# WATER
# THE BOOK

**Inlet chambers at Buckton Castle Water
Treatment Works, Mossley, Lancs.**

# WATER
# THE BOOK

## AN ILLUSTRATED HISTORY OF WATER SUPPLY AND WASTEWATER IN THE UNITED KINGDOM

### Hugh Barty-King

### Special Photographs by
### Heather Angel

### Foreword by HRH The Prince of Wales

**Quiller Press**

DEDICATION
This book is for WaterAid

Text copyright © 1992 Water Services Association for WaterAid.
Compilation copyright © 1992 Quiller Press & Water Services Association.

First published 1992 by
Quiller Press Limited
46 Lillie Road
LONDON SW6 1TN
ISBN 1 870948 74 2

Designed by Tim McPhee and produced by Debbie Wright
at Book Production Consultants, Cambridge for Quiller Press
Typeset by Cambridge Photosetting Services
Origination by Anglia Graphics, Bedford
Printed and bound in The Netherlands by Royal Smeets Offset b.v.

# Contents

As President of WaterAid, the water industry's own charity, I am delighted to write this foreword to a book which not only describes the history and the past challenges of that industry so well, but also places British water services firmly in their world context.

Water, whether in the natural environment or as a utility for people, has always been vital.  Its abundance or its absence determines where civilisations grow and how they survive.

Now, everywhere, the pressures on water resources are increasing.  Even the natural water cycle is threatened by human activities.

The story of water in the United Kingdom is a microcosm of water throughout the world.  It is a story which should now be told, in the hope that lessons can be learned.

In the last century, the growth of population in our industrial cities created the pressures on water which resulted in terrible cholera epidemics and the remarkable Victorian response of effective water and sanitation services.  Now, as population and technological pressures intensify, we are faced with the modern challenge.  This is to protect, conserve and develop the natural cycle so that it can continue to provide the clean, palatable water and the unpolluted water environment which we all need for civilised living.

# WaterAid

Imagine that the most basic necessity of life and health – water – is not at the end of a tap in your home, but is at a muddy hole in a dried-up river bed. Imagine, too, that to fetch that water you have to walk mile after mile over rough ground, carrying it home as best you can.

For nearly half the people living on this planet – two billion men, women and children – there is no need for imagination. For them, fetching and carrying water is part of daily life. The very water they work so hard to get is also the cause of illnesses like diarrhoea or bilharzia which not only weaken and disable people but shorten their lives.

Every day 25,000 children in the world die from water-related diseases. These deaths could be prevented by many quite small investments in water and sanitation systems.

In 1981 the companies and employees of the British water industry created a special charity – WaterAid – to help with some of these problems. From the start WaterAid was able to use the resources and commitment of the industry to develop practical ways of helping.

WaterAid is an independent charity, but the UK water industry remains the backbone of its support. 17,000 employees and pensioners of the industry make regular donations from their pay to support WaterAid's work.

A network of more than 20 active WaterAid regional groups throughout the UK tells the public about overseas needs and organises fundraising events like duck races, pro-am golf tournaments, raffles or sponsored bike rides. Appeals sent each year to most customers with water bills raise hundreds of thousands of pounds to help other people in the world to enjoy the benefits that safe water close to home can bring and to reduce the misery of having no water or having only foul water to drink and use.

From this unique support WaterAid's income has grown from just £25,000 in 1981 to almost £4 million in 1992. It is a testament to the efforts of WaterAid's supporters in the water industry that His Royal Highness The Prince of Wales became WaterAid's President in 1991.

Although links with the UK water industry are close, from the start it was decided that WaterAid would not try to transfer overseas the high technology used in the UK. WaterAid supports only small-scale and local initiatives using simple and practical technologies. In the world's poorest countries the ability to supply and operate a high-technology water service does not exist. WaterAid's approach of low-cost schemes using technologies appropriate to local conditions is the best way to help more poor people enjoy the safe water and basic sanitation that we take for granted in the UK.

It costs as little as £10 per person for WaterAid to bring safe water close to home. Shallow tubewells drilled by hand-powered augers have benefited hundreds of thousands of people in East and Southern Africa. Wells, dug by hand and capped with

**Low-cost improvements can have a great impact on water quality. This spring has been protected to improve the water quality for villagers in Lubanga, Uganda.**

OPPOSITE: **Carrying water, Dodoma, Tanzania.**

For many women around the world, fetching and carrying water is backbreaking work. Bringing the water closer to their homes relieves them from this daily drudgery.

handpumps designed for easy maintenance, provide safe water supplies for many in West Africa. Tapping springs in hills and piping the water by gravity brings water into the heart of village communities in Nepal. These are simple, practical solutions for lasting water supplies.

The projects supported by WaterAid require the full and active participation of local people. Local people help to plan and manage the work and take on the hard, physical labour of mixing concrete, carrying pipes and digging trenches. They build their own water system and they take and keep the responsibility for keeping the water flowing.

WaterAid provides not only the money but technical advice, through country coordinators, and also materials which cannot be purchased locally. WaterAid's staff and advisers visit projects regularly to help make certain the benefits of safe water are long-lasting.

That is not the end of the story; safe water is only part of the solution. Health education, to explain how to keep safe water clean and why basic latrines are needed, is also vital to ensure there are lasting benefits for everyone. And providing simple clean water supply and proper sanitation in overcrowded urban areas means more work for WaterAid.

**Improving traditional wells will help to bring safe water closer to home for these Kenyan women and children in Gardenui, Tana River.**

These approaches mean WaterAid has already helped over 1.5 million people through nine major country programmes throughout Africa and in south Asia – people in Kenya, Sierra Leone, Ghana, Nepal, India, Ethiopia, Uganda, Tanzania and Zimbabwe. There is much to do.

WaterAid works for lasting solutions, not for short-term relief. But aid must not be for ever. WaterAid works always with local partner organisations, often women's groups, churches or other voluntary bodies and sometimes local government. Such partnerships strengthen these organisations; this is essential if the day is eventually to come when international aid organisations are no longer needed. That is the ultimate goal, but it is still a long way away.

Meanwhile WaterAid intends to continue helping ordinary people through simple and low-cost water projects; for such support results in a dramatic change in the quality of life – and the dignity which comes from realising that they have achieved that change through their own hard work and with just a little help from WaterAid.

1 Queen Anne's Gate
London SW1H 9BT
Telephone: 071-233-4800

David Collett OBE
Director, WaterAid
July 1992

# Introduction

**Archimedes screws are used to raise sewage at the inlet of a sewage treatment works so it can then flow through by gravity.**

That those of us who live in the United Kingdom are well served by our water industry there is no doubt. It is a matter of public record in the UK that standards of water supply and wastewater treatment are better than those of most other countries. And these standards are provided to our customers at just about the lowest cost in the world.

The quality of the UK water industry comes from years of enforced or voluntary attention to the careful preparation, storing and supply of clean water and the proper treatment and safe disposal of wastewater. All of us are indebted to so many who have ever worked in the industry and, not least, to those who work in the industry today.

*Water – The Book* is bound to be an incomplete history. Separate books have been or will be written about water industry law and politics, processes and engineering, charging systems, international work and environment and pollution issues. In this book Hugh Barty-King, helped by attractive photographs taken by Heather Angel, describes the history of UK water and what it is now. Mr Barty-King admits the industry itself has provided much support to him in his important task.

*Water – The Book* will be marketed to customers of the water industry as well as through bookshops. Anyway a significant proportion of the profit from the book will go to WaterAid and that proportion increases the more copies that are sold. WaterAid is the UK water industry's own charity and is described on the previous pages.

In addition to those who are mentioned, this book is a testament to all who work in the UK water industry. The book is, I hope, a story that our industry is proud of and that our customers will also be proud of. The list opposite is of the companies and organisations who work in or with the UK water industry who have committed themselves to the risk of producing *Water – The Book*.

Nicholas Hood CBE
Chairman WaterAid Council
Chairman Wessex Water Plc
July 1992

Alhco Ltd
Anglian Water Plc
Aqua-Gas Ltd
ARC Pipes Ltd
Barclays Bank Plc
Binnie & Partners
Biwater Ltd
Bournemouth and District Water
    Company
Bristol Water Holdings Plc
Cambridge Water Company
Chester Waterworks Company
Cholderton and District Water Company
Clyde River Purification Board
Coopers & Lybrand
D'Arcy Masius Benton & Bowles
Department of the Environment
Department of the Environment –
    Northern Ireland
East Surrey Water Company Plc
East Worcestershire Waterworks
    Company
Edward Barber & Co Ltd
Forth River Purification Board
M J Gleeson Group Plc
Sir Wm Halcrow & Partners Ltd
Hartlepools Water Company
Herbert Smith
Kent Meters Ltd
KPMG Peat Marwick McLintock
Mid Kent Water Plc
Mid Southern Water Company Plc

National Rivers Authority
North Surrey Water Company
North West Water Group Plc
Northumbrian Water Group Plc
Office of Water Services
Portsmouth Water Plc
Price Waterhouse
PWT Projects Ltd
Rofe Kennard & Lapworth
N M Rothschild & Sons Ltd
J H Schroder Wagg & Co Ltd
The Scottish Office
Severn Trent Water Plc
Simon-Hartley Ltd
Solway River Purification Board
South East Water
South Staffordshire Water Plc
South West Water Plc
Southern Water Plc
Stanton Plc
Strathclyde Regional Council
Sutton District Water Plc
Tayside Regional Council
Thames Water Plc
Three Valleys Water Services Plc
Water Research Council Plc
The Welsh Office
Welsh Water Plc
Wessex Water Plc
West Hampshire Water Company
York Waterworks Plc
Yorkshire Water Plc

**Rotating arms distribute
sewage effluent evenly
onto biological filters.**

# Author's preface

The two people whose role in this project must be acknowledged before all others are Nicholas Hood, Chairman of Wessex Water Plc and Chairman of the WaterAid Council, and Michael Carney, Secretary of the Water Services Association of England and Wales, who instigated it, and, after I was enlisted to put the idea into words (in conjunction with Heather Angel, who was to put it into pictures), gave the fullest support and help. Colin Skellett, Managing Director of Wessex Water, is another who has given particular help.

They knew of David Kinnersley's pre-privatisation authoritative study of rivers, politics and pollution, *Troubled Water*, and Charles Hall's in-depth essential guide to the Water Services, then run by water authorities and statutory companies, *Running Water,* but felt there was a place for a different kind of book that was not only post-privatisation but had a wider historical embrace which entertained and informed the general reader/water consumer with a general picture of an operation which he or she almost certainly had always taken for granted – as well as telling those involved at the receiving end of the industry how the many functions all contribute to the single end product, clean fresh water.

For the considerable amount of research into past history involved, I am indebted in particular to Arnott Wilson, City Archivist, Edinburgh District Council Archives; Janet Smith, Principal Archives Officer, Liverpool Record Office; Simon Harrison, Senior Assistant Archivist, City of Chester Record Office; Kathleen Topping, Assistant County Archivist, West Kent Archives Office; J S Williams, City Archivist, Bristol Record Office; B Glanfield, British Pump Manufacturers Association; Lesley Bossine, Kew Bridge Steam Museum; R M Palmer, Hon Curator, Coultershaw Water Pump; Guy Brennan, Secretary, The Concrete Pipe Association; Frances Wood, Local History Assistant, Greenwich Local History Library; Guy Holborn, Librarian, Lincoln's Inn Library; D W Atkinson, Senior Keeper, The Yorkshire Water Museum; George Edwards, Hon Secretary, The Ryhope Engines Trust; R I Odell, Corporate Relations Manager, Water Research Centre; Alan Fulton, Head Librarian, and Miss Deans, Aberdeen Central Library; Carl Boardman, County Archivist, Oxfordshire Archives; John Marais, Library Assistant, Trinity College Library, Cambridge; Sarah Penfold, Administrative Assistant, The Institution of Water and Environmental Management; Paul Brough, Senior Assistant Archivist, Devon Record Office; Nicholas Kingsley, Principal Archivist, and Rachel Roberts, Archivist, Birmingham Public Libraries; Steven Tomlinson, Assistant Librarian, Bodleian Library, University of Oxford; W G Hodges, Superintendent of Duke Humfrey's Library; Simon Bailey, Archivist, Oxford University Archives; Mrs Mary K Murphy, Archivist, The Institution of Civil Engineers; Dr Malcolm Graham, Head of Oxfordshire Studies, Oxford Central Library; Miss M Patch, County Archivist, Greater

Manchester County Record Office; B Jackson, Chief Archivist, Tyne & Wear Archives Service; A M Jackson, Principal Archivist, Strathclyde Regional Council; Sheila Hingley, Cathedral Librarian, Dean and Chapter of Canterbury; J C Robinson, Michael Wright and Bob McWilliam of the Science Museum, South Kensington; G Mulholland, Operations Liaison Section, Department of the Environment for Northern Ireland; Dr David Parker, Curator, the Dickens House Museum; Mrs I M McCabe, Librarian/ Information Officer, The Royal Institution of Great Britain; A A Reed, General Secretary, The Pipeline Industries Guild; and the staffs of the British Library, the Guildhall Library of London, and the Science Museum Library.

For information regarding today's scene I am specially grateful to Graham Harrison, the first Secretary and Legal Adviser of Wessex Water, now retired, who made a tour of water supply companies, and fed in greatly appreciated notes about them and a whole range of other relevant matters. My thanks are due to Yvonne Border, Michael Carney's personal assistant at the Water Services Association; Joyce Poynter, Librarian; and Paul Garrett, editor of the *Water Bulletin*, whose weekly report of events has been a main source of information; and also at Queen Anne's Gate, to Michael Swallow, Director and Secretary of the Water Companies Association. To all at the Water Services Association and the Water Companies Association I owe a lot.

I am also grateful to Mary Earnshaw, Head of Corporate Communication, Wessex Water, for escorting me on visits to operations in the region; to Bob Stacey for his erudite talk on water quality research; to Gary Shenton, Duty Controller, for explaining his job; to Jeremy Williams, Public Relations Manager, Bristol Water, for showing me round Littleton Treatment Works; to Hilary Kelle, Technical Development Officer, Avonmouth Waste Water Treatment Works.

I am indebted to the information sent to me by Fiona MacNeil, Head of Public Relations, Anglian Water; Andrew Panting, Public Relations Manager, Northumbrian Water; J W Oatridge, Director of Corporate Communication, and Christine Mosley, Publications and Exhibitions Manager, Severn Trent Water; Janet Fraser, Publicity Manager, Thames Water; David C Highet, Director of Corporate Communications, and Ruth Bradford, North West Water; Stephen Painter, Head of Public Relations, Yorkshire Water; Alan Smith, Public Relations Manager, South West Water; Mrs A Pollok, Three Valleys Water; Sue Lewis, Print/Advertising Coordinator and Martin Watkins, Welsh Water; Michael Franklin, Group PR & Marketing Manager, Southern Water; Roy MacIver, Secretary General, Convention of Scottish Local Authorities; W G Mitchell, Director, Central Scotland Water Development Board; Allan Harrison, Grampian Regional Council, Department of Water Services; Mrs S J Watkins, WS1 Division, Department of the Environment; Miss J W Fisher, Librarian, Office of Water Services; Susie French, Press Officer, National Rivers Authority.

Finally my thanks to Judith McNeill and Mark Robinson of WaterAid.

H B-K
Ticehurst
East Sussex
July 1992

# CHAPTER ONE

# Enough for everybody

THE WATER CYCLE · HOLY WELLS · DOWSING · SANITAS · MONKS AND FRIARS – EARLY WATER PIONEERS · LONDON'S WATER · PROVINCIAL TOWNS FOLLOW THE MONKS' LEAD · PUBLIC EFFORT; PRIVATE CHARITY · WATER PIPES OF WOOD AND STONE, IRON AND LEAD · ELEGANT CONDUIT HEADS · DISTRIBUTION BY WATER CARRIER AND WATER CART · FORCING WATER UP BY PUMPS

It cost Jack and Jill nothing, either in money or ingenuity, to go up the hill from their village to fetch a pail of water. It was only in coming down that they took a tumble and that was human error, no fault of the water supply arrangements.

The aim of this book is to make the story of water supply in the British Isles flow from the holy well and water carrier era to the present-day high technology of computerised control and ring main, without dwelling for too long in any particular pool along the way. It will become obvious to the reader that, so far as the UK water industry is concerned, the operation of treating wastewater – today's euphemism for sewage – is an essential part of the natural process known as the water cycle, one result of which is clean fresh water flowing to our taps. It will also become clear, in subsequent chapters, that the raising and piping of water in adequate *quantities* – which we now tend to take for granted – has in fact tested human inventiveness and engineering skill in this country for centuries.

Long before the Romans came to Britain, there was no need for any man-made arrangements. The water was there for the comparatively tiny population to take from the springs, wells and ponds, streams and rivers – which were part of the scenery, along with the hills and forests, the birds and flowers, the wind and the night sky. It was part of the 'order of things' that kept people alive and made them grow, along with air, food and sleep. Fetching a pail of water was as easy as gathering wood and very much easier than kindling a fire, its fellow element, which needed *making* not just taking.

If there was a problem, it was working out where the water came from and who was making it appear like that. And what about those dew ponds (mist ponds) on Kepi Ring and Cissbury Ring in Sussex, Badbury Ring in Dorset, and Battlesbury in Wiltshire, which were always full of water even when, in a drought, nearby rivers ran dry?

It was beyond the understanding of the early inhabitants to work out that the moisture of the warm air at night condensed on the surface of the cold clay, and that since more water condensed at night than evaporated in the day, the pond filled up. In evaporating under the heat of the sun the small freshwater dew pond was imitating, on a miniature scale, the global water cycle of the oceans which cover three-quarters of the earth's surface. Heated by the sun, the sea water evaporates, a fresh water vapour rises into the atmosphere, and all of it falls back into the sea in the form of rain –

To fetch a pail of water.

OPPOSITE: **Where the fresh water supply starts – the source of the River Severn, a bog 600 yards up on the eastern flank of Plynlimon in mid-Wales.**

except for about one-tenth which falls on the land, where a large proportion of it soon rises once more into the atmosphere as a vaporous mist. A fraction of it escapes evaporation and sinks into the earth away from the heat of the sun, down through the soil to be trapped in sponge-like porous rock, or comes to rest in underground chambers or aquifers from which natural pressure forces it back up to the surface. It breaks through cracks in the stones or rock as springs scattered arbitrarily all over the British Isles constituting the source of fresh water which nature provides.

Some rain falls in such torrents that it never has time to sink into the earth. It pours into the watercourses which the trickle of water from the springs (which has swollen into a stream and then, joined by tributary streams, into a river) has carved out for itself in a route dictated by gravity. It empties into the sea where the water cycle of evaporation and condensation, as with the dew pond, starts all over again. The rain which has escaped being sprung to the surface remains undiscovered and unused, but healthily fresh, in the holes and fissures of porous rock, maybe for centuries, only capable of being raised by man's ingenuity.

Mystified by the apparently miraculous way in which, except in times of extreme drought, the water kept on issuing from holes in the ground of its own choosing, country folk were at a loss to account for the phenomenon, and so dubbed it divine. The writer of the 103rd psalm declared: 'He sendeth the springs into the rivers which run among the hills.' The God of the Christians took over the mechanics from Jupiter, whom the Romans had tried to placate when the supply threatened to dry up. 'Where a spring or river flows,' warned Seneca, writing during the reign of Augustus at the beginning of the Christian era, 'there should we build altars and offer sacrifices.'

The soldiers of the 20th Legion, part of the Roman forces which conquered and then occupied Britain for over 400 years, took due care to erect an altar beside the aqueduct which they constructed to carry water from the spring at Boughton to the fortress they were building at Chester; this they dedicated to *Nymphis et Fontibus* – to nymphs and springs. They did more than erect altars. The Roman water supply systems, largely destroyed by the barbarian invaders in the Dark Ages which followed the withdrawal of the legions, were not paralleled in sophistication for 1,500 years.

## Holy Wells

The superstitions, however, lingered on. Christians dedicated the wells which were the source of so much of their water not to sprites and naiads, but to saints – though for much the same reason. Few would dare to approach St Kilda's Well without making an offering to the genius of the place in the shape of shells, pins or coins:

> The wells of rocky Cumberland
> Have each a saint or patron
> Who holds an annual festival
> The joy of maid and matron.

When people began endowing well water with healing powers, the clergy, alert to discover practices which they would then denounce as pagan, became uneasy. But to little avail. Cornishmen were convinced that St Madern's well water relieved aches and pains; Scots in Kincardineshire believed that water from St John's well in Balmanno would cure rickets and in Perthshire it was widely believed that baptism with water from Trinity Gask well would prevent the onset of bubonic plague.

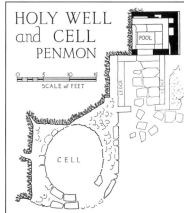

Plan of a small rectangular chamber covering the well where the 6th-century monk Seiriol baptised his converts at Penmon in Anglesey.

LEFT: **Well dressing at Cressbrook, Derbyshire.**

Londoners believed that the drinking of St Bride's Well water would ensure fertility. Outside the city walls, the well in the Strand with its 'sweet, wholesome and clear' water was dedicated to St Clement and this well, which the Romans had known, became a halt on the pilgrims' way to the shrine of Thomas à Becket in Canterbury and a place of pilgrimage in its own right. It is still there.

From St Seiriol's Well in the monastery at Penmon in Anglesey, the 6th-century saint of that name drew water not for washing or drinking but baptising. Bristol had its St Vincent's Well; St Andrew's Well gave its name to the Somerset town of Wells. The dean and chapter of Exeter Cathedral dedicated the 'holy' well outside the east gate of the city to St Satvola (St Sidwell's Well). St James's Holy Well was the water supply for St James's Hospital, Dunwich, in Suffolk.

Most wells were regarded as holy, and were subjected to scenes of 'dressing' and other placatory ceremonies, as on Ascension Day at Tissington near Ashbourne. Well 'dressing' still happens in Derbyshire. Holywell in Shoreditch was one of the three principal sources of water in London along with Clerkenwell and St Clement's Well. The most famous holy well in Britain was that dedicated to St Winefride at Holywell in what was Flintshire (now Clwyd).

In the latter years of the 17th century, water was a source of medicine, leisure and entertainment for the upper and middle classes. The redoubtable Celia Fiennes, a single woman who took to her horse to make several peregrinations across the land, was assiduous in testing the waters, whether the wells or baths or – in some cases – both. After bathing at Buxton, for example, she went on to taste the water at:

**St Winefride's Well at Holywell in Wales – a place of pilgrimage since the 7th century, and the finest example of a mediaeval holy well in Britain.**

> a spring called St Ann's Well which is for drinking, they have arched it up that its much hotter, it heates the cup you take it up in, but not a near so hot as the Somersetshire Bathes and Springs are. The taste is not unpleasant but rather like milk; they say its Diaretick; I dranke a part of a cup full.

By contrast, however, at Eckington, near Rotherham, she found:

> a water which came down a great banck at the end of town like a precipice with such violence that it makes a great noise and looks extremely cleare in the streame that gushes and runns along; it changes the ground and stone or wood it runns on off a deep yellow coullour, they say it runns off a poisonous mine or soile and from Coale pitts, they permit none to taste of it for I sent for a cup of it and the people in the streete call'd out to forbid the tasting of it, and it will bear no soape, so its useless.

### Dowsing

To what extent dowsing – 'divining', 'witching' – is efficacious has long been a matter of debate. Not all divines have been convinced there is any element of mysticism in it. In his *Dictionary of Phrase and Fable* the Revd Cobham Brewer informs his readers that 'the inclination of the rod indicates the presence of water springs, precious metal or anything else that simpletons will pay for.' Writing in 1917, an American government geologist stated confidently that:

> the use of the forked twig or so-called divining rod is a curious superstition that still has a strong hold on the popular mind. . . It is difficult to see how, for practical purposes, the whole matter could be more thoroughly discredited, and it should be obvious to everyone that further tests would be a misuse of public funds.

Seven leading authorities on water supply examined the claims of seven water diviners at Guildford in 1913. Most of the dowsers failed to 'find' the hidden water which formed the test. 'Wherever sensitiveness to underground water may exist in certain persons, of which some evidence is given,' reported the committee who conducted the test, 'it is not sufficiently definite and trustworthy to be of much practical value. . . . It is more a matter of personal mentality than direct influence of the water.' Theories come and go. As late as 1734, the author of *A Universal System of Water and Waterworks* refused to believe that rain was the source of springs and clung to the old idea that they drew their water from the sea through subterranean ducts.

## Sanitas

Although the medicinal qualities of certain springs were widely recognised, the connection between disease and foul water supply was not established until the 19th century.

But, on the whole, water was used almost exclusively for washing, cooking and the watering of stock. Only the very poor habitually drank water: most of the rest drank wine or mead. There was therefore little concern with questions of hygienic drinking water which later generations came to consider an essential element of civilised living.

Indeed the term sanitation was not current in Britain until the middle of the 19th century. The disposal of sewage, a major preoccupation of those who today provide water services in Britain, was not a function which it would have occurred to anyone to carry out on behalf of the citizens, let alone people in the surrounding countryside, nor would they have been expected to.

The disposal of human waste, variously referred to as 'soyle' or 'ordure', was a matter for the householder, who would normally follow the practice of his ancestors by digging a hole away from the living quarters and keeping the deposits covered with earth to facilitate decomposition and reduce smells, though sometimes the contents would be used, or sold, for manure.

## Monks and Friars – Early Water Pioneers

The religious communities were more concerned than most for their personal hygiene and were careful to ensure that there was always enough water on tap for the *lavatorium* or wash-place (from the Latin *lavare* to wash), such as the one at Michaelham Priory in Sussex where there was a stone trough in which the brothers could wash their hands and faces, and sharpen their knives on the whetstone, before going in to the refectory for their meals. They dried their hands on linen towels which, according to their rules, they were not to use for removing dirt or for blowing their noses.

It was unlikely that the spring water in which they washed their hands would be other than clean, let alone contaminated by ordure, since they took the trouble to conduct it into their communities from distant sources by means of pipes. The extent to which they were consciously adapting and continuing the Roman tradition remains unclear. The lead pipes which the Romans had laid in Chester's Eastgate Street had long been abandoned and forgotten when, 1,000 years later, the Christian Abbot of St Werburgh organised the piping of water from a spring at Christleton. He had had to obtain a grant from the spring's owners, the Burnel family, and the permission of the King (Edward I) to push the pipes through the city's walls. They made a reservoir 20 feet square to hold the water from the Abbot's Wells at Christleton, and another one inside Chester Cathedral cloisters known as the Preece or Sprice. Remains of the earthenware pipes which connected the two, and for which part of the city wall had to be demolished and rebuilt, were discovered some 600 years later when workmen started digging the foundations of a house at Barrel Well in 1814. They were some four feet deep and half a yard long. Another water pipeline was laid in the reign of Edward I from a spring near the Gallows at Boughton to the house of the Friars Preachers (the Black Friars). It certainly seems true, as M Fitzsimmons, J E Smith and E Stell remark in their *Brief History of the Water Supply of Chester*, 'certain orders of Friars seemed to have had a special talent for constructing such water supply systems and are mentioned more than once in our historical records.'

The first people to supply Cambridge with pure water from outside the town were

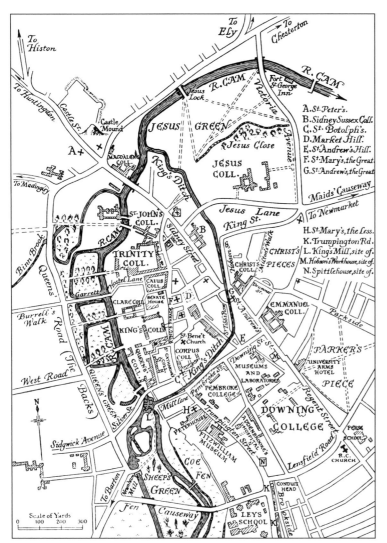

**Mediaeval Cambridge obtained its water partly from wells, partly from the River Cam and partly from an artificial channel known as the King's Ditch which defended the town on the south and east.**

the Franciscans or Grey Friars. Up to the beginning of the 14th century the town had got its water from wells, from the River Cam and from an artificial channel known as the King's Ditch which left the Cam near Silver Street and rejoined it near Magdalene College. Everyone threw their refuse into the river and the ditch, and the water which they drew from it with buckets or pumps was foul and filthy. In 1325 Franciscans laid a pipe from a spring issuing from gravel under rising ground on the west of the town to their community half a mile away, which stood where Sidney Sussex College stands now. In its course the pipe crossed the Cam and passed down a lane later incorporated into the Great Court of Trinity College. When Henry VIII suppressed the Franciscans he granted the whole conduit system to Trinity College in 1546. This remained the college's main source of water for 300 years. It fed the fountain in Great Court, and the tap which still gives water to anyone passing the Great Gate who turns it on.

When people began dying of plague in 1574, Dr Andrew Perne, Master of Peterhouse, blamed water. In a letter to Lord Burghley, Chancellor of the University, he asserted 'our synnes is the principal cause; the other as I conjecture is the corruption of the King's Dytch'. He suggested that a conduit pipe should be laid to the stream issuing from the Nine Wells between the town and Shelford to bring fresh water into Cambridge and flush the King's Ditch. The idea was not taken up immediately, but some 30 years later town and university saw the wisdom of it, and as a joint operation had a new open channel dug from Nine Wells to the outskirts of the town. From there it was piped to a fountain in the market place. Part of the water was diverted to cleanse the King's Ditch and various drains and watercourses belonging to colleges.

Monks applied their talents with equal effect to the even more elaborate water supply system for Canterbury Cathedral from the River Stour and the shallow wells sunk in the alluvium and gravels of its banks. A monk of Christchurch, writing in the reign of Edward II, who died in 1327, tells how:

> In the year 1167 died Wibert of good memory, the Prior of the Mother Church of Canterbury. This same man appointed and caused to be made the conduit of water in all the offices within the Court and Priory, and that water taketh its source about a mile out of the city which under the ground of pipes of lead he caused to come to his church.

A 12th-century drawing inserted in the Canterbury Psalter (the Great Psalter, as it is known), now in the library of Trinity College, Cambridge, shows somewhat vaguely the source of the springs and the route of the pipeline with its conduit house and five tanks before it reaches the city wall, from where it enters the precincts of the monastery – 'Wibert's Conduit'. Another drawing gives the arrangement of the distribution pipes and fittings in great detail within the monastery. A branch pipe was laid to the fine water tower still to be seen on the north side of the cathedral and often called the Baptistry since, as one commentator wrote in 1825, 'it seems too good for the combing of heads and the washing of hands and faces'. The source of the supply was thought to be on rising ground about a mile to the northeast of the monastery called Horsefield or North Holmes (see pp. 24–25).

When the monks of the Abbey of St Peter at Gloucester decided the water they were getting from the River Severn and from wells sunk in the gravel was insufficient, they went to Fulbrook, a tributary of the Twyver. Faced with the same problem, the White Friars laid a leaden pipe from the spring called Gosewhyte Well near Goswite Mill beyond Eastgate; and the Grey Friars were granted use of the spring at Matesnoll called Breresclyff. When some time later a dispute arose between monks and friars over the use of this spring, the King, Edward III, sent his son the Black Prince to settle it. He gave each user the right to extract water from Matesnoll in leaden pipes of equal size.

At Bath monks got water from springs on Beechen Cliff; at Lincoln they laid lead pipes to their friary, thence to a conduit head by St Mary-le-Wigford. Franciscans were responsible for a major scheme in Southampton for which they erected a spring-head building in Hill Lane with three vaulted chambers some six feet high. A lead pipe took the water to a waterhouse in Waterhouse Lane off Commercial Road, and underground by a lead pipe to Havelock Road, to the King's Highway above Bar passing through Bargate, and from there to the Friary (on the site of Gloucester Square) where it divided into north and south branches, with an extension to the medieval hospital known as God's House. In Bristol, Carmelites built St John's Conduit, taking water from Brandon Hill to the Carmelite Friary (in the vicinity of Colston Street). The Temple Pipe was a 125-yard tunnel to an underground chamber of the Knights Templar. In London the Carthusians at the Charterhouse had water brought from the White Conduit at Islington across the fields in pipes, which entered under the cells on the north side of the quadrangle and was received in an octagonal building which disappeared, however, in the 17th century. The monks of St Bartholomew's Priory drew water from Canonbury in lead pipes housed within a tunnel.

Water tower of Prior Wibert's 12th-century waterworks for the monastic buildings at Canterbury.

The priors and abbots, friars and canons of the medieval religious communities had the time and the intellect to master the intricacies of water engineering. Not so the mayors and councillors entrusted with the management of civic communities, who were soon knocking at monastery doors to seek information on how they too could organise a system of the kind which brought water so satisfactorily to the lavatoria and piscinae of those for whom cleanliness was patently next in order of importance to godliness.

## London's Water

The Mayor of London looked to the Abbot of Westminster in 1439 to supplement the fresh water he was able to provide for his 50,000 citizens. In that year the Abbot gave the City of London 'one head of water together with springs to the north and west of

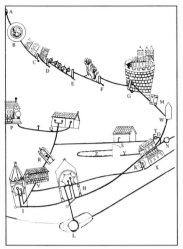

**Sketch by Revd Robert Willis, based on a 12th-century drawing of the Canterbury waterworks.**

A  Spring
B  Conduit house
C – G  Settling tanks

## PIPED WATER FOR THE 12th-CENTURY MONKS OF THE MONASTERY OF CHRIST CHURCH IN CANTERBURY

The two drawings reproduced here show the water supply system devised by Prior Wibert in the 1160s for the complex of buildings comprising the monastery of Christ Church in Canterbury. They are, as Revd Robert Willis noted in his *Architectural History* (1869), 'a most valuable record of the state of hydraulic practice in the 12th century and a monument of the care with which the monks studied the practical science and applied their knowledge for the benefit of their own health and comfort, and of mankind in general'.

Prior Wibert was prompted to devise his system to give himself and his monks a less fatiguing way of obtaining water to wash with, rather than having to carry heavy pails of it up to the first-floor dormitory from the wells in the infirmary cloister, or the outer cemetery, which they had to share with the townsfolk. His scheme was to bring water from springs located in an acre of rising ground called Horsefelde or North Holmes, to the northeast of the monastery and a mile outside the city walls. He had the water diverted at once into a circular receipt or conduit house, illustrated in the top left-hand corner of the smaller drawing.

The water left this round basin through a circular perforated plate which acted as a primary filter of any heavy obstruction – what Willis called 'gross impurities' – which may have included deer's droppings, since Horsefelde was part of a royal hunting ground.

The pure spring water thus filtered passed into a pipe made of stout sheet lead pressed round a wooden core and then seamed and fused along the joint. Gravity took it downhill in the direction of Canterbury. Before it reached the city wall it was taken into, and out of, a succession of five oblong settling tanks, each placed transversely to the pipeline. Each length of pipe entered the tank at its west side and left it at the east side. In this way sediment was deposited in each tank, less and less as the water pursued its course. From time to time a monk would release sediment through the tank's *purgatorium* or purging pipe, also illustrated.

The larger drawing shows the route of the underground pipe on leaving the circular receipt house below the spring, through some fields of growing corn (marked *campus*), a vineyard (*vinea*), and then the orchard (*pomerium*) of the Black Canons of St Gregory's Priory, who were given their own branch pipe off it. To express their gratitude for this service, every September the canons of the priory sent their gardener over to Christ Church monastery with a basket of their best apples.

The final settling tank was placed against the tower in the city wall known as *ye forrins*, and the pipe crossed the moat on a four-arched aqueduct, as the drawing shows. It then went underground through the Prior's gateway, under the infirmary kitchen and to a site near the ancient well in the infirmary cloister which had been the monastery's sole source of supply. Here Wibert had a two-storey tower built – a water

tower (which, because later it housed a font, was mistakenly called the Baptistery). The main water pipe passed through the ground floor of the tower and a junction pipe was taken from it up through the hollow central stone pillar of the tower to the first floor, designed to be the *laver* or washing place. A waste pipe down another hollow pillar carried away the surplus water, which was continually falling from the upper cistern, to the ground floor and away to the town ditch, along with the water used by the monks.

If the North Holmes spring failed to produce enough

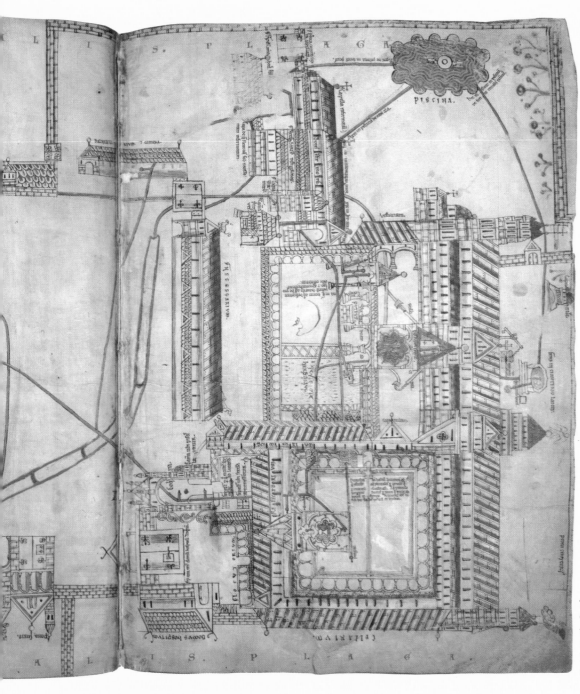

The waterworks of Christ Church Canterbury, from the Canterbury Psalter (*c.* 1150), now in the library of Trinity College, Cambridge.

water, the monks would draw some, as they had done before, from the old cloister well and pour it down the funnel of the vertical pipe at the top of the *laver*. The drawing shows the waste water of the *cupa* being carried under the *necessarium infirmorum* – which is what today is understood by a lavatory – so it would seem that they had some form of water-borne foul sewage disposal. The drawing shows this waste pipe proceeding underground beneath the Green Court and emptying its contents into the town ditch.

On the extreme right of the large drawing is shown the well Wibert provided on the south for the laity, *fons in clositerio laico*. The lever handle is supported in the middle by the fork of a high pole, with a bucket at one end hanging by a chain and a balancing stone tied to the other.

Revd Robert Willis, *Architectural History of the Conventual Buildings of the Monastery of Christ Church in Canterbury*, 1869.
W Douglas Caroe, 'The Water Tower', *Friends of Canterbury Cathedral Second Annual Report*, 1929.

the head in Paddington for a payment of two peppercorns', a grant which was confirmed by King Henry VI in 1442. By a writ of the Privy Seal the citizens were able to buy 200 fodders (tons) of lead for the pipes.

**Seamed lead water pipe of 1516 from Wolsey's Palace at Hampton Court.**

BELOW RIGHT: **Westcheap Conduit.**

London's local government had always been, and was to remain, something of an exception to the laissez-faire conduct of municipal affairs obtaining in most other parts of the kingdom. As early as 1236 the corporation had purchased the liberty to convey water from the Tyburn stream to the city in six-inch lead pipes, the royal grant making it clear that London was regarded as more than just another large town. The water was to be 'for the profit of the City and the good of the whole realm thither repairing: to wit, for the poor to drink and the rich to dress their meat'.

The water was abstracted from the Tyburn near what is now Stratford Place in Oxford Street. Foreign merchants from Amiens and elsewhere, anxious to obtain the privilege of landing and housing wood, donated £100 towards the cost of the scheme and bought the conduit head at Westcheap ('The Great Conduit') from the corporation for a yearly payment of 50 marks.

The Tyburn did not start in Stratford Place; its source was in West End, Hampstead, and it ran on a route which today covers Hay Hill, Half Moon Street, through the hollow of Piccadilly into Green Park, past Buckingham Palace and into the Thames. Known as the Great Conduit of Westcheap, the cistern to which the Tyburn water was conducted, it was the city's first and was castellated with stone.

A Victorian writer on London water in Charles Dickens's magazine *All The Year Round* said the Tyburn:

> supplied water for nothing, as all streams and wells do up to a certain point. Nature is bountiful but uncertain; art is exacting but reliable. Some people left money to establish conduit pipes and maintain them as a charity; others erected these structures and paid themselves by a recognised toll.

The Keepers of the Great Conduit in Chepe recovered the cost of maintenance and repair by levying a water rate on the occupants of houses in Chepe and Poultry of around 12 shillings for two years' consumption. They got some of their money back when on coronation days the lead cistern, which normally poured water into a square stone basin, ran all day with red and white wine – and free for all. They complained, however, that brewers who paid a 'trade fee' took so much of the water that there was often none left for them – and in 1345 the corporation told the brewers that they must find their water for making ale and malt elsewhere.

## Provincial Towns Follow the Monks' Lead

The town authorities of Bristol brought water from Ashley Hill to the quay and to the Tontine Warehouses in the 14th century in what became known as the Key (Quay) Pipe. By a deed of 1376 the Mayor of Bristol, Walter Derby, and one Hugh Derenge engaged to bring all the water rising in the Key Pipe, All Hallows and the St John's Pipe:

> so that the Commonalty of the Town should have no lack of water at any of the said conduits at any time during the life of the said Hugh. And if the said Commonalty shall lack water at any of the said conduits by the space of six days, and that proved before the Mayor, Sheriffs and Bayliffs of the said town, he is to forfeit £10. He is to find 1,000 ft of the rule of strong new pipe every year for all of which he is to receive £10 going out of several houses standing upon the bridge of Bristol, for his term of life.

Determining precedence among the various claimants for what water was available was never easy, particularly when the claims of town dwellers were pitched against those of country folk. By taking the advice of his commissioners to construct a system of dykes to connect the town of Kingston-upon-Hull with springs at rural Anlaby and Haltemprice, Henry IV upset the people in those villages whose own water supply would thus be summarily reduced. They took to polluting the water at their end, so that when it arrived at Hull it was too unpleasant to use. In July 1415, after enterprising town dwellers had appealed to the Pope, the College of Cardinals in Rome wrote to the rural protestors to desist, threatening them with retribution on the Day of Judgement. Refusing to be browbeaten by the Holy Father or anyone else, they returned to their campaign with renewed intensity.

Twenty years after they had installed their system in Southampton, the Franciscans were persuaded to allow the town to have their surplus water 'out of reverence to Henry Archdeacon of Dorset and their goodwill to the community of the town'. In 1420 the Mayor and people of Southampton acquired the whole system on the understanding that they erected a conduit head opposite Holyrood Church, from which two pipes were to take water to a cistern for the use of the town and for the friary respectively. Another 100 years later the Corporation of Southampton acquired the system based on Lobery Mead (the Polygon). John Flemynge, who sold them the spring, retained the right to insert a 'sosprey', a small lead pipe with a stopper, into the conduit head, the water from which was to issue from a brass cock at All Hallows Church. Flemynge enclosed the spring and gave a key to the mayor and another to the friars by which the supply to the sosprey could be cut off should the spring water lose its pressure.

In 1438 the White Friars and Grey Friars of Gloucester granted the bailiffs and community of Gloucester three-quarters of their water supply. The agreement stated that the friars would continue to repair the pipes but the town would have to pay them three-quarters of the cost – and neither party was to do anything to lessen the supply of the other. At the dissolution of these monasteries in 1542 the town took over the whole supply system. In what is regarded as the earliest local Act of Parliament on water supply, the Mayor of Gloucester and the Dean of Gloucester Cathedral were empowered to break ground on Matson's Hill for the conveyance of water to their respective locations. Another 90 years went by and the Corporation of Gloucester bought the whole of the capital of the waterworks and the remaining quarter of the supply for £50, together with the old pipeline from Robins Wood Hill Spring to the High Cross, which had been adapted as a public conduit head by the 1440s. By 1509, at

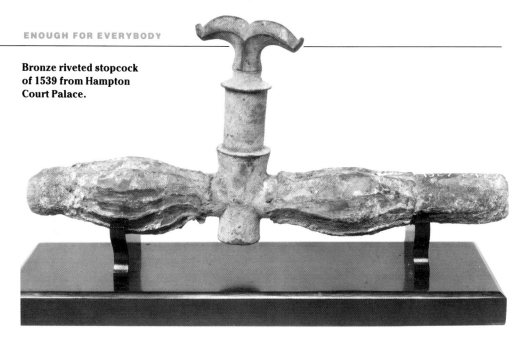

**Bronze riveted stopcock
of 1539 from Hampton
Court Palace.**

least one house in the town had its own private water pipe, and the greater number laid over the next 60 years caused a shortage of water for the public at the town's High Cross conduit head.

## Public Effort; Private Charity

When the smaller religious foundations were suppressed in Chester in 1536, the city authorities took over the water supply systems they had built for themselves, and adapted them to serve the town's citizens – a transfer which took place all over Britain. In some towns, however, the city authorities had already devised a water supply system on their own initiative. The charter of 1440 which created Kingston upon Hull a county, allowed the city to purchase springs at Springhead and build a channel, Spring Dyke, to conduct water to the moat inside the town called Bush Dyke which acted as a reservoir. Twenty years later a wealthy merchant, Sir William Knowles, paid to have lead pipes laid beneath the streets of Hull, so that any householder who could afford to do so could install a pump to draw water from the nearest pipe – the town's first system of water mains.

Sir William Knowles was one of the many well-disposed, public-spirited citizens who saw the funding of a public water supply as an act of charity. As far back as the 12th century, Robert de Berkeley, founder of St Catherine's Hospital, Bedminster, paid for the erection of the Redcliffe Pipe to carry water to Bristol from Knowle one and half miles away. Others left bequests in their wills, like William Canynge who bequeathed a sum for the maintenance of St Edith's Wells in Bristol. The Conduit Charities of Dartmouth raised £400 a year for the corporation to maintain its public water supply. Maidstone Town Council appointed two wardens of the conduit in High Street to collect charitable offerings for its upkeep. With the money given they built a new conduit head which was 'not only a beauty but also of great conveniency to the towne'. When Bath Town Council was hard put to it to find money to run the water supply which had previously been organised by the newly dissolved monasteries, they raised a public subscription to cast new pipes. Some 47 citizens of Bath contributed voluntarily with sums ranging from threepence to 20 shillings. Similarly at Lichfield Conduit, Lands Trustees took over the water supply from the suppressed Friars Minor, and added a reservoir and three new conduit heads to the town's original 'crucifix' conduit.

Not every wealthy landowner saw their obligations with regard to providing a water supply in the same charitable light as Sir William Knowles. The Revd John Edmunds, rector of Petworth in Sussex in the reign of Henry VII, had lead piping laid to carry water to the town and to Petworth House from a source in Petworth Park where water seeped out of sandstone into a ten-foot-high underground chamber made of stone and small flat bricks. The trickle fell onto two feet of gravel, rose to another foot above it and then, filtered by the gravel, drained off down the mile-long pipeline to a stone reservoir in a timber yard beside Petworth Churchyard. A branch pipe went to the manor-house kennels and another to points in the lower levels of the town. A local man, Antony Jonson, left six shillings and eightpence in his will in 1526 'to the mayntaynance of the channell of the cundyte'.

About 100 years later, the owner of Petworth House, the 8th Earl of Northumberland, finding the pipes 'greatly decayed', agreed to share the cost of repair with the town, which he endowed with seven acres of freehold land to the east of Hungers Lane, known as the Conduit Field. His son, the 9th Earl, however, had less concern for his tenants' welfare. He appropriated common land for his new park, and for this and other breaches of manorial custom his tenants sued him in Chancery. They tore down his park railings and cut off the water supply to his house. In a violent manner, he complained in a cross-suit that they had:

> broken and entered those Conduit Houses and hedds apperteyning, and by mere charge belonging to my House stopped and restrayned the water for my necessary use, supposing the same theire lewde behaviour not to come to light.

Tenant–landowner relations were further sullied by the Earl's servants 'washing bullocks entrails at the common tap' for which the Clerk of the Market fined his lordship twopence. They also made themselves unpopular with the locals by watering horses there and washing fish.

There was almost always an element of robbing Peter to pay Paul about making an exclusive duct leading to one set of people out of a natural stream from which all those who lived on its banks, and particularly at its source, had been accustomed to draw. And there was always the dilemma of who should have preference – commercial users like the London brewers or householders who drew it for domestic purposes.

Legend has it that when Sir Francis Drake heard that Plymouth laundresses were short of water, he called for his horse, rode off to Dartmoor, found a spring, bewitched it with his magical powers and made it follow him as he galloped back to town. The reality was more down-to-earth. In 1584 Plymouth Corporation obtained an Act of Parliament to bring water to the town from the River Meavy. This authorised them 'to dig and mine a ditch or trench six or seven feet wide over any land lying between the town and the river and to dig, mine, break, bank and cast up all manner of rocks, stones, gravel, sand, for the convenient and necessary conveyance of the river to the town'. Drake, as MP for Bossiney in Cornwall, was a member of the Select Committee which approved the Bill. In it sums of money were allocated for entertaining the justices when they came to view progress, and for paying a poor man to show them the way across the moor. The corporation had to buy the land from its owners and compensate tenants, farmers and occupiers for loss and injury sustained. The price they paid was on a basis of 16 years' purchase, though payment was accepted in kind. Sir Thomas Wise paid in claret. Owners of watermills on the river were compensated for having their water supply impaired. There was no mention of laundry owners suffering in the same way. The 1584 Act in Plymouth gave the main reason for the

**Drake building the Plymouth Leat at Burrator, attributed to Samuel Cook (1806–59).**

project as the need to supply ships with fresh water, to protect the town from fire, and to scour the harbour which had become silted up with sand by the operations of tinners and other metal workers.

Sir Francis Drake was paid £200 to carry out the work, which he attended to as soon as he had fulfilled a prior obligation to his sovereign regarding the King of Spain's plans for the invasion of England. He cut the first sod one day in December 1590 and the work was finished the following year on 23 April. A grand ceremony, involving the blowing of trumpets, the firing of guns and extravagant feasting, heralded the admission of the first water into Drake's Leat – the old word for an open watercourse. It ran past Drake's front door, and in a typically chivalrous gesture he dipped his scarlet cloak in it 'in exultation that he had obtained his desired end'.

The sides of the leat were lined with granite, and its bottom, some time later, with concrete. Near the Head Weir and through Burrator, the water was conducted across 12 miles of moor in wooden troughs, but because of the twists and turns there were 17 miles of leat. For half the way it ran along an older leat built to take water from the River Meavy to Warleigh Mill. Drake erected six watermills beside it, to which existing mill-owners vehemently objected.

Once in Plymouth the water was taken to conduit heads in the town, for public use without payment, in pipes of wood and lead, and to the houses of those who were ready to pay a 'rent' of four shillings a year. The system served Plymouth for 300 years, the last conduit head being demolished in 1834.

When it came to trying to provide fresh water for their own royal residences, the medieval kings did much as they liked. King Henry III's Palace of Westminster was supplied by means of a hollow pipe 'not thicker than a quill'. The amount of water that could flow through a pipe with the diameter of a goose quill, even though it would have been running continuously, cannot have been very great. Private householders, however, were forbidden to use quills to tap the public water supply, because it reduced the volume available in a way that led to public outcry.

Other members of the royal family had to comply with some rules. When Henry V's brother, Humphrey, Duke of Gloucester, proposed enclosing Greenwich Park in the 1430s with a view to having a house built on the bank of the River Thames, he had to obtain a royal licence 'to make an underground Conduit from a certain well of theirs [the King's] in Greenwich called Stockwell across the highway which runs between their Garden and their Park, to bring water from the well to their manor or inn there'. There was no question of taking water from the river which ran at a lower level. The traditional site of the ancient Stockwell well is above the Duke's Manor House at Ballast Quay, near the corner of Crooms Hill and Nevada Street.

Writing about the underground passages and caverns of Greenwich in 1914, John Stone described the conduit tunnels connecting the two as 'the most venerable systems of water supply within the metropolitan area, complete and in fairly good working order, and producing a supply of water, today'. In the crypt of the Naval College, said Stone, were some cement pipes dug up in Greenwich Park, labelled as having been laid by Duke Humphrey in the 15th century.

## Water Pipes of Wood and Stone, Iron and Lead

Concrete pipes were commonplace in the water supply system of the Roman Empire. Parts of the network at Cologne were found to be in serviceable condition when excavated 1,800 years later. In their British colony the Romans used wood pipes for water supply at Calleva Atrebatum (Silchester, north of Basingstoke). During excavations in 1896 archaeologists traced a 700-foot pipeline across the town. All that remained of it were the iron collars every seven feet which had joined one wooden pipe to the next one. For most of their water supply systems in Britain, however, the Romans used lead pipes, like those unearthed at Bath and Chester.

**Hyde Vale Passage from the sluice under the Vale, part of the 15th-century conduit at Greenwich.**

Britain's main water pipes ('mains') were made mostly of wood right through to the 18th century, with the branch pipes to houses made of lead. In 1745 one London water company alone was using 54,000 yards of wood piping and 3,860 yards of lead. The most popular wood for water pipes was elm. At the beginning of the 18th century, however, Dublin Corporation invited tenders for 200 tons of fir, with its bark on, in lengths of 16 to 22 feet and not less than 12 inches thick at the small end. Each length of tree trunk – hence the continued use of 'trunkline' for long-distance pipe and cable networks, and 'trunk calls' for the latter – was bored through by hand, and later by machines, to form a hollow pipe. One end was tapered so that it fitted into the larger mouth of the trunk next to it. Water pipes made from the trunks of elm trees leaked less than pipes made of lead, which had to have air outlets at intervals. In 1762 Dublin rid itself entirely of its lead water pipes because it cost the city so much to maintain them. They replaced them with wooden ones, as did Bath about the same time.

Various kinds of wood, but mostly elm, were used to make the pipes laid in Belfast in the 17th century. Several lengths from two to ten feet long, and from four to six inches in bore have been preserved. In Stroud in Gloucestershire the 18th-century pipes proved less durable. They were replaced by lead pipes after only 30 years. Yorkshire Water's museum at Hull has wooden water pipes 400 years old.

Though it held water well while serving as a water pipe, wood had a limited life and, compared with the new cast iron, was less economic. Edinburgh replaced its lead

A boring machine for wooden water pipes – the original 'trunk' lines. At the top can be seen how the tapered end of one pipe fitted into the open end of the next one.

main water pipes with five inch cast iron pipes in 1755. Dublin tried out iron pipes in 1797, each eight feet long, half an inch thick with a 12 millimetre clear bore. They laid more wooden pipes in 1806, but had the whole town relaid with iron pipes in 1809. A cast iron tablet on the West Pier of Plymouth's Sutton Harbour commemorates the city's first use of cast iron pipes in 1826. For the most part however, owing to bad jointing, cast iron water pipes were not used to any large extent in Britain until the end of the 19th century.

One of the London supply companies experimented with stone pipes at the beginning of the 19th century but, when they started leaking, took them up as well as the iron ones and replaced them with wooden pipes. When a water company started operations in 1797 they put down stoneware and earthenware pipes. To stop them breaking it was proposed to line them with wood or iron.

There was little consensus about which material made the best water pipe. At the beginning of the 17th century those responsible for water supply for the Court and Priory at Canterbury spent £300 on a set of new lead pipes and £40 on repairing earthenware ones. The following year they paid out £15 on elm timber for pipes: and ten years later treated for a price for leaden pipes instead of 'wooden pipes decayed'.

A pipe was not the only medium devised by engineers to channel water moving downhill in the direction wanted – as opposed to leaving it to take the line of least resistance in a river bed of its own making and get lost in the sea. Before sending it on its diverted journey, the engineer would probably erect over the source, as at Petworth, a chamber where the water's flow would be halted – and perhaps filtered – before it was sent on its way again. This was sometimes called the 'receipt house'. According to the lie of the land and its composition, and the available funds, the water would be conducted from the receipt house in an open duct or a closed tunnel or culvert, or a combination of all types of 'conduit', to the desired location. It might be a question of only slightly altering the

A 200-year-old wooden 'trunk' water main from Lincoln's Inn Fields, London.

direction of a natural watercourse and then making it run down the streets of a town, such as at Salisbury and Winchester. The Earl of Ashburnham wrote in his diary in 1687:

> We came to Winchester safely about 7 of the clock in the evening. We went to see the Colledge founded by William of Wickam. They have excellent Spring Water in this Colledge in great abundance, and indeed the whole Town of Winchester is very well served with water, a river running through most of the streets. Winchester is seated in a bottom among the hills and is one of the sweetest and most healthy places in Europe. I think to send my sonne to school here.

## Elegant Conduit Heads

Into whatever watercourse, man-made or man-altered, the water was diverted from the spring, river or lake which was its natural habitat, its new destination was a conduit head which, because it was more often than not housed in a formidable structure of some kind, was also called a conduit house, or, confusingly, just a conduit. It was referred to by some as a 'fountain', a corruption of Norman French for the head of the stream. The one which the Corporation of London diverted was originally called 'La funtayne de Tybourne'. Built in 1285, it was widely known, however, as the Great Conduit in Chepe.

**The Little Conduit in Cheapside, London.**

By whatever name, the end of the 'waterworks' was a large tank or cistern of lead or stone into which the water poured itself, and out of which, by a free-flowing spout or a controllable tap, it poured into a stone basin below.

This is all there was to a waterworks of those early days. It worked entirely by gravity – 'gravitation works'. Its water was for the use of the public and the head of it was placed prominently in a public place with easy access, probably the market square. Sometimes the market cross was converted to house it. If not, it was given a substantial, stylish housing in keeping with the important role it would play in the life of the town. Its decoration would remind its users of the people by whose public-spirited charity it had been built. The house of the cistern placed at the High Cross in Chester in the 1580s bore the arms of the city, the Earl of Derby, the Earl of Leicester and Dr Wall, a prebendary of Chester Cathedral.

**Elm-wood water pipes of 1797, and the tools used to manufacture them – exhibits in the Sutton Poyntz Museum of Water Supply, run by Wessex Water.**

This stoup, which used to contain holy water, can still be seen outside Fromond's Chantry at Winchester College. Until 1860 'College Men' had to wash, in all seasons, out in the open at an old conduit in Chamber Court.

Lamb's Conduit in London, as rebuilt in 1667 from a design by Sir Christopher Wren.

An ironmonger called John Scriven gave Gloucester a fine Gothic-style conduit head to place at the end of the pipeline from Mattes Knoll (Robin Hood's Hill in Southgate Street). It served the people of the town from 1636 to 1784. A solid structure, it was ten feet in diameter and 25 feet high. It had allegorical figures on top, and panels representing the resources and industries of the River Severn including 'wine manufacture', a reminder that wine was made in this part of England from at least the 12th century.

The Quay Pipe Conduit Head in Bristol, with its large leaden cistern, had a 'fair castelette' adorned with a sculptured head of Momus, God of Laughter. From it mariners filled fresh water casks before leaving the harbour. John Cabot is said to have taken water on board from Quay Pipe before setting out, in May 1497, on a 52-day voyage of discovery, during which he came upon Cape Breton Island and found the north-east coast of America. There was a tradition that Bristol's Quay Pipe water had curative properties. Its conduit head served for some 500 years and was not removed until 1936. An inscription placed on the wall at the junction of St Stephen's and Colston Avenue to mark the last site of Quay Pipe Conduit Head reads:

The springs of Ashley Down supplying this water, before becoming the property of the communalty of the city in 1391, belonged to the Order of Friars Preachers.

Another of Bristol's ancient conduit heads, that for the Temple Pipe which took water from Ravens Well Totterdown, lasted almost as long. Erected in 1366, it was rebuilt in the 16th century when it was surrounded by a statue of Neptune to commemorate the defeat of the Spanish Armada. It was re-erected as a drinking fountain at the junction of Temple Street and Victoria Street in 1872.

All who today walk down Lamb's Conduit Street in London are reminded of the enterprise of William Lamb, Gentleman of the Chapel Royal and Freeman of the Clothworkers Company, who in 1677 paid out £1,500 in restoring the ancient Snow Hill Conduit which had fallen into ruin. He had the water of several springs diverted into a single new stream, which he had conveyed some 2,000 yards through lead pipes to a new conduit head below the Church of St Sepulchre. After being damaged in the Fire of London, it was rebuilt in 1667 to a design of Sir Christopher Wren's, with four equal sides with four columns. Its pediment was surmounted by a pyramid bearing a stone carving of a lamb. This grandiose conduit head was removed in 1746. A hundred years later workmen digging in the yard of the Lamb public house at the end of Lamb's Conduit Street came across a trap door in the paving. Lifting its lid they found a short flight of steps leading to a brick vault. Under a wooden cover they saw the well from which the water was supplied to William Lamb's conduit head. In 1905 other workmen cutting a trench for the electrification of the tramlines in Theobalds Road uncovered a 12-foot length of tree trunk waterpipe with a nine-inch bore.

Otho Nicholson, a wealthy London courtier, diplomat and lawyer, paid for the even more elaborate conduit head, known as 'the Carfax Conduit', which John Clark, a Yorkshire stonecarver, built for the centre of Oxford in 1610. Nicholson's initials O.N. are carved round the top, together with the Empress Matilda riding an ox over a ford. Above each grand arch stand figures of Justice, Temperance, Fortitude and Prudence. In eight niches stand historical figures such as Alexander the Great, the Emperor Charlemagne, Julius Caesar and, tactfully, King James I. 'So Curious and well contriv'd a structure,' observed the writer of a manuscript, now in the Bodleian Library, after the conduit head had been repaired in 1686, 'which for usefullness, beauty and neatness is not to be found in the three kingdoms'. When the road was widened in 1789 it was taken down and given to Lord Harcourt who re-erected it in the grounds of his house in Nuneham Park, where it still stands.

The lead statuette on top of the conduit head which the people of Aberdeen know as the Mannie on the Green once held a bow and arrow for which he was often referred to as 'the somewhat elderly Eros'. He stood in Castle Street for around 100 years, housing the cistern at the end of the lead pipeline which brought water from springs in Carden's Haugh and, from the mid-18th century, from Fountainhall. The conduit head with the little man on top was removed to The Green in 1852.

The Mannie on the Green in Castle Street, Aberdeen. When the figure on the conduit head held a bow and arrow, he was called 'the somewhat elderly Eros'.

A London water bearer in 1624, depicted as old, blind and led by a dog carrying a lantern in his mouth.

## Distribution by Water Carrier and Water Cart

The supplier's responsibility for the effectiveness of the water supply system he had contrived and installed – diverting the source, filtering it (maybe) and channelling it downhill in conduits – ended at the point of delivery, the conduit head. Though water engineers had no influence

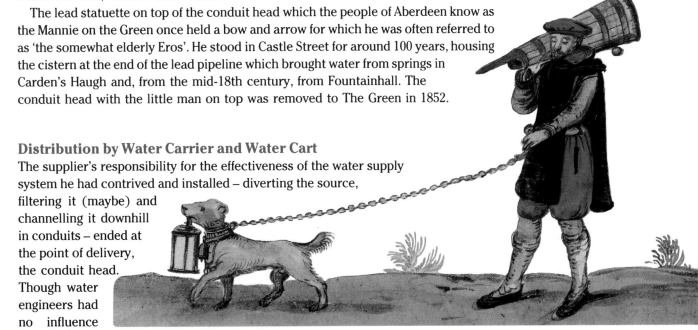

over water consumers, it was the relationship between the two, the fluctuating imbalance of fixed supply on one side and ever-growing demand on the other, which created all the problems that lay ahead.

There were always to be times of drought, decaying and leaking conduits, or diversions made to the king's deer or to watermill owners before the water reached the conduit head. But there was no problem so long as, by and large, the water that flowed from the spouts and taps of conduit heads met the needs of all who came to collect it – which was the case before the Industrial Revolution sent Britain's population soaring.

William Lamb was one of the few who *was* concerned with how the water he had provided was collected. He knew it was the custom for women to do the collecting, and he made 120 pails available for the poorer women of Snow Hill in London where Lamb's Conduit ended. But William Lamb's caring attitude was exceptional. In any event, water was only collected personally by those who lived near enough to the conduit head for carrying away a 'tankard' or two of water not to be too much of a burden. A water tankard held three gallons of water; larger ones held six.

Those who lived at a distance from the conduit head paid water carriers (or water bearers) to bring water to them. In 16th-century London water carriers used a vessel called a 'tyne', a tub made of wooden staves and hoops. Because most of them lived in Cob's Court off Ludgate Hill, Blackfriars, they were known as 'cobs'. Ben Jonson had a water carrier, whom he called Oliver Cobb, in his play *Every Man in his Humour*. They formed themselves into a Company of Water Tankard Bearers which, by the end of the 15th century, had 4,000 members. Their activities were strictly disciplined. In 1585 the authorities ruled that no more than three water bearers should operate in the parish of Ludgate; that all of them should be men and not their wives or servants. They could not carry water to anyone outside the parish. If any of them left a tub in the street to the annoyance of passers-by, they would be debarred from carrying water from the conduit head ever again. They could charge no more than twopence for every seven tankards delivered, and that in winter as well as summer.

In January 1588 the parish councillors of Ludgate ordered that:

> no manner of servant nor no water bearer shall be at the conduit in the [church] service time, nor leave there no tankard nor pail, for if they do so offend, the churchwardens shall take the said tankard or pail and keep them until such time that the offenders do come and put in the poor man's chest fourpence, and then the said part to have his tankard again.

The charges made by water carriers varied. The people of Sunderland paid a halfpenny a 'skeel' in George III's time. A skeel (derived from the Icelandic word *skeola* meaning a milk pail) was a wooden bucket similar to a tankard. In Tetbury in Gloucestershire water carriers were paid sixpence to tenpence a hogshead (52½ gallons).

Delivered by horse-drawn water cart, it cost more. A notice in Sunderland read:

Low Spring water at the Improved Patent Ropery in Bishopwearmouth

> Inhabitants are respectfully informed that they may now be supplied with excellent water at the Improved Patent Ropery in South Street at ¼d a skeel on the spot and by water cart at ½d a skeel at their houses. N.B. This water is found to make excellent tea water and answers well for washing.

In nearby Monkwearmouth water was sold from a water cart for a 'bodle' (half a farthing, or a sixth of an old English penny) a skeel. The cart bore the doggerel:

It's limpid and clear from all mud,
This water I sell for the public good;
Its excellent virtues no mortal can tell,
So sweet is the water from Union Well.

**Donkeys and horses
drew the water carts that
brought water to those
who lived in the suburbs
of London.**

The system of lead pipes which Sir William Knowles had laid beneath the streets of Hull in the 1460s failed to deliver reliably enough for householders to put pumps into them as he had hoped, and they were taken up. So in Hull the distribution of the water from Spring Dyke and the Bush Dyke reservoir was then taken over by water carriers in water carts. Because they filled their carts at Bush Dyke they became known as Bush-Men. They paid the town three shillings and fourpence a year and recovered it from the charges they made.

In Liverpool the water from the Fall Well was distributed from water carts in tin cans. By the end of the 18th century, 60 water carts set out every day, taking ten loads, each amounting to a total distribution of 100,000 gallons. A rough lot, the Liverpool water carriers were constantly brawling about their loads and fighting with their customers. They made a thorough nuisance of themselves. The carts, stated a contemporary account:

> are dangerous vehicles, perpetually encumbering the streets and often either stopping the narrow ones up entirely or unexpectedly crossing the way of passengers, as they seldom proceed but in a zig-zag direction.

In Aberdeen people would never think of getting drinking water from a water cart, only water for washing. Whatever kind of water they carried, water carts not only got in the way but made a terrible mess. In an attempt to prevent them breaking up the streets, the Leeds authorities ruled that heavy carts carrying water from the River Leene must have clogg wheels which were not rimmed with iron or nails. Cart horses and cattle fouling the streets caused even greater nuisance. 'All the streets are so badly paved,' wrote a foreign visitor Andreas Franciscus about his *Itinerarium Britanniae* of 1497, 'that they get wet at the slightest quantity of water, and this happens very frequently owing to the large numbers of cattle carrying water as well as on account of the rain of which there is a great deal in this island.' But at least the water, which splashed over from the tankards they were apparently carrying like pack horses, would have helped wash away what they left on the paving of a more unhygienic nature.

In the estuary of the River Hull it was a case of water on water. Barges were used to carry supplies from Barton-upon-Hull on the south side to Kingston upon Hull.

Apart from being an innkeeper and horse breeder, Thomas Hobson of Cambridge was a water carrier. Far from wishing to fight with his customers – either for ale, a horse or water – he cultivated their goodwill by providing them in 1614 with Hobson's Conduit, for the maintenance of which he settled 'seven lays' of pasture ground. The conduit head was in the market place. But it is not by this charitable act that he is chiefly remembered. It was his custom of obliging dealers to take the horse nearest the stable door, or none at all, which gave rise to the phrase 'Hobson's Choice'.

### Forcing Water Up by Pumps

The carrying of water from conduit head to consumers' premises, whether in buckets and tankards or in creaking water carts, was cumbersome, slow and unreliable. The only people who were happy with it were the carriers who, strongly organised, were the first to oppose any moves for change which they foresaw – correctly as it turned out – would eventually lead to the demise of their calling. But change there had to be. Carrier-based distribution could not keep pace with the growing demand for water throughout the 17th century.

Reliance on the force of gravity alone to move water from source to head was also becoming a severe brake on the ingenuity of the growing band of waterworks makers. Until an effective means of raising water in bulk to a height from which it could then flow to its point of delivery was invented, there was no option but to choose a conduit's course from source to destination provided by the geography. Exeter was one of the lucky towns, enjoying a conduit with a fall of 11 feet in its run of 1,400 feet which thus provided a good 'head of water'. Others were not so fortunate. It was becoming obvious that town water supplies should no longer have to rely on gravity alone.

Thomas More in *Utopia* (1516) nevertheless thought that with careful town planning gravity would suffice. Of Amaurote, his idealised London, he wrote:

> They have a river which runs down a slope through the middle to the city. And because it riseth without the city the Amaurotians have enclosed the head spring of it with strong fences and bulwarks, and so have joined it to the city. This is done to the intente that the water should not be stopped nor turned away or poysoned if their enemies should chaunce to come upon them. From thence the water is derived and conveied down in cannels in bricke divers ways into the lower parts of the citie.

Such a system was to prove less than utopian. Some 200 years after the publication of More's book, developments in British society, population growth and industry had moved beyond the point where the location of urban communities was influenced primarily by proximity to a source of water supply.

But what was to be done? There was really only one choice. Since the location of the city or town at the receiving end was fixed, the water at source had to be moved upwards. But how?

The power human muscle could exert unaided was certainly limited. With a mechanical device such as an Archimedes Screw, however, it could be greatly increased. The improvement was devised, like so much else, in Egypt around 1000 BC,

A 16th-century drawing of an Archimedes screw by which more water could be raised from a river than a human could take merely by muscle power.

Donkey-power could raise even more water – the donkey wheel at Carisbrooke Castle, Isle of Wight.

**This donkey-driven winding wheel, still to be seen in the Sussex hamlet of Saddlescombe, used to hoist up water from a well 75 feet deep.**

and improved by the Greek mathematician Archimedes, who died about 212 BC. It introduced the idea of raising water by 'pumping' – *sucking* it up through a cylinder, which needed very much less exertion than lifting it in a container. It consisted of a spiral screw (originally of leather or lead) wrapped round an axle which could be turned by the crank handle at the top of it. When the bottom end was placed in water, as in the illustration, and the screw was turned, the water was taken up to the top.

Animal power was another option. Horses and donkeys could be made to walk round in a circle, harnessed to the horizontal wooden spigots or a rotor, geared to turn a vertical wheel which wound up a rope with a bucket on the end full of water. A donkey-wheel of the kind still to be seen at Carisbrooke Castle on the Isle of Wight, or a horse-gin, like the one at Preston outside Brighton, could raise water from a deep well in a way that would have been fatiguing, often impossible, for the arms of even the strongest man. It was still laborious and slow. Horses, donkeys and oxen, like human beings, grew tired and hungry, needed resting and feeding. They could only work intermittently. They could easily be worked to death. The wind, which could exert a force of up to ten horsepower on the sails of a windmill on a hill, had no such weaknesses. But whether it blew or not was not subject to human control.

Nevertheless all workable methods of supplementing human muscle power were welcome, and were used. The mayor of Hull arranged for an engineer to build a water house with a pump worked by horses on a treadmill, and a cistern on top of the tower from which water flowed with considerable force through hollowed-out elm tree trunks. The horses remained the motive power of these works until 1773. In 1593 an English engineer called Bevis Bulmer obtained from the Corporation of London a lease permitting him to erect a 'chain pump' – buckets on a moving chain or belt as opposed to the rim of a wheel – worked by horses at Broken Wharf, to raise water from the Thames for a public supply. When it was completed in 1595 he presented the Lord Mayor of London with a cup made of English silver from Combe Martin in Devon.

But what could be depended upon to power a bucket wheel or chain non-stop, without tiring, without having to be fed? Running water, the perpetually flowing river that turned the wheel of the watermill to grind wheat into flour, to beat cloth or to pulp rags for paper-making. In 1573 the Corporation of Chester contracted with an engineer from London to provide, for the sum of £200, a set of waterwheels at Dee Bridge. They paid him 40 shillings a year to maintain the system. The councillors handed it over to a private operator, John Tyrer, in 1600, who erected a high octagonal tower at Bridge Gate with cisterns and engines to force water into the city. The grant entitled him to 'break up, dig, trench and mine the streets, soil and grounds', to drive and pass the water of the River Dee in pipes or instruments of lead to any part of the city for a yearly rent of five shillings.

Tyrer's waterwheel system was incapable of bringing Chester all the water it needed. Seventy years later Chester Corporation gave another engineer, Thomas Evans, a piece of waste ground next to the Bridge Gate waterworks for an engine *operated by horses* to draw water from the Dee and raise it to Tyrer's water tower.

Manpower, horsepower, windpower, riverpower.... Still, those at the cutting edge of the water supply business were looking for a better and more reliable means of raising water. The solution, when it appeared, came not from a native source but from a Dutchman who had learned his skills in the Low Countries, where the constant threat of inundation by the sea had concentrated the minds of engineers wonderfully.

It was the ebbing and flowing of the tide which was to provide the next opportunity for progress in the kingdom's water affairs.

CHAPTER DIVIDERS: **The colour pictures which divide each chapter illustrate the water cycle and aspects of the water environment.**

OVERLEAF: **Rain and snow replenish rivers and aquifers to continue the water cycle. The River Feshie in Glenfeshie, surrounded by Caledonian pines, in the Cairngorms National Nature Reserve.**

# CHAPTER TWO

# Too little and too unhealthy

PETER MORRIS'S LONDON BRIDGE SCHEME • THE NEW RIVER SCHEME • PROVINCIAL IMPROVEMENTS IN SUPPLY • THE SITUATION IN IRELAND • THE GROWTH OF LONDON AND THE GREAT FIRE • SEWAGE DISPOSAL IN LONDON • GEORGE SOROCOLD OF DERBY • THE APPROACH OF THE ENGINE AGE • THOMAS SAVERY AND HIS FIRE ENGINE • NEWCOMEN'S IMPROVEMENTS • QUALITY AS WELL AS QUANTITY? • CHARITABLE INVOLVEMENT IN NORTHERN IRELAND • WATER QUALITY – THE APPLICATION OF SCIENCE • DEVELOPMENTS IN FIREFIGHTING • THE FIRST STEAM ENGINE • WATT MEETS TELFORD • THE ARCHITECTURE OF EARLY WATERWORKS

I t is not known when the Dutchman whose name was anglicised as Peter Morris came to England. By some time in the middle of the 16th century, however, he had won a place for himself in the service of Sir Christopher Hatton (of Hatton Garden), a favourite of Queen Elizabeth and her Lord Chancellor.

It was Peter Morris (or Morice) who saw the potential for obtaining a more reliable and substantial water supply from London's river, the Thames. In 1574 he submitted a scheme to the corporation for installing a paddle wheel under an arch of London Bridge: the tide running up the Thames would turn it in one direction, and the tide running back to the sea in another. The wheel, he told them, would operate a pump which drew fresh water from the bottom of the river and forced it through a pipe into a cistern on the bank. To the city fathers it seemed unbelievable that so preposterous an idea would ever work and they rejected it out of hand. Apart from anything else, they had no wish to offend the Rulers, Wardens and Fellows of the Brotherhood of Saint Cristofer of Water Bearers of London, who had drawn up an impressive list of Rules, Ordinances and Statutes in October 1496.

Sir Christopher Hatton was convinced that his servant was onto something good, and in 1578 persuaded his royal mistress to give a patent to the imaginative Dutch water engineer 'who hath by his great labor and charge found out and learned the skill and cunning to make some new kind and matter of engine to draw water higher than nature itself'. So the city grudgingly gave Sir Christopher's servant permission to put a waterwheel and pumps under the last arch of London Bridge on the city side. They gave £50 towards the cost, but had so little faith in the idea that they declined to give him a contract to complete the system.

It took him two years, and another hundred pounds, to build foundations for the wheel in the river. In the meantime the Earl of Sussex had recommended the employment of a plumber and freeman of the city, one John Martyn, to erect works 'for bringing water from the Thames into some parts of the city'. What this rival scheme was and whether it ever came into being is unclear, but the Privy Council were told that in refusing to give Morris a full agreement the Lord Mayor was treating him very shabbily.

OPPOSITE: **Peter Morris's tidal water wheel tucked under an arch at the north end of London Bridge.**

Meanwhile one Bernard Randolph, the city's Common Sergeant, had become involved with Morris's scheme and according to the record:

> ...had lately charitably agreed to bestow a large sum of money for bringing water out of the River Thames by an engine to be constructed by Peter Morice from London Bridge to old Fish Street ... and by the way to supply the private houses of citizens. Thereupon Mr Randolph entered into agreement with the company of fishmongers for such a charitable deed.

The city's Court of Common Council thereupon granted a licence to Morris for a project, as it was put, 'to profit the whole City and to no hindrance to the poor Water Bearers who would still have much work, as they were able to perform as far as the water of the conduits would satisfy'.

But it seems that during the time it took to bestir the city authorities Morris had 'entangled himself in bonds and bargains upon the faith of receiving money of Mr Randolph who had delayed payment until he had received the assent of his lordship [the Lord Mayor] which he heartily desired, otherwise the work would be in peril of failing, and the benefit of the City in cases of fire and infection would be lost'.

Morris decided that the only way of ridding the aldermen of their misgivings was to complete the installation out of his own pocket and prove to them that it *did* work. When all was finished to his satisfaction, he invited the Lord Mayor and his entourage to a demonstration. They could hardly believe their eyes when they saw Morris squirting water from a hosepipe over the tower of St Magnus Church. There was no question that it worked, and that it did so beyond their wildest dreams. On 30 May 1581 they granted Morris a lease of the arch for no less than 500 years. They charged a rent of ten shillings a year. Dating from December 1582, when the public supply began, the contract will not terminate until the year 2082.

The drawing made by John Bate, reproduced from *Mysteries of Nature and Art* (1635), shows how the paddle wheel riding on the surface of the river, and rotated by the incoming and outgoing tide, did not turn a waterwheel of buckets, but a shaft which pulled a disc to and fro which raised and lowered the two plungers of the two pumps below it. This forced water from the river into pipes climbing up a 128-foot water turret, and discharged it into a cistern. 'There being strayned through a close wyre grate,' wrote Bate, 'it descendeth into the main wooden pipe which is layd along the street; and into it are grafted divers small pipes of lead serving each of them to the use of service of particular persons.' There were nine main pipes.

Of the waterworks at London Bridge at this time, the city's historian Walter Timbs wrote:

> Morice used water-wheels turned by the flood-and-ebb current of the Thames through the purposely contracted arches, and working pumps for the supply of water to the metropolis; this being the earliest example of public water service by pumps to dwelling houses. Previously water had been supplied only to public cisterns from whence it had been conveyed at great expense and inconvenience in buckets and carts.

Not everyone was pleased: the wheel rotated six times a minute and in doing so made a loud and disagreeable noise. It was well known that under the Three Neats' Tongues tavern on London Bridge could be heard 'a strange rattle and creaking and groaning'. In one of their plays Beaumont and Fletcher have a female character compare another female's loud-mouthed behaviour to it – unfavourably:

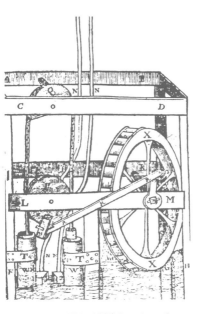

This 1635 drawing of Peter Morris's London Bridge water wheel machinery shows how the wheel rotated the shaft which pushed and pulled a disc coupled by chains to the piston rods of two pumps.

Oh, terribly,
Extremely fearfully! The noise of London Bridge
Is nothing near her.

No matter. It all functioned so well that the Corporation of London had no hesitation in leasing Peter Morris a second 'starling', as an arch was called, in 1583. Only householders in the eastern part of the city – and those able to pay the charges – were at first able to receive Thames water from the London Bridge force pumps. Pipes were laid in the immediate vicinity of the bridge, and in 1583 Morris had a conduit laid to a site near the parish church of St Mary Magdalene in Old Fish Street and, ten years later, to one by the church of St Nicholas Cole Abbey. In 1593 too the horsepowered chain bucket works of Bevis Bulmer were supplying far from pure Thames water to houses around West Cheap, St Paul's and Fleet Street. Shortly afterwards Henry Shaw was given a 500-year lease similar to Morris's to bring water from Fogwell Pond, Smithfield to any customer willing to pay.

## The New River Scheme

Even with the purer water continuing to be drawn from medieval wells and the Tyburn, the supply was still wholly inadequate for London's growing and increasingly fastidious population, particularly in the north part of the city. Raising water to a storage cistern to give it a head 'against nature itself' was all very clever, but to generate the necessary volume, it was perhaps more effective to manoeuvre the pure water that issued naturally from a spring as soon as possible into a man-made river, along which it could move downhill by gravity to wherever it was required.

While the Corporation of London was trying to make up its mind over Sir Christopher Hatton's request to implement Peter Morris's scheme, they heard that a man called Russell had submitted to William Cecil, Lord Burghley, the administrative head of Queen Elizabeth's government, a plan for creating a man-made river to the north side of London in which would flow fresh water diverted from the Colne ('the River of Uxbridge'). A scheme on this scale seemed more likely to provide what was wanted, but it was never taken up.

Twenty years later, in 1600, Captain Edmund Colthurst of Bath came forward with yet another scheme, this time to bring water to London from springs in Hertfordshire and Middlesex. Queen Elizabeth died while his application for Letters Patent was being considered, but they were granted to him by her successor, James I, in 1604. The Common Council of the City of London liked the idea and had a Bill introduced into Parliament, which passed it in 1606 as 'An Acte for the Bringing in a freshe Streame of running Water to the northe parts of the City of London'. By it the Corporation was given the power to make a 'New River' from Chadwell and Amwell in Hertfordshire in the valley of the River Lea near Ware, where there were one-time 'holy' wells positioned sufficiently high to allow a good fall in the direction of Islington. By a second Act the Corporation was allowed to bring the water in a tunnel.

They agreed to allow Edmund Colthurst to carry out the work and had the powers of their two Acts of Parliament transferred to him. A mathematician surveyed the channel's route which, to make it as level as possible, followed the 100-foot contour with a gentle fall of 18 feet over the whole distance, and extended to nearly 40 miles, though the distance as the crow flies was half that. The new ten-foot wide channel was to run past Rye Common, Hoddesdon, Broxbourne, Wormley, Cheshunt, Enfield, Highfield near Southgate, Wood Green, Hornsey and Harringay, Woodberry Down and

Hugh Myddelton took over the New River project from Captain Colthurst, who had run out of money.

Stoke Newington. At Highbury Vale it was to turn west nearly to Holloway and back, and then went through Islington village to ground above Clerkenwell, known as Commandry Mantells.

Captain Colthurst mustered his workforce and plant and work started, but it soon began to cost much more than he had estimated – the final bill came to £18,525 – and he had to withdraw. In his place the corporation found 'a dauntless Welshman', Hugh Myddelton, able and willing to take the project over. Myddelton had made a fortune as a goldsmith in Basinghall Street and as a cloth manufacturer. He was the MP for Denbigh, and a merchant adventurer who in 1600 had sunk a coal mine near Denbigh. This was an engineering project of a very different calibre. It took months of negotiation, including getting power of attorney from the city, before he could agree to restart the enterprise at his own expense, although it was partly funded by 'adventurer' shares. He made Colthurst a partner and appointed him overseer.

Myddelton had probably not anticipated that the New River project would meet with such opposition. In 1610, in a petition to the House of Commons, the owners of land through which the channel was to pass claimed that their meadows would be turned into bogs and quagmires, their arable land would become 'squallid ground', their farms would be mangled and their fields cut up into 'quillets and small peeces'. When the complainants succeeded in having a Bill introduced into the House of Commons to repeal the Corporation's two Acts of Parliament, the work, on which some 600 men were now engaged, had to stop. They had reached Cheshunt. In places they had dug the channel underground; elsewhere they had carried it above ground in wooden aqueducts.

Ten MPs were appointed to view the work done so far in July 1610 and a few months later Parliament was dissolved, which prevented the repeal of the two Acts. Myddelton saw the delay as making it impossible to complete the work in the time prescribed in his contract, and was given five years' extension. But money as well as time was running out. The city refused him a loan, so he went to James I with whom he had had dealings as a jeweller. The New River had to pass through the grounds of the King's palace in Theobalds Park, Hertfordshire. King James had not only given his permission willingly but became intrigued with the whole project, the progress of which he watched from his windows. He agreed to bear half the outstanding cost in return for a 'moiety' or half share of the profits. With a personal interest in the work being completed as quickly as possible, the King forbade any of his subjects hinder its progress on pain of his 'highe displeasure'. Work was resumed in the autumn of 1611.

Gangs of excavators and labourers built some 200 bridges across the river to maintain the 'waies'. Much of their time was occupied with shoring up the left bank of the river which for much of the course sloped away. Between July 1612 and March

New River Head: 'ye Waterhouse', engraved by Wenceslas Hollar (1663).

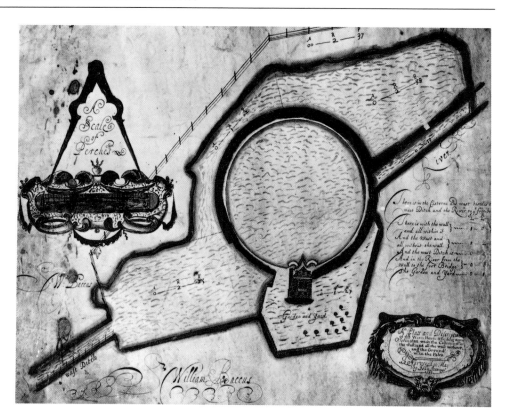

**A plan drawn in 1667 shows the cistern and ditches at the New River Head from which water was piped to nearby houses in Islington.**

1613 they did nothing else but raise and strengthen the banks with clay and piles. They removed hundreds of trees and their roots; they built numerous sluices between which the fall was as little as two to three inches a mile. They reached the terminus in April 1613 – the Ducking Pond, famous for duck shooting, just below Sadlers Wells in Islington, later called the Round Pond and then the New River Head. At a height of 80 feet above the Thames it made an excellent reservoir from which water could be piped to the surrounding north London houses.

The following months were spent on consolidating the river bed and testing the three-feet high stop-gates they had erected where the fall was too rapid and the timber troughs lined with lead which were to carry the water over roads. Hugh Myddelton had achieved much, not least in overcoming the objections of the church leaders who said they would be robbed of their tithes and their privacy and those who accused him of adventuring to the detriment of countryfolk 'to his own private benefit'. He had something to celebrate, and on Michaelmas Day 1613 he staged a public pageant to mark the entry of the waters of the New River into the metropolis, which was witnessed by a large gathering of Londoners. Sir John Swinnerton, Lord Mayor of London, opened the proceedings and the pageant itself was devised by the dramatist Thomas

**A 17th-century receipt for New River water.**

Midleton. Hugh Myddelton's triumph was proclaimed with 'warlike music of drums and trumpets'. Then there entered 'a troupe of labourers to the number of threescore or upwards, well apparelled and wearing greene Monmouth caps all alike, carrying spades, shovels, pick-axes and such like instruments of laborious imployment, marching after drummes twice or thrice about the Cisterne, presented themselves before the Mount, where the Lord Mayor Aldermen and a worthy Company beside, stood to behold them'. A man then stepped forward to deliver Thomas Middleton's declamation, beginning:

> Long have we labour'd, long desir'd and pray'd
> For this great work's perfection.

By the aid of heaven and good men's wishes, it was at last happily conquered by cost, art and strength:

> After five years' dear expense in days,
> Travail and pains, beside the infinite ways
> Of malice, envy, false suggestions,
> Able to daunt the spirit of mighty ones
> In wealth and courage; this a work so rare,
> Only by one man's industry, cost and care,
> Is brought to blest effect, so much withstood,
> His only aim the Citie's general good.

The declamation over, 'the flood-gate opens, the stream let into the cistern, drums and trumpets giving it triumphant welcomes, and a peal of small cannon concluding all'.

Hugh Myddelton and his merchant adventurer partners were the shareholders in the £18,000 enterprise, which in 1619 was incorporated by royal charter as The Company of the New River brought from Chadwell and Amwell to London. They did not at first see any great return on their capital. Myddelton gained a baronetcy in 1622 which James I gave him without asking for the usual fee of £1,095. Sir Hugh, who was the company's governor until his death in 1631, sold 28 of his 36 shares, and with the proceeds financed a project for reclaiming Brading Harbour in the Isle of Wight from the sea. He turned his attention to mining silver in North Wales. Just before Sir Hugh died, Charles I restored to him the Royal Moiety in exchange for what he thought was a more reliable guarantee, a perpetual rent charge of £500 a year.

Others who feared they would lose by the opening of the New River – the water bearers – in fact found their services more in demand than ever. For, once they had brought the well water from Hertfordshire to the New River Head in Islington, the company found they had to spend much more than they had bargained for to pipe it to customers' houses. The owners of ground near the New River Head exacted heavy sums for permission to carry the six-foot elm pipes through their land. The nearby Spa-fields, used as a depot for the pipes, were dubbed the Pipe Fields by the people of Clerkenwell. Since the company had to make high charges for piped water in order to recover their costs, most householders turned to water carriers to bring them tankards from the cistern at a much lower rate. Dressed in coarse aprons hung from their necks and wearing the 'city flat-cap', they walked the streets crying 'Any New River water here!', and making a point of the greater purity of their product with 'Fresh and fair New River water! None of your pipe-sludge!' They charged a penny a pail for their porterage. And when the wooden pipes started leaking or bursting in a frost, they were run off their feet.

'Any New River water here!' was the cry of this 17th-century water carrier who charged a penny a pail for porterage – from Laroon's *Cries of London* (1688).

**Hinksey Well House, built by Otho Nicholson in 1610 to collect pure spring water from a hillside several miles from Oxford. It was piped from here to the conduit at Carfax in the centre of the city.**

## Provincial Improvements in Supply

Otho Nicholson, who had the ornate conduit head erected in the centre of Oxford, as described on page 35, was a member of the Royal Commission of 1605 which considered the first suggestion, rejected by the Corporation, for a water supply of the kind which eventually saw the light of day in the New River project. The success of the latter, and the support given it by King James, led Nicholson to propose a similar scheme for Oxford, in the form of a conduit to carry fresh water from springs in Hinksey Hill to Carfax. Hitherto university and town had obtained their water from shallow wells which were contaminated by their proximity to cesspits and rubbish dumps, or from the Thames from which it had to be carried to its users by water bearers.

Nicholson had the clean spring water diverted into two vaulted gullies leading to a nearby 20,000 gallon lead cistern. This was housed in a stone chamber covered by a stone wellhouse. Over its door were carved the Nicholson family arms (still to be seen). From there the water flowed downhill through an underground lead pipe which, as usual, was encased in a hollowed-out elm tree trunk at the points where it crossed a river. From the cistern in the Carfax conduit head the water was conducted to one cistern at Christ Church and another beside All Saints Church, and from thence to

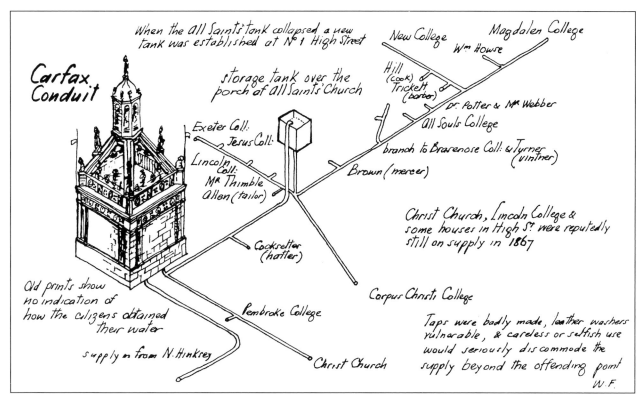

Carfax Conduit

When the all Saints tank collapsed a new tank was established at N°1 High Street

storage tank over the porch of all Saints' Church

New College

Magdalen College

W.ᵐ Howse

Hill (cook) & Trickett (barbor)

Dr. Potter & M.ʳ Webber

all Souls College

Exeter Coll:

Jesus Coll:

Lincoln Coll: M.ᴿ Thimble allan (tailor)

branch to Brazenose Coll: & Turner (vintner)

Brown (mercer)

Christ Church, Lincoln College & some houses in High S.ᵗ were reputedly still on supply in 1867

Cooksetter (hatter)

Corpus Christi College

Old prints show no indication of how the citizens obtained their water

Pembroke College

supply in from N.Hinksey

Christ Church

Taps were badly made, leather washers vulnerable, & careless or selfish use would seriously discommode the supply beyond the offending point

W.F.

A plan showing how the water from Hinksey Hill was distributed by pipe from Otho Nicholson's conduit head at Carfax, Oxford, to colleges and to tradesmen such as barbers, hatters and tailors.

various colleges and sundry individuals (see diagram). This sophisticated piece of water engineering was executed by a London plumber, Hugh Justyce, a member of The London Plumbers' Guild who later became its warden. He had been associated with the New River project. Once completed in 1616, the management of Nicholson's conduit was handed over to a local plumber, William Hobbs.

Oxford was fortunate in having a wealthy benefactor with the ear of the monarch to reduce the town's dependence on unhealthy sources of water and finance the engineering of a purer supply from springs. Liverpool's red sandstone ensured a plentiful supply from shallow wells, but, as at Oxford, the way these wells were used, or rather abused, led to the water becoming contaminated.

The main offenders were people such as Edmund Irlam and Rauff Rughley who in 1568 were charged with 'watteryng felles [hides] and sckynnes, and wasshyng theyre woll at the Fall Well wherebye the Well of the inhabitants of this towne is corruptid'. Fall Well was outside Liverpool on Great Heath at the upper end of St John's Lane. They should have known better. Ten years earlier 'the great sicknesse' which visited the town was traced to 'an Irysshe man, one John Hughes, comyng syckley from Mamchester' and bringing 'his lynen clothes thither to be wasshed'.

However aware they may have been of the connection between misuse of the public wells and the contamination of the public water supply, Liverpool's town councillors took no action until 1583 when they ordered that 'noe person or persons shall washe anie yarne at the common well of this towne called Fall Well upon paine of theire fyne'. The following year they penalised Elizabeth Durninge in that way for doing just that, and others afterwards. But the order was only a mild deterrent. Furthermore, most of the wells in the streets remained uncovered or walled round, and became the depository of every kind of rubbish. In spite of orders imposing fines on all who left their wells unprotected, few took any notice. One reason was the expense. When

The initials O N can be seen clearly on this engraving of Otho Nicholson's Carfax conduit head in Nuneham Park, near Oxford, to which it was removed in 1787 and where it still stands.

Edward Moore sank a well in the new Moore Street in 1667, it cost him six pounds. He had a lucky strike, however:

> Whereas many of the wells in Water Street [*he said*] are above 20 yards deep, it pleased God to send me water at 14 yards. . . . My tenants confess that it makes better ale, boils peas and bears soap better than any water in the town.

He would have had the sense to put a wall round it and a grille and a wooden lid on top. Even so, it seems he did not risk drinking it.

Some 30 years later the town council ordered that Fall Well should be repaired, but nothing was done. They had another try in July 1694 when they ordered new gutters to be supplied 'for conveying away the dirty water that now lies about the well and runs into it, and that some ridge stones may be set round the mouth of the well to prevent servants from washing in it, to the end that it may be kept neat and clean'. A year later those given powers to construct an altogether new water supply system failed to act on them. Another 14 years passed before an Act of Parliament gave Sir Cleave Moore the right to bring water into Liverpool from springs in Bootle, but it was another 100 years before anyone saw fit to use the powers so granted.

## The Situation in Ireland

The water supply situation in Ireland in the early years of the 17th century was no better than on the mainland. In the six northern counties which James I was busy colonising with Scottish and English Protestants, the urban centres, Belfast in particular, were suffering the usual growing pains: polluted sources and insufficient supplies.

The City of London Corporation had contributed £40,000 – extorted (it is hardly too strong a word) from the 55 City livery companies – towards the cost of developing Derry, Coleraine and a large part of the county of Tyrone: but none of the money seems to have found its way into schemes for providing the colonists with fresh water supplies. For that they had to wait 70 years.

Belfast also had to wait until 1678 for an adequate supply system. By then the city's main source, the River Farset, had become badly polluted and supplies were insufficient. Two members of the corporation, George McCartney and Captain Robert Leathes, submitted a report recommending a scheme to convey water from springs outside the city through wooden pipes, at an estimated cost of £250. The preamble to their submission ran:

> WHEREAS many complaints from time to time have been made of ye great want of good and wholesome water to supply ye daily necessity occations of ye Inhabitants of this Towne of Belfast, for ye River that runs through ye said Towne is very much defiled and greatly abused by all manner of things falling into ye said River and other nusances corrupting ye same whereby ye water is made altogether unfit for ye use of man in meats and drinks, and WHEREAS for ye better supply of ye said Inhabitants with good and wholesome water ye springes near ye said Towne have been viewed and an estimate thereof taken by George McCartney Burgesse, and Capt Robt Leathes wch will cost near two hundred and fifty pounds ster[ling] to bringe ye said water in pumps or wooden pipes from ye Upper or Tuck Dame to ye great Bridge of ye Towne (contayneing aboute 200 perch in Length) a place most convenient to supply the whole Towne with water by a Common Conduit...

It went on to recommend the works, 'so well designed by ye said George McCartney and Capt Leathes and feasible to be done' to all the inhabitants of Belfast, who were enjoined to make donations to defray the charge.

The money was forthcoming, and in 1678 Belfast duly had its first supply of fresh water piped from Tuck Mill Dam in the Divis Street area to the Great Bridge of the town near the site of the present Boyne Bridge.

In looking to outside springs from which the water had to be piped a considerable distance, rather than the river that flowed through the town, which was the most accessible and obvious source, though vulnerable to defilement, the burgesses of Belfast and Liverpool stood apart from those of York. York looked to the Ouse for its supply and this was secured by an unusual scheme carried out by Henry Whistler, a London merchant, who in 1677 obtained the lease of Lendal Tower from the city council for the term of 500 years at a peppercorn rent, undertaking to provide the city with a piped supply of water.

The tower, part of York's medieval defences adjacent to the Ouse, was increased in height by Whistler and had a tank constructed on the top; when this was filled with river water by wind-driven pumping plant in the tower, it provided a limited gravity supply to the city. During the 18th century many improvements were carried out including the installation of a steam engine to drive the pumping plant. The tower still stands and the York Water Company's head office is in an adjacent building.

The late 17th century also saw improvements in water supply in other parts of the country. In 1693 Gloucester Corporation had Thomas Nicholls pump water from the River Severn. The Common Council of Newcastle entered into an agreement with a water engineer, William Yarnold, in 1697 to bring water to their inhabitants and to those of Gateshead. Yarnold leased the waterwheel and pumps, by which Cuthbert Dykes had been drawing water from the River Tyne at Sandgate since 1680 for supplying Newcastle, and the waterworks by which the Ellison family supplied Gateshead from springs. Yarnold's idea was to take water from Swan Pond on Carr Hill south of Gateshead, combine it with water from springs on Heworth Common, convey it in wooden pipes to a storage reservoir at Holmes Close and then across the river to cisterns in Newcastle. In 1694 Nottingham Corporation sanctioned the operation of a pump powered by a waterwheel to take water from the River Leene. For the people of Manchester, the Lord of the Manor, Sir Oswald Mosley, put a pumping engine on the banks of the River Medlock at Holt Town and piped it to the Shudehill Pits and Infirmary Pond.

## The Growth of London and the Great Fire

As the 17th century wore on, London's growing population needed all the water that could be obtained. In 1676 the York Buildings Water Works Company was formed with the object of supplementing the supplies from the London Bridge works, the New River system and the countless wells. The company installed pumps powered by horse-driven treadmills at the bottom of Villiers Street in the Strand which, like Bevis Bulmer's Works at Broken Wharf and Ford's at Somerset House, raised water from the Thames.

The Archbishop of York had sold his London residence, York House, to George Villiers, Duke of Buckingham, in 1624. Forty years later the new occupant wrote to the Lord Mayor of London about the house's water supply:

> Having occasion at present to make use of some Conduit water at York House in the Strand; and understanding that the City of London is interested in a Pipe which runs along the Strand; I desire your Lordship and the Court of Aldermen to give licence unto your Plummer that a Pipe of Leade which I have neare abutting to your great Pipe may be so[l]dered thereunto so that I may have the benefit of the said water, which favour shall at all times bee acknowledged unto your Lordship and the rest of your Bretheren.
> (1 July 1664)

Where did this water come from? Presumably from Peter Morris's engine under London Bridge, although there were other engines near at hand. Samuel Pepys noted some of them when he took a stroll in St James's Park one day in October 1660:

> To walk in St James's Park where we observed the several engines to draw up water with which sight I was very much pleased. Above all the rest I liked that which Mr Greatorex brought, which do carry up the water with a great deal of ease.

Perhaps it was these which had supplied the Royal Mews (on the site of Trafalgar Square) in Charles I's day? The monarchy had been restored but not, three years later, it seemed, the water supply. In October 1663, George Monck, Duke of Albemarle, wrote to the Lord Mayor:

I have formerly sollicited your Lordship that you would be instrumental to the Court of Aldermen for procuring the Mewes to bee supplied as it was heretofore with water, which I doe assure your Lordship is so essential necessary both for his Majesty's particular service and for the use of his Equerries that lodge there ...

York Buildings Water Works supplemented the supply from London Bridge works, the New River and countless wells. Watercolour by J. P. Malcolm (1797).

Three years after the letter was written, large parts of the city were consumed in the Great Fire of London, in the course of which poor Morris's wooden wheels and pumps under London Bridge were totally destroyed.

Water, or the lack of it, for firefighting, also featured in one of the many rumours circulating in the aftermath of the fire as to why more effort had not been applied in preventing its spread. Like others, it hinted at a 'Papist Plot'. Gilbert Burnet, Bishop of Salisbury, recounted in his *History of His Own Time* how he was told the story by a Doctor Lloyd and the Countess of Clarendon:

The countess had a great estate in the new river that is brought from Ware to London, which is brought together at Islington, where there is a great room full of pipes that convey it through all the streets of London. The constant order of that matter was to set all the pipes a running on Saturday night, that so the cisterns might be all full by Sunday morning, there being a more than ordinary consumption of water on that day.

A papist called Grant ingratiated himself with the Countess of Clarendon, with

At the end of the 17th century, the directors of the New River Company fitted out this Oak Room at the Water House in Islington for their committee meetings with wooden panelling carved by Grinling Gibbons, a portrait on the ceiling of William III by court painter Henry Cooke and the royal arms above the fireplace.

whose influence he became one of the board that governed the New River Company:

> By that he had a right to come, as oft as he pleased, to view their works at Islington. He went thither the Saturday before the fire broke out and called for the key of the place where the heads of the pipes were, and turned all the cocks that were then open, and stopped the water, and went away, and carried the keys with him. So when the fire broke out next morning, they opened the pipes in the streets to find water, but there was none. And some hours were lost in sending to Islington where the door was to be broken open and the cocks turned. And it was long before the water got to London.

Bishop Burnet says Captain John Grant denied that he had turned the cocks. The officer of the works affirmed that, according to his orders, he had set them all a-running, and that no-one had got the keys from him besides Grant. The captain confessed that he carried away the keys, but claimed he did so without design. Burnet agreed that there were many other stories put about concerning the cause of the fire, and that it did not seem probable that the papists were engaged in trying 'merely to impoverish and ruin the nation':

> for they had nothing ready then to graft upon the confusion that this put all the people in. Above twelve thousand houses were burnt down, with the greatest part of the furniture and merchandise that was in them.

Peter Morris's grandson Thomas obtained an Act of Parliament to give him the power to rebuild the gutted waterworks with timber. Under the original scheme, in the event of *his* water being needed to fight a fire, he could turn off the supply through every pipe except that leading to the scene of the conflagration, in order to give it the greatest pressure; and presumably the same facility was built in to the post-1666 works. There was no Fire Office until 1680. Two men, William Riley and Edward Mabb, had petitioned the King in 1638 for a 41-year patent. They had proposed that the owners of houses in the City of London, Westminster and Southwark, should pay a sum on a rising scale according to rent, which would give them the right to have their house rebuilt if destroyed by fire. A constant watch was to be kept on all parts of the city, they stated in their application for their patent, and fire engines 'to be constructed and kept ready quenching fires with reserves of water in convenient places'. Charles I granted the two of them their patent and instructed his Attorney General to prepare a Parliamentary Bill, but nothing was heard of this incipient fire insurance scheme from then on. But, of course, while insurance was a matter for private enterprise, the quenching of fires and organising reserves of water would have to have been done with the assistance of the Corporation of London. Between 1680 and 1700 four notable fire insurance ventures were launched.

**W. HOWES,**
TURNCOCK to the
NEW RIVER COMPANY,
24, Pudding Lane Eastcheap;
Where it is requested, in case of Fire, or any deficiency in the Supply of Water, information may be given, to which immediate attention will be paid.

**Business card of a turncock to the New River Company.**

## Sewage Disposal in London

The Corporation of London apparently saw no reason to pay attention to the pleas which had been coming to successive lord mayors for the water pipe at Charing Cross to be reconnected to the royal mews. To assuage the thirst of the royal horses and wash down their looseboxes required complicated tidal machinery, pipes, pumps, cocks and cisterns. A simpler operation met the needs of those poor men and women of the Vintry Ward who daily answered the call of nature at the Longhouse. For them the waters of the Thames, rising and falling with the tide, did all the cleansing unaided.

The Longhouse in Greenwich Street (close to the present Bell Wharf Lane south of Cannon Street station) was built in the 15th century by Lord Mayor Richard Whittington. It was the biggest public latrine – house of easement – the city had ever had. Sixty-four men and 64 women could sit on two long rows of seats face to face. 'Longhouse' became a general term for a privy as a result. Underneath the wooden seats was a narrow gully open to the river.

Dick Whittington's Longhouse was burnt down in the Great Fire of 1666, along with Peter Morris's waterwheels, and rebuilt with only 12 seats. In 1685 the local residents told the Corporation that whatever convenience the place might be for some, for them it was an annoyance. It was reported in 1690 that George Peck, to whom the site had been let after the fire, had arched over the gully when rebuilding the edifice, although it should 'lye open'. He was ordered to take care 'that all impediments of the water flowing to the same be removed'. Otherwise, they said, 'the tide cannot have sufficient ingresse and regresse to purge away the soyle of the said Longhouse as it ought to have.'

However unpleasant it must have been for the neighbours, it must have been even more so for the six old-age pensioners for whom Whittington provided almshouse chambers on the floor *above* the latrine. None of it could be described as exactly environment-friendly but then, as Philip Jones has pointed out, Whittington 'saw nothing unhygienic in people living above the privies, for there was at that time a cesspit under or adjacent to most houses'.

Was this early example of water-borne sewage disposal taken up by other municipal bodies who saw themselves as responsible for water supply? There is no evidence that it was. In any event it was not a matter of their having to spend money on *engineering* it: all that was necessary was to position the convenience so that a fast-running river could do the dirty work on its own – though little thought was given to the effect this would have on rivers which were more and more being used as a source of fresh water supply. It was to be some time yet before water suppliers assumed responsibility for sewage disposal as an integral part of their service, and treated the soiled effluent *before* it was discharged into water which was later to be abstracted for distribution to the public.

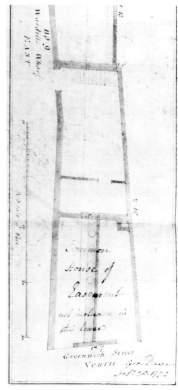

**A plan of Whittington's Longhouse, drawn by George Dance in 1772.**

## George Sorocold of Derby

More reliance was put on the power of a river along its whole length, as it rushed downhill in a constricted watercourse to the sea, than the cleansing role of a tidal estuary. The man who was contributing more than any other in Britain at this time to the improvement of water engineering was to be found not in London but in Derby. A contemporary wrote:

> Nothing can be more fit for serving cities and towns with water except a crank-work by the force of the river. In composing such sort of engines I think no person has excelled the ingenious Mr George Sorocold.

There was no direct water supply to houses in Derby: it had to be carried to them from rivers and wells by water bearers, although the friars had laid a conduit pipe to their monastery from Becket Well. Derby was George Sorocold's home town; he was born there probably in about 1668. As a young water engineer he had been intrigued to learn of the waterwheel pumping system which a Frenchman named Rannequin had designed to provide water for the French king's palace and gardens in Versailles. It had 14 waterwheels, operating 253 pumps. Sorocold designed a similar 'forcing pump' and proposed a plan to the Mayor and Burgesses of Derby for bringing fresh water to houses direct.

They liked the idea and in March 1691 gave him the building known as Gunpowder Mill 'with free liberty to erect a water-house, a water-wheel and other engines, laying pipes for conveying water into the streets, lanes and passages within the borough, to hold for a term of 99 years at an annual rent of £3'. Derby Corporation financed the whole project and, when it was completed in 1692, managed it. It did not supply the whole town, but only that part between the River Derwent and Markeaton Brook (then called Odde Brooke). The waterwheel could be set high or low, and when the river was in flood the engine ground malt. Normally it pumped water into a cistern standing in the nearby St Michael's churchyard. From there it flowed downhill through elm pipes to the town and what Celia Fiennes described as 'a fine stone conduit in the Market Place which is very spacious, well pitch'd, a good Market Cross'. The installation served Derby for much longer than 99 years, till at least 1829.

During a tour of the North Midlands which included a visit to Derby, Daniel Defoe commented on what he called a throwster's mill – 'the only one of its kind in England' – which was erected, he said, 'by one Soracule, a man expert in making mill-work, especially for raising water to supply towns for family use':

> But he made a very odd experiment at this place. For, going to show some gentlemen the curiosity, as he called it, of his mill, and crossing the planks which lay just above the mill-wheel, regarding it seems what he was to show his friends more than the place where he was, and too eager in describing things, keeping his eye rather upon what he pointed at with his fingers than what he stepped upon with his feet, he stepped awry and slipped into the river.

He fell close to the sluice which let the water in on the wheel and it was difficult for anyone to catch hold of him. The force of the water carried him through and pushed him under the great wheel 'which was going round at a great rate':

> His body being thus forced in between two of the plashers of the wheel, stopped the motion for a little while, till the water pushing hard to force its way, the plasher beyond him gave way and broke, upon which the wheel went again and, like Jonah's whale, spewed him out, not upon dry land, but into that party they call the apron, and so to the mill-tail where he was taken up and received no hurt at all.

News of the successful fresh water supply which George Sorocold had given Derby Corporation soon spread. In 1694 he joined with a Londoner, Richard Barry of Westminster, to obtain a 99-year agreement to install a similar system in the ancient city of Norwich. The partners promised to lay lead or wooden pipes in all the principal streets inside six years. In the same year, with a surveyor Henry Gillert, Sorocold negotiated a deal with Leeds Corporation to lay an engine to carry water from the River Aire through the streets of the town to householders willing to pay for it. 'It will be a worke of publique benefitt' declared the Corporation 'and deserves great encouragement'. Sorocold erected a waterwheel beside the Aire Pitfall near the northeast end of Leeds Bridge and a reservoir near St John's Church at the top of Briggate. In August he began laying lead distribution pipes in Kirk to take the water into houses. Visiting the

Daniel Defoe, who described George Sorocold's waterworks in Sheffield and Derby in his *Tour Thro' the Whole Island of Great Britain*.

New Waterworks in October, one Ralph Thoresby described it in his diary as 'a most ingenious contrivance'.

When a London draper, two London merchants and two citizens of Bristol formed a partnership in August 1696 and contracted with Bristol Corporation to supply the town with fresh water at reasonable rates, they had Sorocold build one of his waterwheels on the bank of the River Avon two miles above Bristol Bridge. The engine pumped river water into a large pond a mile from Lawford's Gate and then in elm pipes to the town. He was to install his water-engines, reservoirs, conduit heads and pipes all over Britain – at Macclesfield, Wirksworth, Yarmouth, Portsmouth, King's Lynn, Deal, Bridgnorth and Sheffield, where the waterworks were described by Defoe in his *Tour Thro' The Whole Island of Great Britain*:

> Here is a fine engine or mill also for raising water to supply the town, which was done by Mr Serocoal, the same who fell into the river at the throwing-mill at Derby.

He saw no fine engine in Chester, however, when he visited the town in 1690:

> They had no water to supply their ordinary occasions but what was carried from the River Dee upon horses in great leather vessels like a pair of bakers' paniers, just the very same for shape and use as they have to this day in the streets of Constantinople and at Belgrade in Hungary to carry water about the streets to sell for the people to drink.

Six years later Sorocold was called to London by Hugh Marchant who had obtained Letters Patent authorising him and his fellow venturers to erect over-shot wheels in the Thames and extract river water for public purposes. For what became Marchant's Water Works in St Martin's Lane, Sorocold built three such wheels, one on top of the other, geared by a three-throw undershaft. The whole lot were driven by one stream. In this enterprise he was joined by John Hadley who had invented the mechanism for adjusting the height of a wheel to the rise and fall of the tide. Sir Godfrey Copley, who gave his name to the Royal Society's 'Copley Medal', said Sorocold's engine at Marchant's was the best piece of work he had ever seen.

Richard Soame, a London goldsmith, bought the rights in the rebuilt water-works at London Bridge from Thomas and John Morris, Peter's grandsons, for £38,000, and engaged Sorocold to construct the engine for a third arch – the fourth from the bank – the lease of which, just granted to Thomas Morris, he obtained in 1701. He also arranged for Sorocold to reconstruct the machinery in the

A pamphlet, *The CASE of Thomas Morris Esq*, reproduced here from the Corporation of London archives, regarding the controversy over the letting of a third arch of London Bridge for the erection of more waterwheels.

New River Head in 1733. The New River Company had this new head dug at Islington on higher ground, with a pumping engine powered by horses.

original two arches, which had been in constant use since being renewed after the fire – and indeed to overhaul the whole system. The new waterwheel which Sorocold designed for the third arch was 20 feet in diameter and had 14-foot floats. The seven-inch bore pumps displaced 880 gallons of water a minute against a head of 120 feet, equivalent to 32 horsepower. Sorocold incorporated John Hadley's raising and lowering mechanism, but it was rarely used. The whole London Bridge Water Works, as redesigned by George Sorocold, consisted of four waterwheels – he put two new ones under the third arch – driving 52 pumps of similar type which raised 1,820 gallons a minute.

It is not known when George Sorocold died, but it is to be hoped that he lived to hear of the remark made to the Royal Society in 1731 by the distinguished civil engineer Henry Beighton – that the machines installed at London Bridge were far superior to those at Marly, which pumped water from the River Seine for the palace at Versailles, and which had inspired Sorocold to embark on his career as a water engineer.

### The Approach of the Engine Age

The New River Company was responsible for supplying the greater part of London's water and did so, as it had done now for 100 years, without any recourse to water-wheels. In the 1720s Defoe reported that the company had been obliged to dig a new head at Islington on higher ground, up to which water was raised by 'a great engine worked formerly with six sails now by many horses constantly working, so from that new elevation of the water they supply the higher part of the town with some advantage and more ease than the Thames Engines do it'.

Many new entrepreneurs now sought to compete with the old guard and reap some of the rewards, which they saw as substantial. (The New River Company paid a dividend of £33 2s 8d in 1640; at the end of the 17th century it was valued at £200 a share; at the end of the 18th century £500.) A Water Bill was introduced in 1720 for 'the better accommodating the inhabitants in and around the cities of London and Westminster with water'. A couple of years later a proposal was laid before the House of Commons for yet another new river to bring the fresh water of the Cowley Stream from Drayton to Marylebone, with the intention of employing 'the useful inventions and engines to raise and force water' of John Fowke of Ten Foot Lane, Wapping. A Chelsea Water Company was formed in 1723. In the speculation mania of the South Sea Bubble, the £10 shares of The York Buildings Water Works Company rose to £305.

> You that are blessed with wealth by your Creator
> And want to drown your money in Thames Water
> Buy but York Buildings, and the Cistern there
> Will sink more pence than any fool can spare. . .

wrote a rhymester in *The Bubbler's Mirrour, or England's Folly* of 1721:

> Come all ye Culls, my Water Engine buy
> To pump your flooded Mines and Coal-pits dry.
> Some projects all are Wind, but ours is Water,
> And, tho' at present low, may rise herea'ter.

The choice of investment was not as irrational as most of the fantastical schemes into which so many were induced to pour their money by dealers in Exchange Alley, such as extracting butter from beech trees and making square cannonballs. The water engine at York Buildings was no fantasy, but a redesigned version of a very real and

**One of the many plans for another 'New River' to augment the water supply of central London – submitted in 1722, it would have brought water from Drayton to Marylebone.**

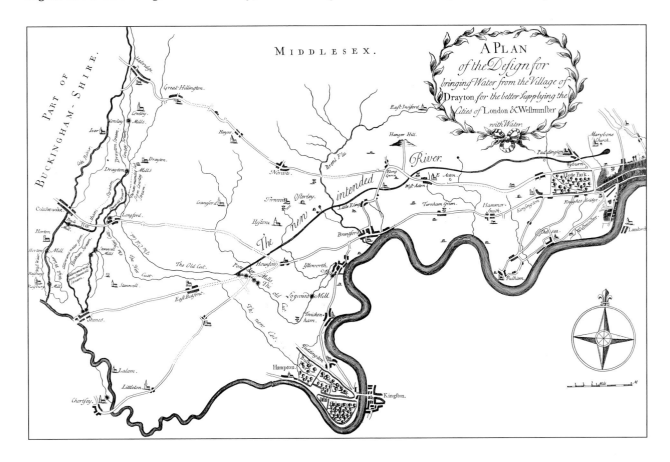

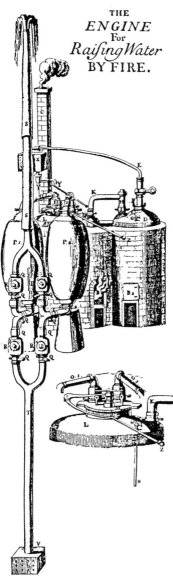

THE
*ENGINE*
For
*Raiſing Water*
BY FIRE.

**Close-up of the Savery Engine from the Captain's book of 1702, *The Miner's Friend, or an Engine to Raise Water by Fire Described*.**

OPPOSITE: **Savery's engine working in a mine, from Harris, *Lexicon Technicum* (1704).**

proven water-raising system worked out and built by the very down-to-earth Cornishman 'Captain' Thomas Savery.

Throughout the reign of Queen Elizabeth many had tried to find a better means of raising water. Between 1561 and 1599 some 55 patents were taken out for various 'engines', of which seven were for apparatus for raising water. Between 1617 and 1642 one in seven patents in the Patent Office Index were for new water-raising ideas. As R. D'Acres pointed out in *The Art of Water-drawing* in 1659, instruments for so doing were either natural or artificial. Natural syphons ('the Philosopher's Engine') were of little or no use; they were only a make-sport in the world except among vintners. No suction pump had ever managed to lift water higher than 30 feet. Animate movers – man's muscle and animal strength – were not well suited for working water machines; the inanimate *elements* were best. So far only air (the wind) and water had been used:

> CHAP. II.
> *Of the various Species, or differing kinds of Water Gins, and wayes for Drawing of water.*
>
> THe firſt, beſt, and fureſt ( if the Mine be worth it ) of a l other, is the Addit, Sough, or Shore, as ſome call it, where it may be obtained, but where they cannot be had, we muſt be compelled to uſe other Artificial wayes and meanes for to force up the water.
> The *Machins*, or *Inſtruments* wherein *waters* are raiſed from lower Deeps, are for their *various forms* innumerable; but for their diſtinct kinds and ſorts, but few.
> The *world* hath laboured more to have them differing in figures, forms and ſhapes, than in effects or ſervice ; raſhly ſuppoſing, that if the *Water-Gins* and *Machins* were but of a ſtrange contrivance, and a ſort, never yet ( for what they knew of ) experienced (though it may be others have long ſince tried them, as I know ſome have been of very late, and alſo of very chargeable tryals ) preſently, greater ſervice muſt needs be expected and performed by them.

> Most men have expected greater matters from the Water-Gins than can ever be effected, supposing that as they can take water from below so they should alter the nature as well as place of the water by making a grave and heavy body (instantly) to be of no burden (thinking as it were, with smooth language, to court and complement up that solid and weighty body). Whereas it is never to be hoped for by any experienced sober men that water should become less of burden than his own natural weight.

All a water engine could do was to lift the pure weight of water in 'an apt, convenient and durable way'. Better than air or water was fire.

## Thomas Savery and his Fire Engine

David Ramsay had produced apparatus 'to raise water from lowe parts by fire' as early as 1630. It was open to anyone to note the distilling action of the heat of the sun in raising water from the sea to the clouds. How to engineer this natural phenomenon to serve human needs? The Marquis of Worcester obtained an Act of Parliament in 1663 entitling him to receive the benefit and profit of 'a water-commanding engine' to drive up water by fire, but he managed to solve only half the problems. It was left to Thomas Savery to work them out in a way that enabled him to build the first full-sized apparatus for raising water by 'fire' and introducing it into commercial use.

In *Hydrostaticks & Hydraulicks* (1729), S. Switzer suggested that the inspiration for Savery's fire engine was a tobacco pipe which he immersed to wash or cool:

He discovered by the rarefaction of the air in the tube by the heat or steam of the water, and the gravitation or impulse of the exterior air, that the water was made to spring through the tube of the pipe in a wonderful surprising manner.

Captain Thomas Savery was no army captain: that was just what he was called by the gang of Cornish tin miners whom he led with such enthusiasm in the 1680s. The copper mines of Cornwall had been famous since the 5th century BC. Tin came later, and by the end of the 17th century the area around Camborne and Redruth in Cornwall was the largest source of tin and copper ore in the world, and was to continue to be so until the 1870s. The 17th-century miners were prevented from extracting the ore, which they knew lay deep down, by the water which could not be removed by the pumps then available. In 1698 Thomas Savery conceived the idea of placing a pipe running from the floodwater at the bottom of the mine up to the surface, widening it out 30 feet up to form a chamber. If, he reasoned, steam could be forced into the chamber, the water in it would be forced into the pipe above. If he closed a valve below it, it would stay put. Dowsing the chamber with cold water would create a vacuum which would suck the water up from below and refill the chamber. It was what had happened when he cooled his tobacco pipe.

In July 1698 Savery took out a patent for his 'new invention for raising of water . . . by the impellent force of fire'. The book he wrote some four years later, *The Miner's Friend, or an Engine to raise Water by Fire Described*, enumerated the uses to which it might be applied:

1. The working of mills by raising water.
2. The supplying of palaces or noblemen's and gentlemen's houses with cisternfulls of water, for domestic use through the house, for fountains, or in case of fire.
3. The serving of cities and towns with water.
4. The draining of mines and coal pits.

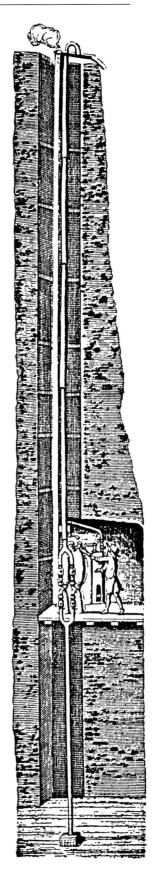

It is significant that Savery himself placed the draining of mines and coal pits in fourth place in his list of uses, for though that was the prime aim of the invention, not one engine was installed for this purpose; miners thought it too dangerous. He installed one, however, at Campden House, Kensington, in 1712 for a Mr Balle; one at Sion Hill for the Duke of Chandos; and another to drain Broad Water at Wednesbury in Staffordshire. Prior to that, he had exhibited a working model to King William III at Hampton Court Palace. His patent was for 14 years, and he obtained an Act of Parliament extending it by another 21 years. The Royal Society invited a demonstration and was duly impressed. He set up a factory to make his engines at Lambeth, and in 1702 moved to Salisbury Court off Fleet Street near the old Dorset Gardens Playhouse. People flocked to see the remarkable new engine perform, as *The Post Man* reported in March: 'with less expense than any force of Horse or Hands, and less subject to repair'.

It was probably true to say that it was less expensive than a horse-powered or man-powered plant, but the cost of the large amount of coal required to raise enough steam was soon found to be out of proportion to the work done and it all proved somewhat more costly than anyone had anticipated. A man had to be employed to open the valve by hand to allow steam to pass into the 'receiver' and displace the air which passed up the force pipe. When the receiver was full of steam, he had to shut off the valve and throw cold water on it so that the steam condensed and produced a vacuum, which would force water up the suction pipe into the receiver.

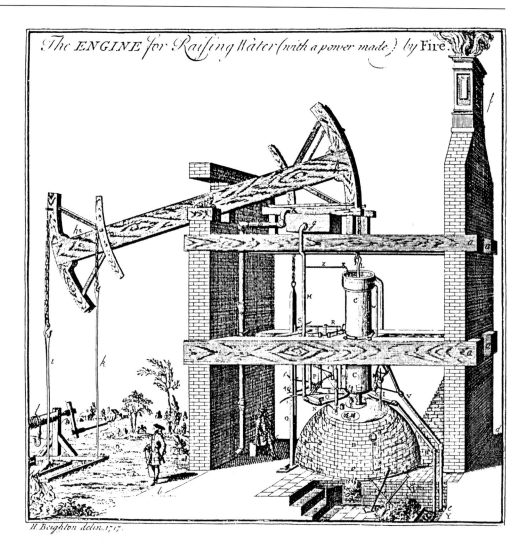

**Thomas Newcomen's improvement on the Savery Engine, engraved by H. Beighton (1717).**

### Newcomen's Improvements

In 1712 a greatly improved fire engine was erected and started to function at Dudley Castle. This was the handiwork of Thomas Newcomen who, stated a magazine of 1725, 'by applying the weight of the atmosphere instead of the elasticity of steam brought it [Savery's engine] to the perfection wherewith it is now used'. A Newcomen engine replaced Savery's at the York Buildings Water Works, but the locals were alarmed by it and it needed just as much coal. It was taken out of service in 1731 as too costly, although it remained on site for some time afterwards for the benefit of sightseers. Newcomen engines were better suited to draining mines and by 1715 they were to be found in the northeast at Washington, Tanfield Lea, Chester-le-Street and Byker. As many, if not more, were installed in Cornish tin and copper mines. By 1716 Newcomen engines were working in eight counties; by 1775 there were 100 in the northeast coalfields. In the story of water supply, power pumping by an inanimate atmospheric engine began a new era.

The York Buildings Water Works saw it all – horsepower, Sorocold's waterpower, Savery's firepower, Newcomen's atmospheric-power – and possibly machinery designed by a Dr Desaiguillières. It was a well-ordered progression, each step serving contemporary water consumers in its own way, and the contribution of each inventor recognised by his improver – the tribute to George Sorocold on page 61 was from Thomas Savery.

However much the plant at the foot of Villiers Street may have alarmed Londoners, six years before it closed it seems to have impressed foreigners. M. de Saussure, who visited London from Switzerland in 1726, wrote that everyone who understood machinery admired it greatly:

> Smoke issuing with force through a little tube and corresponding with a large and tightly covered boiler full of boiling water sets in motion a large piece of machinery composed of wheels, counterpoise and pendulum, which in their turn cause two large pumps to work continually. This piece of machinery and the two pumps are placed at the foot of a wooden tower which is, I think, about 100 feet in height, in breadth diminishing, after the manner of pyramids, gradually. At the summit of the tower, which is octagonal, there is a small leaden cistern . . . which receives the water the pumps send up and from thence it flows into the great reservoir or pond of Marylebone. The inventor of this machinery is a very clever mathematician, Dr Desaiguillières. [See the illustration on page 57.]

He had words of praise not only for this one waterworks but for the capital's entire water supply system:

> One of the conveniences of London is that everyone can have an abundance of water. The big reservoir or cistern near Islington, the York Buildings machinery near the Strand and that of the Bridge supply every quarter abundantly. In every street there is a large principal pipe made of oak [he probably meant elm] wood, and little leaden pipes are adapted to this principal pipe to carry water into all the houses. Every private individual may have one or two fountains in his house, according to his means, and pays so much a year for each fountain. Water is not obtainable all day, these fountains giving three hours water in every 24. The large leaden cisterns are replenished during the time the water does not run into the houses. . . . Besides the distribution of water by means of pipes, there are in many streets pumps and wells where poor people who cannot afford to pay for water, can obtain it for nothing.

He was astonished at the amount of water the English used. Most of it seemed to go on cleaning their houses. 'Absolutely none of it is drunk,' he said. 'The lower classes, even the paupers, do not know what it is to quench their thirst with water.'

## Quality as well as Quantity?

There might be more of it now, good enough to see and feel, but was it good enough to taste? 'If I would drink water,' declared Tobias Smollett, the Scottish satirist, writing under the guise of Humphrey Clinker in 1769:

> If I would drink water, I must quaff the mawkish contents of an open aqueduct exposed to all manner of defilement from the river Thames, impregnated with all the filth of London and Westminster – human excrement is the least offensive part of the concrete, which is composed of all the drugs, minerals and poisons used in mechanics and manufacture, enriched with the putrefying carcases of beasts and men, and mixed with the scourings of all the wash tubs, kennels and common sewers within the bills of mortality. . . . This is the agreeable potation extolled by the Londoners as the finest water in the universe.

He found it no better in Bath where he was as much afraid of drinking as of bathing. Much of Bath's supply at this time came by open channel from the Beechen Cliff to Walcot Street, and thence in lead pipes, later replaced by wooden ones from which there was less leakage. When more water was required, in 1769, a waterwheel was erected to raise water from the River Avon into a cistern and into a new reservoir, the ceremonial opening of which Smollett may have attended. But however clever the engineers had been in raising and conducting the water from its source, they did not regard it as part of their job to ensure that it ended up in a fit state for consumption. Smollett was convinced that 'the filthy composition' of the water at Bath was due to its contamination by 'the scourings of the bathers'. At his lodgings in Milsom Street he had:

> a precarious and scanty supply from the hill, which is collected in an open basin in the Circus, liable to be defiled with dead dogs, cats, and every species of nastiness which the rascally population may throw into it from mere wantonness and brutality.

Such behaviour was common throughout the kingdom. Manchester issued a proclamation in 1765 against persons making a practice of drowning cats and dogs and washing dirty linen in the Shute Hill reservoir. At Berwick-on-Tweed the water was contaminated with blood from the shambles. To make river water at all usable, the people of York felt obliged to pour it into large water pots to let it settle for a day or two. When they had emptied one pot, they washed out the sediment and refilled it with newly drawn river water to wait its turn.

## Charitable Involvement in Northern Ireland

Wells to the south of Belfast in the Fountainville and Sandy Row areas were the sources of water which Belfast Corporation leased to William 'Pipe Water' Johnston in 1710. By then the town's population had grown to more than 1,000, and the borough consisted of about a dozen streets and lanes and some 200 thatched cottages. George McCartney was still running the watercourses and mill dams which had been granted to him in 1678. In 1762 when Johnston found that the operation was more costly than he had anticipated and that he was running into debt, he sub-let it to James Hall, who was, however, unable to raise enough revenue to keep the wooden pipes in repair. The town's water supply system had virtually ground to a halt by 1790, when the Belfast Charitable Society stepped in with a relief measure to sell pure well water to any of the town's 18,000 inhabitants who wanted it at four gallons a halfpenny. Five years later, with the corporation unable or unwilling to regard water supply as an essential public service which it had been elected to provide, the Charitable Society formally took over responsibility for it and obtained the leases of a number of other springs necessary to meet the demand. It laid pipes to the principal streets, so that by 1800 there was a proper system for distributing fresh water to all parts of the town, including public conduit houses where poor people could fill their tankards with fresh water without payment.

The background to a charity shouldering so vital a public service was one of political change. In 1782 a Protestant patriot party forced the British government to remove a number of commercial restrictions and grant the Irish parliament independence. When those who wanted further disengagement from Westminster rebelled in 1798, they were suppressed. In 1800 the Parliament of Ireland passed an

Act providing for the improvement of the waterworks' administration, the regulation of its expenditure and the levying of rates to meet it and to provide an income for the Charitable Society which, as it recognised, had many other calls upon its resources apart from water supply.

In the meantime, the demand for fresh water in Belfast was mounting and the Charitable Society, in the absence of any other body, felt obliged to act in the interests of public health by renovating the whole system and developing new spring sources to extend it. Its aim was to supply every inhabitant with one four-hundredth part of a gallon of water a minute – three and half gallons per head a day. This good work continued right up to the accession of Queen Victoria, when at last it was recognised that it should become the responsibility of a body devoted exclusively to water supply.

## Water Quality – The Application of Science

While most water users were not unduly concerned about the product's purity, there was little incentive for water suppliers to do anything about it: it would only add to their costs and deplete their profits. In any case no-one had, as yet, devised a scientifically satisfactory technique for water purification, in spite of much theorising and experimentation. It was not until 1791 that the English architect James Peacock took out a patent for his process and apparatus for water filtration.

It was the first of its kind. In a pamphlet describing the system, Peacock observed that among the various objects evidently designed by Providence to receive amendment at the hands of men, there was one of immense importance which had not yet received it in the degree it was capable of, and that was *water*:

> This element, necessarily of such universal use, and particularly in food and medicine, is suffered to remain laden with a great diversity of impurities, and is taken into the stomach by the majority of mankind without the least hesitation not only in its fluid state, however turbid it may happen to be, but also in the forms of bread, pastry, soups, tea, medicines and innumerable other particulars.

A

SHORT ACCOUNT

OF A

NEW METHOD

OF

FILTRATION BY ASCENT;

WITH

EXPLANATORY SKETCHES, UPON SIX PLATES;

BY JAMES PEACOCK,

OF FINSBURY-SQUARE, ARCHITECT;

Author of OIKIDIA ; or NUTSHELLS, SUPERIOR POLITICS, &c.

*Adde quo l e parer ac Ler l'as d clements
Nec facile eft tali nature obfifier: quicquam
Inter enim fu git ac penetrat per rara viarum.*

LUCRETIUS.

LONDON:

PRINTED FOR THE AUTHOR;

AND

SOLD BY LACKINGTON AND Co. CHISWELL-STREET,

1793.

James Peacock's patent process for water filtration was the first of its kind.

It had been his study for several years past, he said, to supply the inhabitants of the metropolis and its environs with more than a sufficiency of perfectly clear soft water from the inexhaustible sources contained in the noble rivers in its vicinity. He had made a very great variety of experiments in order to arrive at the simplicity and perfection of nature in her process of percolation, 'by using the same medium, and the same mode, taking away by human art her hurtful and disgusting redundances only'. The patent was for:

> Invention of a new Method for the Filtration of Water and other fluids which

would be of great public and private Utility . . . for public service, reservoirs or cisterns for private use . . . by impelling the ascent of the fluid through the filtering medium instead of the common method of descent.

Another novelty was cleaning the filter by reverse flow, the descending water carrying with it 'all foul and extraneous substances'. His system involved three tanks, one for the turbid (muddy) water, one for the filter, and one for clear water. The theory of filtration by ascension was that gravity would cause some of the sediment to be deposited in the chamber beneath the false bottom, and the remainder would be intercepted by the increasingly fine material. The reverse flow would cleanse the filter and the settling chamber.

James Peacock's filter cleaning by reverse flow was one of the basic elements of the later mechanical filter. Contemporaries regarded it as 'ingenious', as 'highly desirable in point of delicacy', but many years had to pass before water purification became an integral and essential part of the role of the water supplier. And, of course, for one important use, there was no need to have it pure, clean and sweet.

### Developments in Firefighting

A French visitor to London who wrote an account of his *Voyage Philosophique D'Angleterre* in 1783 was very impressed by the way water was everywhere on tap for extinguishing fires:

> There was provision of water for internal use in houses either by *pompes a feu* set up in different points of the Thames, whose invention, like the major part of those things with which England distinguishes itself, is due to a religious refugee; or by the little river that Sir Hugues Myddelton laid down at the expense of the Earl of Hertford by canals and aqueducts which form a line of 60 miles.

These waters, he wrote, were designed originally for domestic consumption. They were distributed twice a week to each house by wooden conduits which ran through the entire town under the paving stones of the streets. However the government, looking to benefit from new enterprise and not to increase its revenue from taxation at the expense of the interested company, but to procure for the public the advantages to which everyone was rightfully entitled, had found a quick and ample means of help in the event of fire. Wooden fire hoses (*tuyaux de bois*) had been put up in the streets at distances not too far apart, placed perpendicularly on the conduits, always open and at the service of houses. Their exterior orifice was fitted into a square-hewn stone (*une pierre de taille*), placed on a level with the pavement and closed with a wooden bung which, easily pulled out as soon as the need arose, let escape a jet of water four or five inches in diameter, to which two pumps could then be applied.

> This aid, it is true, even if applied at the moment the fire shows itself, does not always save the house where it started; but at least it preserves part walls [*batiments mitoyens*] which gives town dwellers very great peace of mind where one never ceases to fear not only the imprudence of servants but the negligence of neighbours.

These *tuyaux* were the 'fire plugs' which all water suppliers had for some time been inserting into the water pipes they laid in town streets, often as a condition of their being given the contract. In 1769 Ralph Lodge took over William Yarnold's waterworks at Newcastle upon Tyne, and was given permission by the city's Common Council to construct a reservoir on the town moor so long as he provided 100 fire plugs for the benefit of the town. When Lodge's waterworks failed to serve Newcastle as the Common Council wished and they terminated their agreement after 30 years, the operation was given to the Newcastle Fire Office, one of the town's insurance companies, who wanted to take control for themselves of the means of extinguishing fires. To give themselves more water for firefighting, the new proprietors of the town's waterworks sank a shaft 48 feet down into the flooded coal workings on the Coxlodge estate and pumped the water up with a windmill, into a new reservoir on Town Moor.

The amount of water available, however, allowed them to turn on the supply only twice a week. Water for firefighting had to be constant; if it was to provide a strong jet, furthermore, it had to have a higher pressure behind it than any waterwheel or windmill, let alone gravity, could provide.

## The First Steam Engine

Thomas Savery and Thomas Newcomen had put more power behind water pumps with their atmospheric fire engines, but even greater power was needed if pumps were to force greater weights of water up to higher and higher water towers and push greater volumes of water along greater distances to the factories and new towns of the Industrial Revolution.

When in 1756 a Newcomen engine came in for repair to James Watt, the Scottish

**The Boulton & Watt steam engine installed at Chelsea Pumping Station, London, in 1820 and transferred to Kew Bridge Pumping Station (now a museum) in 1840.**

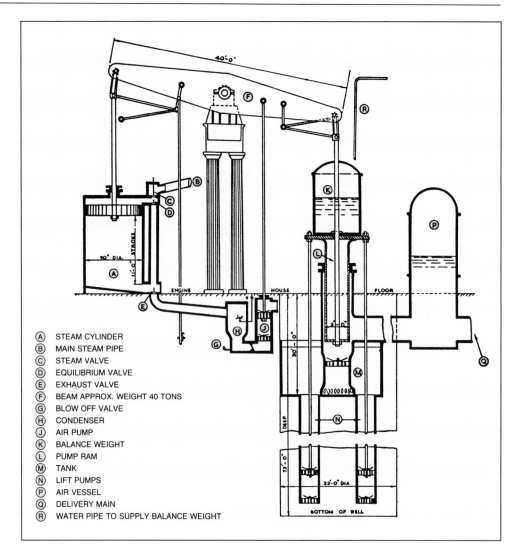

**Among the Cornish pumping engines that survive, an important example is this 'Woodhouse' engine, installed at the Springhead Pumping Station of the City of Hull in 1876 and now an exhibit at the Yorkshire Water Museum.**

(A) STEAM CYLINDER
(B) MAIN STEAM PIPE
(C) STEAM VALVE
(D) EQUILIBRIUM VALVE
(E) EXHAUST VALVE
(F) BEAM APPROX. WEIGHT 40 TONS
(G) BLOW OFF VALVE
(H) CONDENSER
(J) AIR PUMP
(K) BALANCE WEIGHT
(L) PUMP RAM
(M) TANK
(N) LIFT PUMPS
(P) AIR VESSEL
(Q) DELIVERY MAIN
(R) WATER PIPE TO SUPPLY BALANCE WEIGHT

mathematical instrument maker employed by Glasgow University, he saw that its failure was due to its wasting three-quarters of its heat by condensing the steam in the cylinder itself. The vacuum which was at the heart of the atmospheric engine should be created, he thought, in a separate condenser. Moreover steam, and not the atmosphere, should drive the piston down.

The model he made of what had become a steam engine worked well, but it was not until 1768 that he was in a position to apply for a patent. Watt formed a partnership with Matthew Boulton, at whose Soho Works in Birmingham in 1776 he built a full-size steam engine. This had proved his theories to be correct. The following year he went to Cornwall, where the demand for efficient water pumping engines was greatest, and had no difficulty in persuading the owners of copper and tin mines, where flooding was still seriously hindering production, to share his enthusiasm and place orders. After the installation of one of his engines at Chacewater, he wrote to a friend that 'the velocity, violence, magnitude and horrible noise of the engine gave universal satisfaction to all beholders'. It 'forked' water as no engine had done before.

The news of the steam revolution spread rapidly. His 'sun and planet' mechanism secured the rotary motion which had defeated all others. He sent an assistant, William Murdoch, to develop the Cornish market after his return to Birmingham. To travel across country from one mine to another, Murdoch built himself a steam carriage. He often had to drive at night, so he mounted bladders of coal gas on the vehicle which, when lit, became gas headlights. He developed the idea for lighting his house in Redruth, sold gaslighting (from an in-house producer plant) to factories and lit the Boulton & Watt works at Soho. Piped gas, developed by Frederic Winsor, together with the system of water supply, were the two main public utilities for which municipal authorities assumed responsibility during the next century.

James Watt's contribution to Britain's water supply was not confined to giving it steam-powered water pumps. He was consulted by the owners of Glasgow Waterworks, who were having difficulty in laying pipes to bring pure spring water across the River Clyde to their pumping engines at Dalmarnock. The channel of the river was covered with mud and shifting sand, and subject to the pressure of a great body of water. To solve their problem Watt invented a 'crustacean tube', a long, articulated suction-pipe with joints formed on the principle of those in a lobster's tail so that it would be capable of accommodating itself to any possible irregularities in the bottom of the river. They accepted his recommendation and had a 1,000-foot length made on the lines he suggested, two feet in diameter, by Boulton & Watt. The idea worked perfectly. His services, he said, were 'induced solely by a desire to be of use procuring good water to the city of Glasgow and to promote the prosperity of a company which had risked so much for the public good'. The water company expressed its gratitude, nevertheless, by presenting him with a piece of plate worth 100 guineas.

The art of drawing water was transformed. Steam engines replaced horse-treadmills and waterwheels, but only gradually. Though Watt's invention constituted a leap forward in technology, the pace at which it could be applied to water was limited by the capacity of the Boulton & Watt works, and by the demands for steam engines from the textile industry, the Cornish tin miners and Durham coal miners.

But others had their own ideas for developing Watt's innovations. In 1784, John Smeaton FRS, 'the father of civil engineering', who had invented the compressed air pump, designed a steam engine for the York Water Works Company, of which he was one of the proprietors. It was not only horsepower and waterpower which had become old-fashioned. At Hull in 1773 they installed a new-fangled atmospheric engine to take over from the horse-treadmill which had powered their water pump since 1616; then in 1795 they replaced it with a Boulton & Watt steam engine.

## Watt Meets Telford

Four years later James Watt met the man who more than any other perhaps promoted the application of the new power unit to water supply. 'I have just got acquainted with Mr Watt and his son,' wrote Thomas Telford to a friend in February 1799. 'He is the Steam Engine man from Glasgow – he is great and good, so is his son.' It was the beginning of a close association. Telford was a fellow Scot; born in Eskdale, he was then 42. He had come to London as a young man of 24. In 1794, as engineer of the Shrewsbury Canal, he had built a cast iron aqueduct, and then another on Ellesmere Canal. They were projects which brought him a national reputation.

Telford's meeting with Watt was over a project in northwest England. 'I am presently engaged,' he wrote to his friend Andrew Little in June 1799, 'in conducting a plan for supplying the Town of Liverpool with water by means of pipes in the same manner as London is now supplied':

OPPOSITE: **The aqueduct on Llangollen Canal at Pontcysyllte in Wales – one of Thomas Telford's greatest civil engineering achievements. Eighteen stone piers were built to raise it 121 feet above the River Dee.**

**A pump driven by an undershot wooden water wheel was first installed at Coultershaw in 1792 to supplement the spring water supply to Petworth House and town, 1½ miles to the north. The present breast-shot wheel was cast by Robert Chorley at Cocking Foundry in the mid-19th century. The pump was in service until about 1960 and subsequently lay derelict. Restoration by the Sussex Industrial Archaeology Society was started in 1976 and by 1980 the pump was again in working order.**

This is a business of some magnitude, and we have some opposition to contend with – no less than the Corporation of Liverpool. Thus circumstanced you will readily conceive that my mind must be occupied in forming proper arrangements.

Water carts and water carriers were still bringing water from the Fall Well to Liverpool when agitation against so wholly inadequate a system led to the passing of an Act in 1786 which empowered the corporation to compel landowners to dig wells, collect springs, construct dams and reservoirs and have water piped into the town. A sum of £95,324 was subscribed, but work did not begin until 1799, when a well was sunk in Berry Street and others in Hotham Street and Copperas Hill. It was all somewhat half-hearted, and by a private Act of Parliament the Company of Proprietors of the Liverpool Waterworks was formed to organise a water supply from springs in Bootle. It sank a few boreholes on land owned by the Earl of Derby. There was no follow-through, however, and another company was formed with Telford as engineer, who at once contacted Boulton & Watt for assistance and information. In August 1800, Telford obtained quotations for the delivery and erection of an 18-inch cylinder steam engine and 12-inch pumps. When he inspected the waterworks on Lord Derby's estate in 1802, he confirmed that supply was at a rate of 120,000 gallons an hour.

While big municipal corporations, that could afford a steam engine and take on the responsibility of operating the far-from-simple mechanism, were able, however hesitantly, to take advantage of the new technology, many village councillors and private home-owners were installing new waterwheels to power pumps in the old familiar way, by which they would run no fire risk and have no need of coal.

To supplement the spring water supply to Petworth House in Sussex and the neighbouring town, one and a half miles away, a beam pump driven by an undershot wooden waterwheel was installed at Coultershaw in 1792. Robert Martin's drawing shows what it looked like. The Coultershaw Beam Pump is thought to be peculiar to West Sussex; the only similar one known is in Bignor Park. With the iron wheel cast in the mid-19th century to replace the wooden one, the installation was restored by the Sussex Industrial Archaeology Society in 1980, and as a Scheduled Ancient Monument is on public view. The pump was powered by the waterwheel until as recently as 1960.

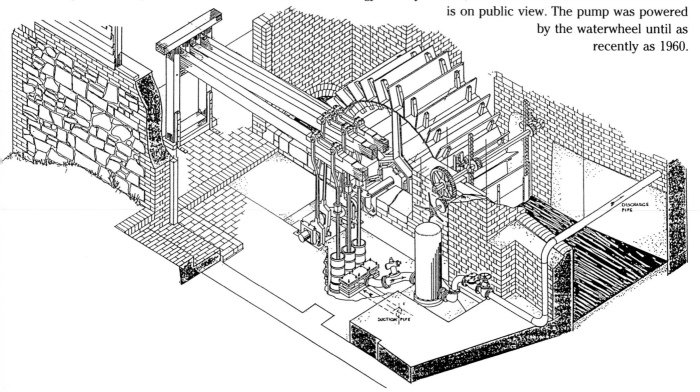

The water cistern and public water pump at Rye in Sussex were completed in 1735. Situated inside St Mary's churchyard, Rye, seven shillings were paid to the vicar as compensation for digging the reservoir.

The New River Head Works in 1856, constructed to a stylish symmetrical design.

## The Architecture of Early Waterworks

In the country there was more incentive to have a waterworks which, by its design, its lack of noise and smell, was in keeping with its rural surroundings. If it could also be aesthetically pleasing, so much the better. Vanbrugh took pains to see that the cistern he placed over the gateway to the kitchen court at Blenheim Palace was not at odds with the architecture of the rest of that grand mansion. When Henry Joynes designed a small water tower for rural Kensington Palace Green, and the Carshalton Water House for a director of the South Sea Company, he took care to make them ornamental.

In 1730 the Mayor and 'Jurats' of Rye voted for £600 to improve the town's water supply and to pump water up by horse-gin from springs below the cliffs to a water house at the bottom of Conduit Hill. They acquired a corner of St Mary's churchyard, the only available open space, on which to build a cistern; such a sensitive site demanded an original and distinctive design. The cistern was built of brick and was half underground. Its oval plan-form with its saucer-shaped bottom, eight feet below the ground, held 20,000 gallons. It was roofed with a continuous half-vault leaning against a central tight oval brick tower, rising ten feet above it.

'Rye Cistern is possibly unique,' wrote Ralph Wood in *Sussex Industrial History* (1976). 'It is a most sophisticated yet simple design, having qualities of great strength and durability – both well proven – and low liability for maintenance. It is quite beautifully built and thoughtfully detailed in every way; the shape is fascinating and it bears sufficient embellishment to increase its visual interest at close quarters.'

The waterworks of a sizeable town involved many more buildings, of both a functional and residential nature, and the early architects made great efforts to lay them out in an integrated plan, often linking them by flower beds, lawns and trees. The

New River Head complex at Islington was pleasingly stylish. The so-called Marble Gauge, built in 1739 to control the water passing into the New River from the River Lee, was of classical proportions. There was distinctive elegance too about all the buildings of the five water companies of the 18th-century inner metropolis: the Ravensbourne, later Kent, Waterworks (1701); Chelsea Waterworks (1723); Southwark & Vauxhall Waterworks (1771); Lambeth Waterworks (1785); and the Grand Junction (1789).

**Built in 1883 to supply water to Nottingham, Papplewick Pumping Station is the most complete and ornate of all Victorian stations. Highly decorative columns support the huge beam pumping engines built by James Watt in 1884. Egyptian ibises and other decorative aquatic animals and plants adorn the columns supporting the beam engines and feature in stained glass windows. The engine house and boiler rooms designed by Marriott Ogle Tarbottom are situated with the cooling pond in attractive grounds.**

**OVERLEAF: River Wharfe at Kettlewell, Yorkshire.**

# CHAPTER THREE

# Water and sanitary engineers to the rescue

WASTEWATER AND ITS CONVENIENCES • CONTAMINATION FROM PIPES • EXPERIMENTS IN FILTRATION • LOW PRIORITY FOR PUBLIC HEALTH • ASIATIC CHOLERA • DISEASE WAS WATER-BORNE • EDWIN CHADWICK CALLS FOR SANITARY REFORM • WATER-CARRIAGE SYSTEM POLLUTES THE RIVERS • GETTING RID OF THE CESSPOOLS AND MIDDENS • GENERAL BOARD OF HEALTH RECOMMENDS RE-SEWERING

Today, in common parlance, the word 'sewage' denotes what people in the water industry call 'foul sewage', but it did not have that meaning originally. That was not what a person meant when he accused another of having a mind like a sewer. It was water. The English word is a derivation of the Latin word *asaquare*, to de-water, to take water away.

The first proper sewers were watercourses, pipes and tunnels into which rain water was taken away from streets to prevent them becoming flooded and impassable; away from the roofs of houses, via gutters, to protect their walls and foundations (house drainage); from fields to keep them ploughable and the roots of the corn and fruit trees from rotting in stagnant soggy soil. These were what the commissioners were appointed by Henry VIII to maintain under his Bill of Sewers of 1531. They were not designed to take anything solid.

These sewers also came to serve as the channels for carrying away not only surplus clean water but water that had been soiled by the dirt that people washed off themselves, their clothes, and cooking utensils and plates (kitchen slops), and by the soap they used for that purpose. This was the washing-up water and bath water disposed of down the plughole and washed along the wastepipe, down the drain. People had converted clean water into dirty water which was therefore wastewater – dirty waste but not foul waste.

Up to 1815 the main role of sewerage and sewers was to prevent flooding, not to carry away dirty waste and foul waste. Up to the Industrial Revolution – and indeed for some time after – people were left to dispose of their ordure, their foul waste, themselves. It was a private matter. Their place of ease, set apart from other rooms, was a privy (*privatus*). Indoor privies had pail-middens which had to be continually cleared, but people in the country were used to going down to the garden to do what was necessary behind a bush. In his poem *The Panegyrick of the Dean*, Jonathan Swift has Lady Acheson say:

> The bashful Maid, to hide her Blush,
> Shall creep no more behind a Bush;
> Here unobserv'd, she boldly goes,
> As who should say, to Pluck a Rose.

On the mediaeval map of Canterbury Cathedral's buildings the hospital's latrine is marked NECESSARIUM INFIRMORUM. 'Necessary' had the meaning commodious and convenient. While commode and convenience denote places of easement to this day, the term 'necessary houses' has dropped out of usage. It was the term, however, which barristers of the Honourable Society of Lincoln's Inn used in their petition to the Masters of the Bench as late as 1759:

> That tho' Necessary Houses for the Barristers and Students of this Inn are becoming extremely inconvenient and want [lack] regulation that they are often so dirty as to be unfit to be used, and that it is scarce possible to keep them clean from the number of people of all kinds that frequent them, for not only most of the Clerks and writers about the Inn but even people of the neighbourhood have keys to them.

> Your petitioners therefore humbly pray that either more convenient Necessary Houses may be built and set apart for the Gentlemen of the Bar, or that the present ones may be put under such regulation with respect to the keys, and the keeping them clean, as this Honourable Bench shall think proper.

Members of the Inn more commonly referred to the place as the Boghouse. One had been built behind 1 New Square under the Serle's Court Agreement of 1682.

A privy in a mansion house or castle went by the name 'garderobe' and was built in the thickness of a wall approached by a right-angled passage into which any offensive smell was meant to be trapped. For the Dutchman who recorded his impressions of a visit to England in 1560, the idea was obviously effective:

Gardy Loo! (Gardez l'eau!)

> Their chambers and parlours strawed over with sweet herbes refreshed me; their nosegays finely intermingled with sundry sorts of fragraunte floures in their bedchambers and privy rooms, with comfortable smell cheered me up and entirely delighted my senses.

The remains of such built-in privies can still be seen at Langley Castle, Chepstow Castle and Peveril Castle. Sometimes the privy was built out from the wall so that the ordure dropped into the moat – as can be seen at Ightham Mote in Kent.

More a necessary than comfortable convenience was the privy in the small bottle dungeon in the 14th-century Scottish castle of Cawdor whose thane Shakespeare featured in *Macbeth*. The dungeon, to which the only access was a trapdoor in the floor of the room above, was used not only to conceal ransomed prisoners but for hiding women and children in times of terror.

As the King made royal progress from castle to castle throughout his kingdom, he took with him a portable commode befitting in comfort and decoration his regal status – a 'close stool' of the kind to be seen at Hampton Court, and Knole in Kent, with elbows covered with velvet and garnished with lace. For the less fastidious royal retinue, Hampton Court had a monster garderobe which seated 28. Huge Greenwich Palace had a unique system of outside urinals in the courtyards called 'pissing places'. To encourage the use of these, rather than the nearest corner, the walls of the inner court were given a white dado with red crosses painted on them so there was no excuse for anyone who claimed he could not find them. Far into the 18th century, people at the lower end of the social scale who lived in towns had no scruples about emptying their chamber pots and pails of kitchen slops out of their windows onto the pavement – and any hapless passer-by – below, with the only warning a shout of 'Gardy loo!' (*gardez l'eau!*) as it was already on its way.

Foul sewage disposal, either out of the window or into earth middens, was no part of the business of the water supplier or water engineer until 1775 when an English watchmaker, Alexander Cumming, was granted the first patent for 'a Water Closet upon a new construction'. The event signalled the last days of the dry closet and the (very gradual) introduction of water-borne/water-carriage sanitation.

Cumming's 'new construction' gave the installation an S-shaped trap. The design was improved a couple of years later by Thomas Prosser and altered yet again, and indeed perfected, by Joseph Bramah in 1778. By 1797 Bramah had sold some 6,000 WCs. But the idea of these engineers was not entirely original.

Alexander Cumming had, in fact, reinvented the valve WC which Queen Elizabeth's godson Sir John Harington had devised for his home at Kelstone near Bath in 1596. 'This device of mine,' he wrote in *A New Discourse of a Stale Subject called THE METAMORPHOSIS OF AJAX*, 'requires not a sea full of water but a cistern, not a whole Tems [Thames] full but halfe a tunnefull, to keep all sweet and savourie.' He opened his description of the workings of his invention by telling the reader:

> In the privy that annoys you, first cause a cistern of lead containing a barrel or upward to be placed either behind the seat or in any place either in the room or above it, from whence water may, by a small pipe of lead of an inch be conveyed under the seat in the hinder part thereof (but quite out of sight); to which pipe you must have a cock or a washer to yield water with some pretty strength when you would let it in.

The brass sluice was fixed by a strong screw 'to which you must have a hollow key with a worm fit to that screw' which stood four inches wide of the back of the seat.

> Item. That children and busy folk disorder it not, or open the sluice with putting in their hands without a key, you should have a little button or scallop shell to bind it down with a vice pin, so as without the key it will not be opened.

When all was put in place it was 'passing close' plastered with good lime and hair so that no air came up from the vault. If water was plenty, the oftener it was used and opened the sweeter, 'but if it be scant, once a day was enough for a need though 20 persons should use it'.

> If the water will not run to your cistern you may with a force of twenty shillings [?] and a pipe of eighteen pence a yard, force it from the lowest part of your house to the highest.

Harington installed another one for his royal godmother at Richmond Palace. They were the only two ever made. No one followed it up, though Queen Anne seems to have had something of the sort at Windsor Castle. The English traveller, Celia Fiennes, records in her journal how she saw there 'a closet that leads to a little place with a seat of easement in marble with sluices of water to wash all down'. Queen Anne died in 1724. A few decades later Robert Adam had a water closet installed in Shelbourne House in Berkeley Square, London, another two at Osterley and four at Luton Hoo. These had a marble vessel with a long handle attached to a plug which, when pulled *up*, released the ordure into a D-shaped tray full of water with a pipe leading from the top of it. Someone had written a verse in 1697 called *Piss-Pot's Farewell*, but virtually two centuries had to pass before the 'pot' finally left the scene. From Cumming's patent of 1775 to 1885 the adoption of the WC as improved by Bramah and others was very slow.

Sprinto non spinto.   More feard than hurt.

'A godly father, sitting on a draugth
To do as need and nature hath us taught.'
Illustration of Harington's water closet of 1596 in *The Metamorphosis of Ajax*.

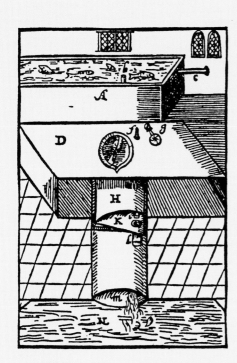

*A priuie in perfection*

A. the Cesterne.

B. the little washer.

C. the wast pipe.

D. the seate boord.

E. the pipe that comes from the Cesterne.

F. the Screw.

G. the Scallop shell to couer it when it is shut downe.

H. the stoole pot.

I. the stopple.

K. the current.

L. the sluce.

M.N. the vault into which it falles: always remember that ( ) at noone and at night, emptie it, and leaue it half a foote deepe in fayre water. And this being well done, and orderly kept, your worst priuie may be as sweet as your best chamber. But to conclude all this in a few wordes, it is but a standing close stoole easilie emptied.

And by the like reason (other formes and proportions obserued) all other places of your house may be kept sweet.

**The mechanics of Sir John Harington's water closet of 1596, which was reinvented by Alexander Cumming in 1776.**

## Contamination from Pipes

When the use of WCs became universal the water supply system was transformed, but in the meantime water suppliers were fully occupied with still unsolved pre-WC problems and, in particular, making sure the product was acceptably wholesome. Where the source was a deep well or an aquifer to which a small diameter borehole had been bored, they could reckon on the water being sweet and clean, but they learnt to live with the risk of it becoming contaminated after it had risen pure from underground and been conveyed to the town where it was wanted.

Not all well water was considered wholesome. The medical authorities of Manchester ruled that the well water raised to supplement that from the River Medlock was decidedly harmful. No one took any notice, however, and the two-pronged supply continued until 1809 and the formation of the private enterprise Manchester and Salford Waterworks Company. Town councillors said the water supplier of Manchester (whose population was to expand by 70 per cent between 1801 and 1821) must give priority to purity. The aim of whatever organisation was chosen for the job, private or municipal, must be 'the furnishing and control of this important article of food and cleanliness on which the health and comfort of the inhabitants depend'. They recommended adopting a municipal scheme as preferable to any other 'which may be equally or more expensive, and less eligible with respect to purity'.

They opposed the Parliamentary Bill which the Manchester and Salford Waterworks Company promoted, in spite of knowing that it would use stone instead of iron pipes designed to make the water supply pure, but they failed to prevent it being passed. The new company thereupon bought out Sir Oswald Mosley's interest in the existing waterworks and set to work. It had been formed by The Stone Pipe Company, the brainchild of Sir George Wright who had taken out a patent for a machine which cut circular cores from solid stone. With it he manufactured, in London, water pipes from limestone, at first from Dorset and then the Cotswolds, which he held would carry water without tainting it as iron pipes did. John Rennie was Chief Engineer.

Though the stone pipes would undoubtedly have given the people of Manchester a thoroughly wholesome water supply, the waterworks company was mismanaged and ran into debt – to the delight of John Bateman who accused it of more than bad management. In his *History of the Manchester Waterworks* he asserted that once the Bill was passed, there commenced 'the perpetration of one of the most barefaced and nefarious pieces of jobbery which has ever disgraced the annals of private companies replete as they are with instances of dishonesty'. Manchester Corporation took over the insolvent company which, said Bateman, enabled them to execute their original objective of 'preserving the health of the poor' and so preventing an increase of the rates for their relief 'and by adding to their comforts and happiness procure for themselves the gratifying sensations of benevolence'.

Bateman accused The Stone Pipe Company of creating the waterworks company purely as a means of selling more stone pipes. If they had known as much about organising an urban water supply as manufacturing stone pipes, both Manchester's water users and the water company's shareholders might have benefited. Two years later The Stone Pipe Company, under the direction of John Rennie, promoted an Act for the water supply of London. However, as Dr Hugh Torrens of the British Society for the History of Science at Keele University has pointed out, when stone pipes were tested in four London streets in 1812, 135 failures were discovered. The pipes were unable to stand the pressures involved. 'This saga was important in the development of town planning in Britain as pipe-laying was then regulated and new pipes required to be of iron from 1817.' All the pipes of Manchester's system were cast iron by 1816.

The harm which Manchester well water could inflict was *sui generis* – a result of its own make-up. In Harwich it was chemically sound but soiled by an outside contaminator. 'They have no fresh water in this town' complained an 18th-century visitor to the famous seaport in the Tendring Hundred of Essex:

> the nearness of the sea making all the water in the wells of their pumps so brackish that it is fit for nothing but to wash their houses with, to supply which they make conveniences to catch and keep rain water for the washing of their clothes. But for other uses they either have it brought in water-carts from a spring near a mile from the town by the road to Dovercourt, or it is brought in water-schuyts [a Dutch cargo-carrying vessel] from a spring in Arwerston.

The location of the spring described as Arwerston is probably Erwarton, eight miles upstream from Harwich.

About a quarter of a mile from the town on the London Road was a well where the Master of the Brewhouse used to have his water:

> But his being overflow'd by a great Tide three or four years ago, the water was thereby so spoiled that they have not since thought fit to make use of it.

It was the state of affairs which half a century later Peter Bruff inherited and formed the Tendring Hundred Waterworks to remedy – a company which still operates today.

People who were worried about the possible harmfulness of their well water sent bottles-full to Michael Faraday who made a chemical analysis of it in the Royal Institution Laboratory below street level in London's Albemarle Street – it is still there. Lord Harewood sent him a bottle of water to analyse from his 'Spring at the temple' in May 1818, and Faraday recorded in the laboratory notebook (see the portion of the page reproduced overleaf) that it contained very little muriate acid, 'scarcely any Sul[phate] Acid and a very small quantity of lime – a pint contains only $^6/_{10}$ of a gram of dry salts'. It was all part of his work at Albemarle Street along with probing Spanish Brandies, Palm Wine, Apple Juice and Colonel Duckett's Elder Flower Wine, tucked in between what was gradually interesting him more and more, experiments of the kind he conducted on 17 February 1818 and noted under the heading 'Voltaic Electricity and the Magnet'.

The great physicist, whose discovery of electro-magnetic induction revealed the principle of the electric motor and dynamo, had the time and the interest to analyse the water from Holy Well near Rock House, Malvern and declare it 'as nearly pure as may be; only a very little Muriate of Lime in it'; to examine Margate's water, a sample from Mr

**Michael Faraday, who challenged the government of the day to clean up the Thames.**

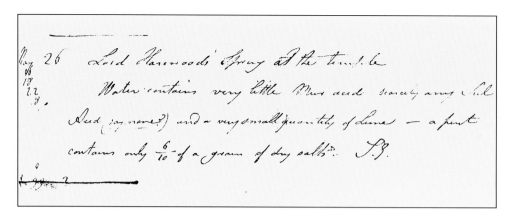

**Entry by Michael Faraday for 26 May 1818 in his Royal Institution Laboratory notebook, recording his analysis of water from Lord Harewood's spring at the Temple.**

Arnold's pond in Guernsey, from St Osyth's Well, from the Duke of Marlborough's Blenheim estate, Lord Spencer's at Althorp, from Knightsbridge Barracks, from the notorious Grand Junction Waterworks, from Tilbury Fort for the Board of Ordnance, from Keal Water and Bolingbroke Water. He continued to do so right through to the 1850s.

However clean at source, water could become harmful by acting on the inside of a pipe as it travelled through it, detaching material to mix with it and contaminate it. Michael Faraday found that the purest water any man could drink was obtained from melting pure ice, yet such water would act on lead. Water which had been carefully distilled did not. The choice of pipe was therefore vital. Water could enter a pipe 100 per cent clean and, after collecting impurities en route, could leave it far from wholesome, if not poisonous.

When a newly formed water company asked Thomas Telford to advise them on how best to improve Glasgow's water supply in 1806, he laid great score on choosing the most suitable pipes. He experimented with Rutherglen Quarry's stone pipes, but when the results varied, he recommended using cast iron pipes. All the previous proposals failed, he said in his report, in the primary object which was to supply *pure* water. 'At Glasgow', he told James Watt, 'I had to combat the phantom of crude projects for supplying that city with water.' He told them to erect Boulton & Watt steam pumping engines two miles up the River Clyde and *pump* water to the city. He estimated the population of 80,000 would consume 500 gallons a minute.

The importance of choosing the right pipes was also high on the agenda when, four years later, Telford was asked to account for the indifferent quality of Edinburgh's water supply from springs at Comiston, Swanston and Bonaly. His report condemned the lack of any fixed principle in the type and size of the existing pipes. Wood, lead, cast iron and earthen pipes were frequently found on the same pipeline, he said. Such a system could not be improved, it should be replaced. Moreover, spring water and surface water should be conveyed, stored and distributed separately. Spring water should be reserved for domestic use and stored mainly in the Castle Hill cistern; surface water in a new reservoir they should build at Bruntisfield Links. No action was taken on his report of 1811, nor on John Rennie's of 1814. It was not until the Edinburgh Joint Stock Water Company was formed in 1819 that the problem of the Scottish capital's water supply was tackled in earnest. Telford was given responsibility for the works plan, James Jardine was the engineer and John Rennie acted for the landowners affected by the scheme.

The mere choice of the right material for pipes reduced the chance of polluting naturally pure spring water, though not, of course, well water which had been soiled by an overflowing cesspool on higher ground which was not being regularly or properly emptied, as so often happened. Once laid, the pipeline required no attention other than ensuring no impurity leaked into it from outside. Purifying water that was impure by nature, particularly any which was required for an industrial process, was an altogether more complicated operation, however.

The water of the River Cart in Scotland was naturally muddy and quite unfit for the Paisley textile manufacturers who needed it for bleaching. To enable them to use it, in 1804 John Gibb devised a system of lateral filtering which became famous as the Paisley Filter. He passed the river water through a stone-filled trench to a ring-shaped settling chamber and then through lateral-flow filters to central clear water chambers. A small Boulton & Watt steam engine lifted the water to an 'air-chest' 16 feet above the river and forced it to a settling chamber through 200 feet of three-inch bore pipes made of Scots fir. It was the first known filter for city-wide supply in the world.

## Experiments in Filtration

At the beginning of the 19th century filtration was still in the experimental stage. Each water engineer had his own pet theory. As engineer for the Glasgow Waterworks Company in 1806, Thomas Telford said if there was any difficulty in getting the water of the River Clyde to subside or filtrate so as to be perfectly good, 'then instead of one reservoir six feet in depth it will be advisable to have two of three feet in depth each, and each one acre in superficial area'. But Telford's settling reservoirs failed, and an altogether different approach was adopted, that of Dr Andrew Ure, a lecturer at Glasgow University, which had won a competition. The Glasgow Waterworks joined forces with the Cranston Hill Waterworks Company who had a so-called 'filter gallery' devised by the company's founder, Richard Gillespie, in 1808. This was a settling basin of several days' capacity in which grosser particles of sediment were removed. Finer particles were removed in a filter of several feet of sand and gravel with tunnels below it. It was the first experience of artificial filtration on a large scale. Glasgow was the third city in the world to have a filtered water supply. In the 1820s Robert Thom in Scotland and James Simpson in England pioneered mechanical and slow sand filtration – Thom with his first self-cleaning municipal filter at Greenock in 1827, and Simpson for the Chelsea Waterworks in London in 1829. Hull Corporation started partially filtering water from Spring Ditch as it left their Spring Bank Waterworks Reservoir in 1830 – one of England's earliest instances of water treatment. A pump powered by a steam engine shifted 2,700 gallons a minute.

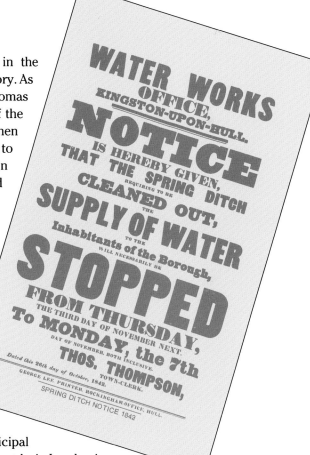

**Poster in the Yorkshire Water Museum, Hull.**

James Simpson's sand filtration was eventually widely adopted. At Chelsea and Lambeth he used a small reservoir with layers of large and small stones, gravel and sand, in that order from the bottom upwards. The water flowed over the top and sank to the outlet at the bottom. The system depended on the gradual formation of a film of diatoms, green algae and other forms of life on the sand.

Filtration was optional where the source was a spring, but essential when water was drawn from a river, which companies were doing more and more after the hot and dry

**James Simpson's slow sand filtration principle, which he pioneered in the 1820s, is still applied effectively 170 years later at Dunmore Point Water Treatment Works on the shores of Lough Neagh in Northern Ireland (*above*) – the largest freshwater lake in the British Isles.**

summers of the 1820s. After the particularly dry summer of 1826 Aberdeen's Water Commissioners, who had been responsible for the burgh's water supply since 1795, considered turning to the Loch of Skene, the Culter Burn and the Aberdeenshire Canal at Stoneywood. In the end they decided to use the River Dee. They sunk a well 660 yards above the Bridge of Dee and drove a tunnel 200 yards along the riverside to collect filtered water. A thousand gallons a minute flowed to the new Waterhouse in Union Place. In 1826 Chester's first waterworks company with statutory powers built a powerful steam engine with double pumps near Barrel Wall, and apparatus for purifying water by deposition and filtration from *their* River Dee.

In London, as seen, the southern part of the metropolis had been supplied with river water from the Thames ever since the 16th century when Peter Morris had conceived the novel idea of putting a tidal waterwheel under an arch of London Bridge to pump water up to a water tower on the bank. Other companies were formed to extract water from further up the river. The proprietors of London Bridge Waterworks, overhauled and extended by George Sorocold, had been hard put to it to supply the quantity required – London's population had reached a million by 1800 – let alone the quality, which in any event most seemed to accept as part of the unalterable scheme of things. Few of London's water suppliers thought it necessary to follow the example of James Simpson at Chelsea and filter their water through sand. When the people of Southwark complained of having too little fresh water in 1767, they were happy to be given a supply from a new waterwheel erected for the purpose under the second arch of London Bridge from the south end.

After two and a quarter centuries the noisy London Bridge Waterworks were still supplying customers with nearly four million gallons a day – 160,000 gallons an hour. In 1822, however, the wheels and pumps which blocked five arches of the bridge were deemed a navigational hazard. The campaign to rid London of this 'nuisance' was headed by the rival New River Company:

LONDON BRIDGE WATERWORKS
Reasons why the waterworks ought to be removed and observations
upon the refusal of the London Bridge Waterworks Company to
the proposition made by the New River Company
15 March 1822

But the waterwheel obstruction apart, London Bridge was falling down. In 1800 a Parliamentary Select Committee on the Port of London (which had first considered the problem in 1796) invited architects to submit plans and estimates for a new London Bridge. One of those who submitted his ideas in May 1800 was Thomas Telford. His plan was for an iron bridge, with embankments and wharves. He went into the problem of how to deal with the waterworks with his usual thoroughness. He obtained information from Boulton & Watt about suitable steampowered pumps and prepared a scheme for replacing the wooden waterwheels. His proposal was not accepted. Londoners had to wait for a new London Bridge until 1831 when John Rennie's was opened. In the meantime the New River Company got its way and succeeded in having an Act of Parliament passed in 1822 for the London Bridge Waterworks to be removed. The shares of the London Bridge Waterworks Company were transferred to the New River Company (taken over by the Metropolitan Water Board when it was formed in 1904).

It was perhaps good riddance to the London Bridge murky water supply. Two years after the new London Bridge was opened the New River Company built two reservoirs beside the channel at Stoke Newington to be used partly as a reserve and partly to purify the water by allowing suspended matter to settle. But it was another 20 years before they built a proper filtration works at New River Head.

## Low Priority for Public Health

Potability was only gradually becoming a factor in water supply. It was a step in the right direction when, in 1827, the government appointed a commission of three men to report on London's water supply: one was engineer Thomas Telford and the other two, an able physician and 'one of the most eminent chemists of the present day'. They had been appointed, said Sturgess Bourne, the Secretary of State, 'that the public might have the benefit of the ablest opinions of the *potability* of the water'. Sadly however, in tune with the uncomprehending other-worldliness of the legislators of the time, both central and local, when their commission reported at length in 1828 they chose to disregard it:

The growth of the population and with it of pollution; the establishment of gas works and factories; the hopeless disorganisation of supply and distribution, and the ruinous competition between rival water companies, had brought matters to an impossible state. It was a perennial subject of petition and complaint. It came before every session in Parliament. Certainly the situation was unsatisfactory. (Sir Alexander Gibb, *The Story of Telford*)

Looking back on it three-quarters of a century later, Henry Jephson writing of *The

*Sanitary Evolution of London* regarded as 'most strange and remarkable' the slowness with which England as a nation awoke to the idea that the public health was a matter of any concern whatsoever:

> It seems now so obvious a fact that one marvels that it did not at all times secure for itself recognition and acknowledgement. But men and women were growing up amidst the existing surroundings, foul and unwholesome though those were, and some at least were visibly living to an old age; the population was increasing at an unprecedented rate; wealth was multiplying and accumulating; the nation was reaching greater heights of power and fame. Whatever was there, what could there be wrong with the existing state of affairs?

Perhaps what novelist Benjamin Disraeli had diagnosed as 'Two Nations'. 'I was told,' he has Lord Egremont remark in *Sybil*, 'that the Privileged and the People formed Two Nations, governed by different laws, influenced by different manners, with no thoughts or sympathies in common, with an innate inability of mutual comprehension.'

Sidney and Beatrice Webb thought the worst feature of the so-called 'vestry' system of local government was the total lack of knowledge or capacity to deal with the problems involved in the government even of the smallest village:

> Right down to 1835 the Vestry, in the vast majority of the English parishes, retained all its important and multifarious duties, and continued to be the same little oligarchy of intimate neighbours, tenants of the squire, and employers of paupers, presided over by clergyman or Senior Churchwarden, and dominated by the neighbouring Justices of the Peace.
> (*English and Local Government: the Parish and the County*, 1906)

What was wrong? The lethargy of central government? The incompetence of local government? The greed of the joint stock companies whose combining and high charges led to the formation of an Anti-Water Monopoly Association and protest meetings organised by aggrieved consumers unwilling to tolerate a state of affairs that most took for granted?

In London resentment was strongest against the Grand Junction Water Company, formed in 1810 to take water out of the canal of that name (now the Grand Union Canal) near what is now Paddington Railway Station, and which made no attempt to purify it. Presumably the businessmen who launched it believed they were reacting positively to the accusation that London's water supply was 'scanty and precarious' and 'feeble in power and remote in source' which a House of Commons Committee were that year investigating. The MPs were also probing the alleged 'tardy manner in which water was furnished in cases of fire'. It was said that water had taken one and a half hours to reach a fire in Covent Garden, and was too late to have any effect whatever. Fortunately such occurrences were only occasional. Those whose only supply was water from the stinking Paddington canal had to suffer every day.

## THE DOLPHIN or GRAND JUNCTION NUISANCE

was the title of the broadsheet by John Wright whose aim was:

> proving that seven thousand families in Westminster are supplied water in a state offensive to the sight, disgusting to the imagination and destructive to health.

The company's intake was only three yards away from the outlet of a large foul sewer. The outcry forced it to extend its suction pipe further into the canal and install

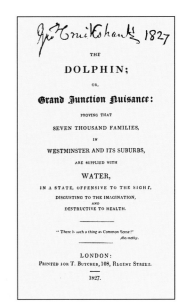

**George Cruikshank's signed copy of *The Dolphin*.**

**OPPOSITE: The New River Company, which built two new reservoirs at Stoke Newington in 1833, continued to supply North London with water throughout the 19th century – an *Illustrated London News* panorama of 1884 depicts the course of the channel from Ware to Clerkenwell.**

The Dolphin, the spot on the Thames from which the Grand Junction Company outrageously drew their water beside the mouth of the Great Common Sewer (2), by Chelsea Hospital (4). On the right is the company's steam engine house which pumped up the water (3).

precipitation reservoirs. In 1820 the company built an entirely new station at Chelsea where a pair of Boulton & Watt steam engines pumped water from the River Thames to the reservoirs at Paddington. But the water was no purer, so it closed the station and moved the two engines to the Kew Bridge Pumping Station, its third attempt to establish a pollution-free source from which to supply Paddington, Kensington and later Ealing. One of these engines has survived, and was the first set to work by the Kew Bridge Engines Trust at Kew Bridge Steam Museum in 1975.

The other new London companies such as the West Middlesex (1806), the East London (1807) and the Kent (1809), under attack from pressure groups, strove to achieve a balance between quantity and quality, reconciling their works with the environment, and satisfying the shareholders. Some, like John Martin, thought an answer was to build an entirely new system which would provide the necessary increased volume and greater purity.

For even the usually reliable springs were letting them down in the 1820s. At Pentonville, a place abounding in springs and formerly abounding in conduits, (remembered William Hone), all the conduits were destroyed and the pumps there in the midst of that healthy and largely growing suburb, during the hot days of July 1825 were not equal to supply a tenth of the demand for water:

> They were mostly dry and chained up during the half of each day without notice, and persons who came perhaps a mile went back with empty vessels. So it was in other neighbourhoods. Well may we account for ill. Mischievous liquors sold, in large quantities, in some places, for soda water and ginger beer were drank to the great comfort of the unprincipled manufacturers, the great discomfort of the consumers' bowels and the great gain of the apothecary. (*The Every Day Book*)

John Martin's grandiose scheme was to bring to London 'a current of pure water and at the same time materially beautifying the metropolis'. He planned to bring it from the River Colne three-quarters of a mile to the northeast of Denham near Uxbridge and convey it alongside the Grand Junction Canal to a reservoir at Paddington. He reckoned that the height of the latter would ensure distribution of the water, without the use of a steam engine, to the whole of the West End except the highest parts of Paddington and Marylebone. 'To combine other objects of utility with that of affording a supply of wholesome beverage', he suggested building a swimming pool near the reservoir for a thousand bathers. His new stream would then carry on to the Serpentine in Hyde Park and thence underground to the garden of Buckingham Palace where it would 'spread itself into an ornamental water', continue into the lake at St James's Park and discharge into the Thames. The project, however, was stillborn.

There was plenty of advice but little action. Huge sums of money were found to build railways, but there were few willing to justify expenditure on the less glamorous operation of providing Britain with a wholesome water supply network. For most of 'the authorities' it was not urgent enough, and central government supported them in that view. Sir Francis Burdett, the radically minded MP for Westminster, urged that one

Chelsea Water Works, where James Simpson introduced sand filtration – a print of 1752.

man, Thomas Telford, should be instructed to report to the House of Commons on the current system of sewerage in the metropolis and submit a plan on how London *should* be drained. In the place of the multiplying of authorities and corporations whose powers and knowledge were equally limited, there was a growing demand for a complete unified sewerage system. Burdett wanted to see London placed under the inspection of an *engineer*, one person whose duty it would be to see that proper sewers were established over the whole of London according to a single plan. But, as Sir Alexander Gibb observed, 'such an attempt to take the matter out of the hands of the authorities and put it under a single engineer reporting to the House was hardly likely to be accepted, in spite of Burdett's powerful advocacy; and Burdett did not press it on the Government's assurance that it would take action.'

Telford was consulted, however, in 1831 over the proposal to lay a sewer under St Paul's Cathedral. He was brought in as arbitrator. 'However practicable it may be, with due caution, to construct such a sewer,' ruled the Commissioners on Sewers, 'it is in consequence of the originally insecure state of the foundation of the cathedral, inexpedient'. The idea was abandoned, and a route taken further removed from the cathedral 'lest in any future time the further dilapidation should be, even remotely, attributed to your works'.

It was easy for laymen to reach a decision of this non-technical nature but they found themselves out of their depth if confronted with any more complicated issue. It was not the mark of a gentleman in any case to show familiarity with scientific or engineering matters. Ignorance and reluctance to show acquaintance with technicalities could lead to the wrong conclusions, like those made by vestrymen who believed that because a flame would issue from the end of a gaspipe if a match was applied to it, the whole pipe must be dangerously hot. As D'Arcy Power wrote in his article on 'The Public Health' in *Social England*:

The broad principles of drainage were less understood than they had been in Nineveh, and were certainly not as good as they were in Rome under Augustus. In Rome at any rate we know that the sewers were cleansed occasionally, for the magistrate under whose auspices such work was accomplished would afterwards descend the newly cleansed channel in a boat; but no one ever heard of the sewers in this country being surveyed by any municipal authority. The sanitary appliances were of the rudest description; cesspools were frequent and were usually placed in the basement of houses; the water supply abominable; the streets were badly paved, badly lighted and badly guarded.

## Asiatic Cholera

William Warden, brewer and well-borer, who for several years tried to convince Hull Town Council of the adequate capacity and purity of the water from Springhead against the contrary view of London 'experts' who recommended developing other local resources.

The authorities, local and central, were persuaded, though only very gradually, that maybe providing a sanitary water supply, constant and not intermittent, *was* urgent, that it might save money, not waste it, and that the public health *was* part of their responsibilities. In 1831 news reached their ears that a large number of people were going down with Asiatic Cholera and many of them were dying from it – though few at first connected the outbreak with their neglect of public sanitation. It was not until some years after 1831 that they cleared their minds of the myth and guesswork that surrounded its cause. It took at least ten years for ministers of religion and medicos to reach the conclusion that cholera was not a Visitation of God, and that it was not transmitted through the air – the Miasma Theory that poisonous germs floating in the atmosphere were responsible for disease. Before then, in the face of the unknown, cholera with its unpleasant symptoms of diarrhoea and vomiting, became an epidemic. Its extent brought national panic.

The first cases occurred in Sunderland where 31,000 of its inhabitants were to die before the disease had run its course. Out of a population of 2,800 some 400 died of it in Exeter and another 800 were stricken with it but survived. In York 185 died; in Newcastle many more. When the disease hit Hull in August 1849 and raged for three months 1,860 died – one in 43 of the entire population. Even at this date there was still ignorance as to the cause of it:

> The medical services were unable to cope with the epidemic. It was soon out of control in the horribly unsanitary conditions in which many people lived. Strange as it may seem to us, brandy was prescribed as a preventive and a cure. This left liquor sellers at their wits' end trying to prevent those likely to be infected from coming into contact with their other customers. In one instance in Prospect Street a hole was made in the outer wall of the building through which cholera sufferers were supplied. These licensed premises became known as *The Hole in the Wall*. (The Yorkshire Water Museum, *The History of the Water Supply to Kingston-Upon-Hull*)

In spite of the brandy, deaths soared. As many as 700 were buried in a single grave in the General Cemetery, Spring Bank. Hull became a 'forbidden city'; people who now travelled away from their homes on the new steam trains thought twice of buying a ticket to Hull. When the fever died down the people of the town led by their clergy held a day of fasting 'to acknowledge the hand of the Almighty in the present awful visitation and to implore the removal of the existing calamity'.

In London the greatest number of cholera victims were among the poor who lived in squalid, filthy surroundings like Jacob's Island in Southwark which Charles Dickens described in *Oliver Twist* and Alderman Sir Charles Gurney, one-time Lord Mayor of London, refused to believe was other than a figment of the novelist's imagination. It was a neighbourhood surrounded by a muddy pond eight feet deep known as Folly Ditch, a creek from the Thames filled at high water by opening the sluices at the Lead Mills. There a stranger would see:

> the inhabitants of the houses on either side lowering from their back doors and windows buckets, pails, domestic utensils of all kinds, in which to haul the water up; and when his eye is turned from these operations to the houses themselves, his utmost astonishment will be excited by the scene before him.

Crazy wooden galleries looked down on the slime beneath; rooms so small, so filthy, so confined, that the air would seem too tainted even for the dirt and squalor which they sheltered:

> Dirt-besmeared walls and decaying foundations; every repulsive lineament of poverty, every loathsome indication of filth, rot and garbage; all these ornament the banks of Folly Ditch.

Dirt and squalor are the most frequently recurring words in descriptions of the living conditions of the poorer classes of the period, along with references to the failure of the authorities to do anything to remove them. The urgent need to provide Bristol with an additional water supply had become 'a pressing public question' at least in the 1830s, according to John Latimer, author of *The Annals of Bristol in the 19th Century*:

> The state of the poor in many districts was lamentable in the extreme; and the high rate of mortality which generally prevailed was held to be largely attributable to the consumption of impure water, and to the dirt and squalor that prevailed amongst the labouring classes.

When the Mayor of Bristol presided over a meeting in March 1840 called to remove the slur of an official report, which described Bristol as 'worse supplied with water than any great city in England', and to form a Bristol and Clifton Waterworks Company, the scheme was dropped from lack of support.

The Sussex town of Worthing showed the greatest increase of fever at this time – and no wonder, said *The Medical Press*. The news need not excite surprise when it was learnt that on the side of the water-tower of the town was a shed containing the engine which performed the double duty of distributing water to the houses and the sewage to the land. One well had been sunk in porous soil for drinking water and another 50 yards away for the reception of the sewage.

This of course was foul sewage. It could not be too distinctly understood, pronounced the medical doctor of the Privy Council in the 1850s 'that the person who contracts cholera in this country is *ipso facto* demonstrated with almost absolute certainty to have been exposed to excremental pollution'.

Cholera, he said, was not Nature's only retribution to Britain's neglect of sanitation. Typhoid fever and much endemic diarrhoea were incessant witnesses to the same deleterious influence:

> The mere quantity of this wasted life is horrible to contemplate, and the mode in which the waste is caused is surely nothing less than shameful. It is to be hoped that, as the education of the country advances, this sort of thing will come to an end; that so much preventable ill will not always be accepted as a fate; that, for a

'Every loathsome indication of filth, rot and garbage' in the open sewers of Victorian London.

POISONOUS ACCUMULATION

GRAVEL MIXED WITH SAND

**Part of the Thames shore in 1858. The accumulation of the contents of cesspools and sewers resulted in a series of cholera outbreaks.**

population to be thus poisoned by its own excrement, will some day be deemed ignominious and intolerable.

Organic matter in water was also unhygienic, but that of animal origin more dangerous that any derived from the vegetable kingdom. The former contained nitrogen and was usually derived from the contents of cesspools or sewers percolating into springs. In decomposing it produced nitrous and nitric acid and ammonia, which, however, did not communicate any bad taste or smell to the water but in many cases made it particularly palatable.

### Disease was Water-borne

This would have made it more difficult for laymen to comprehend that disease could be water-borne, and to look for a remedy in the mechanics of water supply. However the medical evidence for the link between disease and contaminated water was there for all to read in the reports of London anaesthetist Dr John Snow, who examined the mortality statistics in London's Soho, and William Farr, a statistician in the Registrar General's Office, who scrutinised the incidence of cholera in London's East End. Surely it could be no coincidence, asked Snow, that there were eight times the number of cholera victims among people who had drunk their water from the company which drew its water from the Thames at a point where the foul sewage of 2¼ million people was discharged? Snow created bacteriology as a new branch of medical science.

These reports revealed a picture of destitution of which the general public had no conception. Clearly the victims of the first cholera outbreak of 1831/2 were those whose homes were the unventilated and undrained hovels of the kind found in the East End of London, while the middle and upper classes of society escaped. Cholera was 'a disease of society', claimed *The Economist* in 1849, the year of the second great outbreak.

The disease also took hold in a very different environment: there was nothing particularly dirty or squalid about the living quarters of the people of York who fell victim to the disease. Their misfortune was to draw water from the river at a spot near to the mouth of one of the town's sewers and next to a public convenience, the contents of both of which were discharged daily into the river. Respectable householders in Newcastle started going down with cholera as soon as the Whittle Dean Water Company supplemented its supply (from the Whittle Burn and springs ten miles out of town) with water from the River Tyne, which it drew at a point past which the tide flowed, carrying with it the foul sewage of the town. Within two days of the company cutting out the Tyne supply the deaths started diminishing and the epidemic was on the wane.

It became clear that the violence of the epidemic exhibited a close relation to the degree of foul sewage contamination of the water supply which, when drawn from a river like the Tyne or the Thames, depended on *where* it was abstracted. When water was taken from the Thames at Battersea between Hungerford and Waterloo bridges, where the river water was decidedly foul, the death rate from cholera in 1849 was 163 in 10,000. Among the inhabitants of Belgravia, Chelsea and Westminster, whose water came from below Chelsea Hospital, it was 47 in 10,000. The death rate among those who had water from the Thames at Kew was 8 in 10,000.

There seemed to be no pattern about the duration of each 'visitation', though John Snow thought it was usually in direct proportion to the population. It remained in a village for only two or three weeks, two to three months in a good-sized town, while in a big city it often remained a whole year or longer. Moreover the disease hit unevenly. It caused havoc in Newcastle in 1831, returned with less virulence in 1849 but became 'a centre of horror' in 1854.

It was for the water suppliers, municipal or otherwise, to tackle the shortcomings of their systems with regard to the misplacing of their river abstraction point, but it was for government to take heed of the picture of 'Darkest London' revealed by the reports of Snow and Farr – and to take action.

It was the Age of Reform. Not only parliamentary reform, with the revolutionary Reform Act of 1832, but of reformed attitudes to social life so long regarded as traditional and therefore sacred, such as promotion for army officers by purchase and punishment of other ranks by flogging; imprisonment for debt; and the climbing boys whose sad existence Revd Charles Kingsley exposed in *The Water Babies*.

Not least among these issues was sanitary reform, but the principal agent who set the changes in motion antagonised the old guard by wanting to move too fast. They made sure he had no more than 20 years in the driving seat. Tact and diplomacy were never strong points in the make-up of Edwin Chadwick, the barrister and amateur reformer who was as appalled as everybody else by the revelations of those who sought to find the causes of the cholera epidemic, but he was alone in allowing them to take over his whole life. To his detractors he may have seemed a man possessed; indeed he made no secret of his belief that he was battling against Fate. His fellow crusader, Charles Kingsley, identified sanitary reform with the Will of God.

Chadwick was convinced that if the ills of society were to be remedied, 'searching sanitary reform' must come before all else; that 'even Education and Religion can do nothing where they are most needed until the way is paved for their ministrations by Cleanliness and Decency.' And the key to effecting the change was by replacing the vestry system with centralisation. Britain now had the tools to make the change. The chief remedies were 'the application of the science of engineering of which the medical men know nothing':

> The suddenness with which the people of England appeared for the first time to acquire a sense of sight and smell, and realise that they were living on a dung heap was due to the impact of industrial change. By the 1840s the slow procession of piecemeal alteration in modes of production had produced a qualitative change visible to all. England was rich. England lived in towns.... Engineering skill and the new riches made a sanitary science possible... and necessary.
> (S E Finer *The Life and Times of Sir Edwin Chadwick*)

The open sewer from Bow Common passes houses in Limehouse, 1858.

Edwin Chadwick.

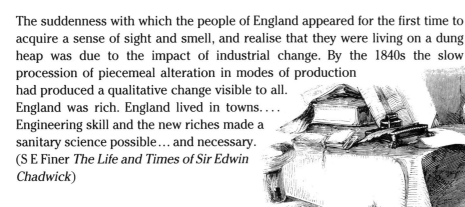

Sanitary reform went hand in hand with sanitary science but, as Asa Briggs has said, progress was very slow. Delay in implementing legislation was made worse by the tardiness of the Victorians in developing the necessary skills for managing growing cities – civil engineering skills, for example, and medical skills:

> The noisy opposition to Chadwick made the most of his self-confident dogmatism, his eagerness to provide non-expert answers to highly complex technical problems. If half the technical skill applied to industry had been applied to the Victorian cities, their record would have been very different. As it was, Victorian cities were places where problems often overwhelmed people. (*Victorian Cities*)

### Edwin Chadwick Calls for Sanitary Reform

At the age of 32 in 1832, two years after he had been called to the bar, Edwin Chadwick became a civil servant as an Assistant Commissioner on the Poor Law Commission. As such he was the chief architect of the Poor Law Amendment Act of 1834. The following year saw the enactment of the Municipal Corporations Act which gave borough councils and urban district councils control of public utility undertakings, including sanitation and water supply. Ratepayers were soon querying the economics of sanitary reform, and it took time to convince them of the principle that it cost more money to create disease than to prevent it; that, as a medical journal of the time put it, 'there is not a

**Building the tunnels for the main drainage of London – work in hand at Wick Lane near Old Ford, Bow.**

single structural arrangement chargeable with the production of disease that is not also in itself an extravagance.' Sewerage and waterworks were expensive and a burden on the new 'rates' paid by the more prosperous section of the community. In the main the beneficiaries were those who did not pay rates.

In 1838 Chadwick joined Benjamin Disraeli, Lord Shaftesbury and Dr Southwood Smith, distinguished reformers all, in creating The Health of Towns Association to promote public health. Dr Southwood Smith had himself investigated conditions in London's Bethnal Green and Whitechapel. In Lamb's Fields he found a stagnant pond in which there was always a quantity of putrefying animal and vegetable matter 'the odour of which, at the present moment, is most offensive'. Into an open filthy ditch all the uncovered privies of North Street opened.

Edwin obtained first-hand evidence of similar conditions all over Britain when he toured the country as head of the Royal Commission on the Health of Large Towns and Populous Districts in England and Wales. The members of the Royal Commission visited 50 large towns, where for the most part the water supply was organised by companies operating under special powers conferred on them by an Act of Parliament. Under these they could only lay water pipes in a town's main streets. In only six of the 50 towns did they find 'good' water supply; 13 'indifferent' and 31 'bad'. They pointed to the inconvenience of road stand-pipes, and the pollution of wells. In Birmingham they found that only 8,000 of the town's 40,000 houses – a fifth – had water 'laid on'. Bristol was one of the worst supplied of the largest places. In Manchester 33 privies served 5,095 people – one for every 150 of them. They found 'the authorities' at loggerheads. In Liverpool the town council were responsible for water supply, but two mutually hostile commissions for the general sewerage.

The Royal Commission sat under the chairmanship of the Duke of Buccleugh from 1843 to 1845. Before it issued its report, Parliament passed the Metropolitan Buildings Act which made it compulsory to connect house drains to sewers, which effectively turned the Thames into a cesspool, and was largely responsible for the second cholera outbreak in 1849. The star the reformers followed was 'improvement', and in pursuit of it they founded groups such as The Metropolitan Association for Improving the Dwellings of the Industrial Classes (1841) and The Society for Improving the Condition of the Labouring Classes (1844). Edwin Chadwick produced his blueprint for improvement in 1842 in his monumental *Report on the Sanitary Condition of the Labouring Population of Great Britain.*

There could be no improvement in sanitation without water, he said. It was central to the entirely new concept of town sanitation which was *circulation* in place of stagnation – the arterial system of town drainage. Water closets shot foul sewage into road sewers which had never been designed to take solids. Many ran uphill so that the solids fell back to the level and stayed there. A WC was patently the most convenient, clean and economical way of disposing of domestic refuse, but not when it discharged into sewers made solely to draw off flood water. Fortunately, the main defect of the rain water sewer as the disposer of foul sewage had been remedied by one John Roe, the engineer to the Holborn and Finsbury Commission of Sewers. In place of the sewer with a flat or semi-circular base, he produced an egg-shaped sewer with steep gradients. Water with the sewage had to force itself through the deep and narrow channel and swept all solids with it at once without leaving any deposit. A WC connected to one of John Roe's sewers via the house drain would reach the river in a matter of hours. To make it work there had to be a *constant* stream of water, and enough of it to dilute the refuse and carry it rapidly away. The lifeblood of the arterial system was water flowing at high velocity.

Chadwick championed the arterial system as more economical than having to maintain and clean out private cesspools, but he was well aware of its most damaging feature which he met full on:

> The chief objection to the extension of this system is the pollution of the river into which the sewers are discharged, but an evil of inappreciable magnitude beside the ill-health occasioned by constant retention of several hundred thousand accumulations of pollution in the most densely populated districts.

He realised it meant using the Thames as an open sewer, but he thought the water of that river so bad that what the WCs emptied into it could never make it worse. An even bigger obstacle to its acceptance was that it made the water companies' existing equipment obsolete, if not the private enterprises themselves. Indeed Chadwick was all for a clean sweep: no half measures, in fact no 'improvement' but replacement. Asked why he had tried to stop the Lambeth Water Company from moving its intake from the pool of London to above Teddington Lock, he said that the ills of the country's water supply system would only be cured by uniting drainage and water supply under the same public jurisdiction. The new supply would therefore be 'ineligible and unsuitable'. The new investment of capital needed for the new intake was inexpedient, since it would probably have to be repurchased.

Something less radical was probably more acceptable, something more akin to what Edmund Burke called 'the habit of compromise': trading off one benefit against another. The advantage of being able to put foul sewage from WCs into rivers would seem to be worth keeping, but then it would have to be *treated* before it entered the river and that would be costly and time-consuming.

Whether Britain's water supply service of the 1840s needed improving or removing and replacing, the process was bound to be long-term. The rot had already set in, but with every month of non-action it worsened. As S E Finer has described, years of neglect had played havoc with the London scene:

> The service provided was disgraceful. Only the richer areas were adequately served and over 17,000 houses had no water whatsoever, but relied on the 'poison wells', thick with scum and oozing with sewage; 70,000 out of London's 270,000 houses were supplied in groups of twenty or thirty by stand-pipes running an hour per day, three days a week. The evil was exaggerated by the companies' system of intermittent supply, which necessitated the use of storage receptacles. This was no hardship to those who could afford capacious lead cisterns, but to the poor with their winepipes or butter-tubs it was quite another matter. Sometimes the stand-pipe was out of order, or the water cut off because the landlord had not paid his water-rates; sometimes the housewife missed her place in the queue. Whatever the cause it meant going without water for days.

**Filling up buckets from a stand-pipe.**

As a result the poor used water very sparingly. Children went unwashed, washing water was used over and over again; drinking water which stood for days in rotten tubs and uncovered butts 'carpeted with dust and soot, was nauseous to the taste and flocculent with dirt and sediment'. Half London's population got their water from the Rivers Chadwell and Lee, receiving the pollution of 20 miles of villages on the way. But it was more wholesome than that received by the other half who received theirs 'from the very tideway of the Thames, a stretch of water into which no less than 209 public sewers discharged themselves'. And not only that but also, as a writer in the *Edinburgh Review* pointed out, 'dead animal and vegetable matter – the blood and offal of slaughterhouses – the outpourings from gas-works, dye-works, breweries, distilleries, glue-works, bone-works, tanneries, chemical and other works'. Thoroughly stirred up and finely commuted by the unceasing splash of 298 steamboats, it was then pumped for the use of the wealthiest city in the world:

> The twentieth century looks back upon the 1840s with a puzzled wonder of an Alice stepping into the world behind the looking glass.

## Water-carriage System Pollutes the Rivers

The contamination was not, of course, an entirely new phenomenon. Rivers were already being polluted by discharges from surface-water sewers and by domestic and industrial waste waters from riverside communities and factories. The contents of privies and middens and overflowing cesspools drained into surface-water sewers, but as H H Stanbridge points out in his *History of Sewage Treatment in Britain*, it was the introduction of the water-carriage system which led to the *gross* pollution of rivers. Chadwick was the first to pinpoint the solution as removing the refuse from built-up areas before it had time to decompose and give offence, an operation best effected by water, which meant providing more of it than was available.

Much of the water that *was* available was wasted by the design of the early flushing WCs. The water for these came from a cistern in which there was a valve at the outlet of the flush pipe. Pulling the chain raised the valve and released the water. The action pulled the plug out. For many, having to pull the plug was a bore, and they tied the chain down to keep the valve open, so that the water kept on flowing down the pan non-stop. If everyone did this the Board of Trade believed it would drain the country's reservoirs dry. Even if the valve was tied open, it was often only half effective in its closed position for not being made to fit closely enough. It never returned to a fully watertight position after each flush, and water trickled through all day.

The man who solved that problem was Thomas Crapper with 'Crapper's Valveless Waste Preventer, One Moveable Part Only, Certain Flush With Easy Pull, Will Flush When Only Two-Thirds Full'. At the Marlborough Works in Chelsea, Crapper & Co, Sanitary Engineers, produced the cistern, fitted to all water closets today, by which water comes into it as soon as it is emptied by means of the floating ball on a metal arm which turns the water off when it rises to the top. The water remains in the cistern, with none of it draining out, until someone pulls the plug again and lets it go.

Thomas Crapper's firm received the royal warrant as Manufacturing Sanitary Engineers, a distinction that came at the end of Crapper's career from King Edward VII. Among his patents was Crapper's Seat Action Automatic Flush. With Thomas Twyford of Stoke-on-Trent he produced a whole toilet unit – the 'Combination' – which could be installed in a house or premises of any kind. But perhaps today, for more than anything else, he is known for having giving the English language the word 'crap', meaning nonsense, exaggeration and lies. As Wallace Reyburn said in his excellent biography of the man, *Flushed with Pride*:

> It is *crap* in this connotation which has drifted across the Atlantic from America to England in recent years. One hears it from time to time in this country, as in 'You're talking a lot of crap.' But the English are hesitant about using it in polite society, associating it in their minds with the good old Anglo-Saxon word.

In the more salubrious environment of Scotland the water supply situation was a little better. In his 1842 report Edwin Chadwick quoted the observations of a Mr Burton who

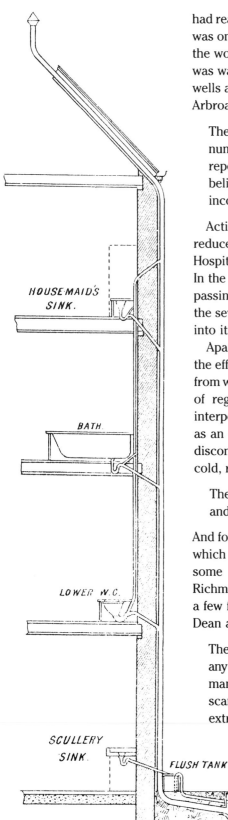

HOUSEMAID'S
SINK.

BATH.

LOWER W.C.

SCULLERY
SINK.

FLUSH TANK.

OUTFALL SEWER.

had reason to believe that in many parts of Scotland the want of a good supply of water was one of the most material impediments to the furtherance of cleanly habits among the working people. Besides the immediate evils of an inadequate supply, much time was wasted and many bad habits acquired by those who had to wait their turn at the wells at a time of drought. He believed that Dundee, Stirling, Dunfermline, Lanark and Arbroath were all imperfectly supplied:

> The evil is rendered more serious by the demand for cooling water for the numerous steam-engines, and the article is so precious that is for these purposes repeatedly re-cooled by exposure and evaporation after it has been heated. I believe that in many of the colliery and manufacturing districts there is inconvenience, amounting to suffering, from want of water.

Action taken in Ireland by moving troops into new barracks in Cork immediately reduced the occurrence of dysentery – a case which Chadwick quoted from Dublin Hospital Reports to show the extent to which the nature of the water influenced health. In the old barracks the troops were supplied with water from the River Lee which, in passing through the city, was rendered unfit for drinking by the influx of the contents of the sewers from the houses, and was likewise brackish from the tide which ascended into its channels.

Apart from the effect of impure water on health, Chadwick was extremely worried at the effect the lack of piped water had on people's lifestyle. Supplies of water obtained from wells by the labour of fetching and carrying in buckets did not answer the purpose of regular supplies of water brought into the house without such labour. The interposition of the labour of going out and bringing home water from a distance acted as an obstacle to the formation of better habits. It was a serious inconvenience and discomfort to have to fetch water at a distance out of doors whenever it was wanted, in cold, rain or snow:

> The minor comforts of cleanliness are of course forgone to avoid the immediate and greater discomforts of having to fetch the water.

And for some there was the discomfort of having to pay to have water brought to them, which required them to choose which was the preferable evil. In Bristol in the 1840s some 100 houses near Richmond Terrace were supplied from wells known as the Richmond and Buckingham springs; another 400 were connected with Sion spring, and a few families were provided from Jacob's Wells, the pipes being the property of the Dean and Chapter. But, as John Latimer pointed out:

> The poor, excepting those living near the public conduits, were generally without any provision. Water-carrying was therefore a common and lucrative trade, and as many as a thousand poor families had to pay on an average a penny daily for a scanty supply, as it was not surprising that they should be stigmatised as extremely dirty in their habits. Unfortunately, too, much of the water drawn from private wells was affected by neighbouring cesspools and was pernicious to health.
> (*The Annals of Bristol in the 19th Century*)

Welcome change came with the formation of the Bristol Waterworks Company by Act of Parliament on 16 July 1846 – and still operating today.

Designs of the "Twycliffe" Patent Syphon Closet Basin.

No. 2—Plain Surface, White or Ivory, 50/-

"Corinthian" Pattern, in Relief.
No. 4—With Slop Top, White or Ivory, 75/-
No. 1—Without    „      „      54/-

No. 3—Strong Fire Clay.
Enamelled inside, 44/-

"Poppy," Printed.
No. 26—Blue on White Ware } 58/6
No. 27—Brown on Ivory Ware }

"Cactus," Printed and Coloured.
No. 33—Brown on Ivory Ware, 78/6

"Mikado," Printed.
No. 28—Blue on White Ware } 58/6
No. 29—Brown on Ivory Ware }

"Japanesque," Printed.
No. 30—Blue on White Ware } 58/6
No. 31—Brown on Ivory Ware }

"Corinthian" Pattern, in Relief.
No. 25—Blue and Gold, 136/-

"Cactus," Printed.
No. 32—Brown on Ivory Ware, 58/6

LEFT: **A page from Twyfords' 1889 catalogue.**

**The first one-piece WC bowl, developed by Twyfords in 1884.**

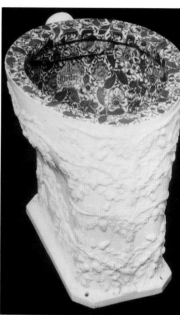

OPPOSITE: **Different kinds of wastewater that drained into the public sewer in 19th-century Britain, including the housemaid's sink at the top and the pedestal wash-down WC on the first floor.**

## Getting Rid of the Cesspools and Middens

The cesspools which were still contaminating the water supply were the shallow trenches or pits dug to receive the wastes from privies and closets which had been made more permanent by lining them with brick or stone. A cesspool was built near a house, in the garden or yard. Where there was little space it might be built *under* the house, in the cellar. Members of the Health of Towns Commission of 1843 reported that 'one of these wells, four feet deep, filled with this stinking fluid, was found in one cellar under the bed where the family slept'. In the same year Robert Rawlinson reported that between 1827 and 1843, 51 cesspools had been abolished at Windsor Castle. In a closely built-up area of Liverpool three tunnel-middens received the excreta from 76 dwellings

Those who did not have water piped into their houses were condemned to having to draw heavy pails of it from the nearest well, which may have been some way distant.

Illustration of 'The Water-Man' from the title page of *Sketches of Pumps* 'handled by Robert Cruikshank with some temperate spouting by Alfred Crowquill', 1846.

in which 529 people were living. They were underneath the houses; the only exit for the gases from the middens was through the closets and they penetrated every room.

So that cesspools did not have to be emptied so often, the builders often made walls which were purposely not watertight, so that the liquid part of the sewage they contained could percolate into the surrounding soil. In some cases, Stanbridge points out, as at Guildford, where the cesspools were sunk into chalk, and at Northampton where they were excavated in porous sandstone, they rarely needed emptying at all. Sometimes they were sunk until a layer of sand was reached, so that the liquid could be drawn into it. Often a cesspool would be given an overflow pipe leading to a nearby stream, or the cesspool overflowed without any encouragement onto a garden or yard. It was commonplace for the well supplying a family with water to be polluted by the contents of a cesspool which it was the custom to empty only 'at uncertain intervals', once in two or three years or maybe 'not for a dozen years or more'. When it was done the emptying was carried out during the night, and when this became more frequent scavengers warned residents by ringing a bell so they could close their windows against the stench. Under the pressure from the flushing WCs of a continually growing population, the cesspools in the crowded slums were soon unable to handle the huge volume of waste water poured into them. The only thing they could do was to flow over into yards and streets or into the nearest river.

When foul sewers were built to receive the overflows from cesspools, water closets were connected directly to the sewers. Chadwick said that these should use glazed earthenware pipes as drains, of the kind first produced in 1842. Robert Rawlinson, Chief Engineering Inspector to the General Board of Health, set out his ideas on how sewerage systems should be arranged and recommended straight lengths of pipe between manholes, manholes at each change of direction and lamp shafts at intervening points. His suggestions were so patently sound both in theory and practice that they were accepted and adopted in probably every country in Europe.

Up to 1852 those responsible for re-sewering a town could do one of several things. They could connect their old surface-water sewers together with an interceptor sewer, thus discontinuing discharge into a watercourse; they could lay a new sewer to receive the sewage and take it away for treatment; or they could arrange for new sewers to receive both sewage and surface water, and abolish the old sewers, instead of leaving them to take surface water and ground water to a watercourse.

When a Committee of the British Association of the Advancement of Science carried out a survey in 178 towns in England and Wales of methods in use in 1870 for removing excreta from houses, it found that in 146 towns it was removed by sewers, while in 19 towns sewers and some other methods were used. In 13 towns there were no sewers, reliance being placed on cesspools, surface-water drains and the rest. In only 46 towns did the sewage receive any form of treatment before disposal.

In 1852 the General Board of Health recommended that when re-sewering a town, two sets of sewers should be provided: one at the rear of a house to receive rain water from the roof and yard, as well as the sewage from the house, and one at the front to take rain water. This separate system of sewerage came into being when new systems of pipe sewers were installed in towns to take domestic wastewater to a suitable point for treatment and disposal, leaving the existing brick sewers to convey storm water and subsoil water direct to a stream. One John Towle was granted a patent for such a separate system of sewerage in 1868. Leamington was the first town to adopt it – it had a population of 20,000. At Fareham, with a population of 4,600 and some 500 WCs, storm water was carried off through special drains. In 1884 most of the witnesses appearing before the Royal Commission on Metropolitan Sewage Discharge supported the separate system principle, and in 1892 the Private Street Works Act empowered local authorities to install separate drains for sewage and rain water.

Cost inhibited many local authorities from changing over to a water-carriage system. Manchester still had an improved form of privy-midden in 1871 and her councillors were worried about what a change would mean in terms not only of cost but also the increased demand for it on their short water supplies, and the pollution of the rivers. They introduced the 'Rochdale Pail System' in that town around the same time, but it still had 4,000 privies and only 372 WCs. Of Nottingham's 18,000 houses, 15,000 were served by privy-middens. The introduction of WCs was more advanced in the south of England, with more in seaside towns than inland. In the industrial towns of the Midlands and North usually only houses in the upper-class districts had WCs.

The sewage from such WCs as Birmingham had was fed into the sewers the town council laid in the valleys of the River Lea and the Hockley Brook in 1852. It was, of course, untreated, but in 1859 a sedimentation tank was built at Saltley, and in 1871 a Sewage Inquiry Committee were able to report that 'the whole of the Borough is drained to one outfall at Saltley with the exception of a small part which is drained into a tributary of the River Cole.' Outside London, the main thrust of the campaign to sewer towns, so that domestic waste was flushed away from dwelling houses, started around 1865; the Sanitary Act of 1866 for the first time gave the government power to take action against any local authority who had received a complaint about the lack of sufficient sewers or the maintenance of existing ones.

Under a further Act of 1876 a local authority could prohibit the throwing into a public sewer of anything which was likely to hinder the free passage of the sewage in it, or

East London Waterworks Company were universally unpopular – a *Punch* cartoon of 1896. The caption to this cartoon read:
EAST LONDON WATER SUPPLY!
Company's Turncock. "Now, look 'ere, don't you go a wastin' all this 'ere valuable water in washin' and waterin' your gardens, or any nonsense o' that sort, or you'll get yourselves into trouble!"

**George Scharf painted these workmen laying mains in Tottenham Court Road in 1834. London's drainage system was severely criticised when the Metropolitan Sanitary Commission reported in 1848.**

which could be considered injurious to health or likely to damage the fabric of the sewer. The Act of 1890 specified the penalties which could be imposed if the wastewater on its own, or mixed with other matter, either actually damaged the fabric of the sewer or caused a 'nuisance'.

## General Board of Health Recommends Re-sewering

The body which made the recommendations regarding the re-sewering of towns, the General Board of Health, was new. It had only been in existence for four years in 1852. It was established by the measure with which the government showed its belated concern for the public's health, the Public Health Act of 1848. It had the power to create local boards of health, either at the request of ratepayers or where the death rate in a locality exceeded a specified limit. In a municipal borough the local board of health would be the town council; elsewhere one would be elected by ratepayers.

The General Board had no power to control local boards who could and did defy it. The government's Commission of Enquiry into a further outbreak of cholera at Newcastle in 1854 reported that the filthy condition of the town was due to nuisances which Newcastle Corporation had the power but not the will to suppress. The General Board of Health, of which Edwin Chadwick was Secretary, could do nothing. It was not answerable to Parliament, and its terms of reference could not be amended by the legislators until the end of its five-year term of appointment.

The Public Health Act of 1848 and the Waterworks Clauses Act of 1847 both subscribed to Chadwick's conviction that only centralisation could bring the wholesale reorganisation of Britain's water supply, the neglect of which, by so many and diverse warring parties, had given the British Isles so unhealthy a reputation. The 1847 Act standardised waterworks practice by consolidating all the provisions obtained by water companies in their individual Acts of Parliament – all those that is, that were deemed necessary and relevant. The Waterworks Clauses Act covered not only the construction of waterworks but the laying of pipes, installation of fire plugs, the protection of water and the fouling of water, as well as water charges.

To protect drinking water against contamination, the 1847 Act made fouling water an offence, and vested a statutory duty in town commissioners to put out fires; the water suppliers had to fix fire plugs into their mains at least 100 yards apart, but the Commissioners had to pay for them. Fire plugs were on their way out, however. In 1848 Alfred Moore, resident water engineer of Warrington, and J F Bateman the Lancashire water engineer, invented the Ball Hydrant. By this the pressure of the water in the pipe held a wooden ball in position against the outlet. When water was needed, someone removed the wooden ball plug, by tapping it until the pressure forced it out, and then inserted a stand-pipe against the flow of water which had to be constant. The invention gave rise to a new piece of firefighting equipment, the hose reel.

The Act made it a duty for suppliers to make their supply constant. It had, too, to be in sufficient quantity and at a reasonable pressure. Together with the amending measure of 1863 it remained the backbone of water legislation for almost 100 years.

However, whatever bright new ideas might issue from Westminster, the last word was still with the local authorities of the kind castigated by the Chief Surveyor of the Westminster Court of Sewers as 'totally incompetent to manage the great important works committed to their care and control,' where jobbery, favouritism and incompetence was rampant. Slackness and indifference in the front line thwarted Chadwick's hopes that the second round of cholera in 1849 would galvanise 'the authorities' into appreciating the seriousness of the situation – which it lay in their power to improve, though not instantly to remove.

Oxford's answer to an 1848 questionnaire was categorical. Had they done anything to obtain an abundant and economical supply of water? No, they had never done so, and 'were not likely to do so till compelled by Parliamentary interposition . . . the *laissez faire* system prevails and nothing but the interference of government will change it.' They were not aware of the advantages of a constant water supply.

Any form of town improvement cost money and, as Nottingham said, 'popular men will not hazard their popularity by using money for such purposes, though convinced of the necessity of such improvements.' It was a widespread attitude which owed much to civic pride. 'While we are most anxious that every town in the kingdom should have the benefit of good sewerage and pure water,' wrote a leader writer in the *Leeds Mercury* in 1848, 'we could not consent to purchase these blessings by a permanent infringement of the rights of municipal bodies and through them of the people at large.'

'Self-satisfied bumbledum in town and parish, incapable of grasping the implication of the crisis,' groaned Edwin Chadwick, 'cried out aloud against centralisation.' The Central Board of Health, attacked by local authorities and all those with vested interests, was dissolved in 1854. With it ended Edwin Chadwick's crusading. He was 54. He was knighted in 1889 and died the year after.

Maybe he felt frustrated in his lifetime, but Samuel Smiles, editor of the *Leeds Times*, would have given him full marks for perseverance. In the story of Britain's water supply Chadwick holds an honoured place.

George Scharf's drawing of the sewers in Bloomsbury Street, London, in 1845 – constructed to an improved design by John Roe, Holborn's sanitary engineer, and commended by the Commissioners.

OVERLEAF: A family of mute swans on the River Itchen, Alresford, Hampshire.

'The Cold Water Cure' by Robert Cruikshank.

# CHAPTER FOUR

# A prime necessity

ENGINES AND PUMPS • LONG JOURNEYS TO DISTANT RESERVOIRS • WATER FOR FIRE-FIGHTING • FLORENCE NIGHTINGALE JOINS THE AGITATION • THE YEAR OF THE GREAT STINK • CHOICE OF WATER PIPE • CONTROL WATER RESOURCES! • MUNICIPAL OWNERSHIP OF WATER SUPPLY • SANITARY SCIENCE

Water engineers and sanitary engineers sustained their vision of what Britain – and any civilised society – needed by way of a constant sanitary water supply, unaffected by the doubts of the local politicians. There were so many problems asking to be solved and they got on with solving them. Encouraged by members of the Reformed Parliament, and men like Edwin Chadwick and Michael Faraday who shared their vision, they conceived and executed schemes which an earlier generation could never have contemplated.

The first problem was to find the means of shifting the huge volumes of fresh water which the mushrooming towns were needing every day. Between 1801 and 1831 Bradford's population rose from 29,000 to 77,000; Leeds's from 53,000 to 123,000; Halifax's from 63,000 to 110,000. The size of London grew from 958,000 in 1801 to 1,948,000 in 1841. In 60 years the number of people living in the British Isles doubled from 15 million in 1821 to 30 million in 1881 – hard to comprehend today.

Gravitation had been enough to keep the water flowing so long as the distances were not too great and it was all downhill. It still served the needs of many towns, but the wooden pipes which formed the conduit tended to leak and were often impregnated with the flavour of town gas which it gave to the water. The tool which enabled the engineers to force water against gravity up hill and down dale in the volume required, and over very long distances, was the steam engine, now greatly improved since James Watt (who died in 1819) installed the first Boulton-made 'Cornish' engines to pump water out of the tin mines in Cornwall and the coal mines of Durham. Many other manufacturers had entered the field and were producing their own versions to the designs of men like Richard Trevithick, Arthur Woolf and Jonathan Hornblower, Edward Bull and Thomas Hawksley.

Maudslay Sons & Field of Lambeth built the steam engine which the Grand Junction Water Works Company installed in its Kew Bridge Pumping Station in 1838 (and which is still to be seen there in 1992). Its role was to share with the old Boulton & Watt 1820 'West Cornish' engine, moved there from Chelsea in 1840, the job of pumping water to Paddington. During its trials in December 1838 the Maudslay engine delivered an average of 601 tons of water an hour for an average consumption of $4\frac{3}{4}$ cwt of Wylam Moor coal, working at a speed of 13 strokes a minute. In 1845 two 40-inch diameter cylinder 'grasshopper' Cornish beam engines, built by Sandys, Carne & Vivian at their Copperhouse Foundry, Hayle, were laid alongside it to pump raw water

The magnificent Western Pumping Station, a protected part of London's Victorian water heritage, today provides an operating centre for ten out-stations located to the west of London, north and south of the Thames, linked by telemetry.

Abbey Mills Pumping Station, an impressive Italianate building, serves the low-lying parts of the inner London sewerage system, north of the River Thames.

into the filter beds which Grand Junction felt obliged to provide after all that criticism about pollution. This was part of a major plan to update and augment the pumping capacity at Kew Bridge initiated by the young engineer Thomas Wicksteed. In 1846 the biggest waterworks engine in the world was put to work, a 90-inch Cornish beam engine also built by Copperhouse Foundry. As a stand-by, they had the 90-inch cylinder, 10-foot stroke inverted Cornish Bull engine built by Harvey & Company of Hayle in 1857; this pumped water to Grand Junction's Campden Hill reservoir near Notting Hill Gate, where three more 'Bull' engines were erected for pressurising the mains at that elevation. The designer of these was Edward Bull, another Cornishman.

The Southwark firm of Easton & Amos built the beam engine installed at Cliftonville Pumping Station, Northampton, in 1863. It had an American-type centrifugal governor on the lines of the Porter-Allen design, introduced into Britain the year before the engine was built, and was more sensitive than the Watt pendulum type which preceded it.

All these engines are to be seen today in the Kew Bridge Steam Museum, along with several others, assembled by the Kew Bridge Engines Trust.

Two compound rotative beam engines made by Easton & Amos between 1856 and 1875 are to be seen in the museum of The British Engineering Trust in Brighton. This was Goldstone Pumping Station which had to adapt itself to providing a water supply to the famous Sussex coast resort, whose population between 1800 and 1840 more than doubled. When Edward Cresy, a superintendent inspector appointed by the new General Board of Health, visited the station in 1849 he found the three beam pumping engines wholly inadequate to meet the demand. Together they totalled 80 horse power and delivered an average of 700,000 gallons of water daily into a reservoir with a capacity of two million gallons. Because of leakage and engine failures, the supply was never constant. So the Brighton Water Company invited James Easton to submit a

Beam engine at Kew Bridge Pumping Station, now the Kew Bridge Steam Museum.

**Lifting one of the beams of the Hawksley engine into position for the Sunderland & South Shields Water Company's Ryhope Pumping Station in 1868.**

plan which could extend the water supply throughout the area, particularly to the ever-increasing residential area of Hove. James Easton had teamed up with Charles Amos to form their famous partnership in 1836, and by 1850 the two of them had gained international prestige designing and installing Woolf compound engines in major cities in Britain and abroad; this continued for 30 years. Other promoters engaged the services of Thomas Hawksley, who recommended obtaining water from Goldstone Bottom between Dyke Road and Portslade, which the water company bought in 1862.

Thomas Hawksley designed and built waterworks for many of Britain's large towns including Newcastle and Nottingham. In 1852 he supervised the erection of a large pumping station at Humbledon for the new Sunderland & South Shields Water Company; the engine house still stands. In the next 25 years the company had to build four more large pumping stations to meet demand. With the erection of the steam engines and boiler houses, the building of reservoirs and the laying of pipelines, it was a major operation. It began at Fulwell in 1852; Cleadon followed in 1863, and the scheme rounded off with the works at Ryhope and Dalton in 1868 and 1879.

In the care of Ryhope Engines Trust, Thomas Hawksley's installation still stands as a striking reminder of Britain's water heritage. The problem of constructing the engine house presented Thomas Hawksley, engineer of the Sunderland & South Shields Water Company, with a challenge. Into its foundations had to be bedded the foundations of most of the engine's components as well as provide supports for the well heads. The massive rocking beams had to be supported some 22 feet above ground level, so engine and engine house had to be constructed together, and without interfering with the sinking of the wells. Hawksley estimated the station would cost £50,000, but in the

OPPOSITE: **Massive Eastons and Anderson compound beam engine at Goldstone Pumping Station which pumped water to Brighton. Built in 1876, it pumped 2¼ million gallons of water a day; it is now exhibited at the British Engineerium, Hove.**

end it cost the company another £5,800. The two double-acting, compound rotative beam engines, made by R & W Hawthorn, alone cost £9,000. The pumps delivered three million gallons of water a day from Ryhope's deep wells. Commissioned in 1869 – see the photograph of one of them being erected reproduced on page 115 – they provided Sunderland and district with water for nearly a century, and with what elegance!

One of the original pair of steam turbines installed for the Weymouth Waterworks Company at Sutton Poyntz by the Glasgow engineer David Cook in 1856 has been scheduled as an ancient monument. The two of them, costing £920, could each pump 300,000 gallons of water a day to the company's reservoir. The teeth of the large gear wheels were originally made of applewood, but when the wrongly grained wood began to break up they were replaced by cast iron wheels. The massive machine, which was used in conjunction with the steam engines up to 1958, can still be seen in the turbine house of Wessex Water's Sutton Poyntz Pumping Station and Museum.

Bells, Lightfoot & Co of Walker Engine Works, Newcastle upon Tyne, made the 40-ton 'Woodhouse' Cornish beam engine for the City of Hull Waterworks, now in Yorkshire Water's Springhead Museum, in 1876. It could pump 6¾ million gallons of water a day, and it did so until 1910. The diameter of its cylinder was 90 inches and it had a stroke of 11 feet. Two pumps lifted water to a tank fixed 20 feet down the 73-foot

**Turbine installed by David Cook of Glasgow in 1857, now in Wessex Water's Museum of Water Supply, Sutton Poyntz, Dorset.**

deep well. From the tank a plunger forced the water into the main pipes. The 40-foot long beam, weighing 40 tons, was not made, as most others were, of cast iron but built up of wrought iron plates rivetted together. It is supported on a massive iron casting (entablature), itself carried on four cast iron fluted columns – another work of art, as is the majestic pumping station which houses it.

## Long Journeys to Distant Reservoirs

To give a *constant* supply to towns across long distances, powerful pumping with steam engines such as these shared the role of conveyance to not one, but several reservoirs, with gravitation.

In 1847 the Merchant Venturers Company of Bristol built three service reservoirs at once – at Bedminster Down, Whiteladies Road and Durdham Down. From springs at Barrow Gurney and Harptree Combe, five miles away, the water flowed to Whiteladies Road by gravitation, and was then forced 300 feet up to the Durdham Down reservoir by pumps. The other Bristol source, the springs forming the head of the River Chew at Litton and Chewton Mendip, was 16 miles away. It was a laborious journey. The water had first to be conveyed via a two-mile aqueduct to East Harptree, then through a quarter-mile tunnel, an iron tube over Harptree Combe, a four-mile pipeline, a three-quarter-mile tunnel through North Hill, a stone aqueduct over Leigh Down valley, and finally the mile-long Winford Tunnel. The four million gallons of water brought from Chewton Mendip to the 25-acre Barrow reservoir travelled 11 miles – and still had five miles to go before it reached customers' houses.

To reach Liverpool the water had to flow 17½ miles in the scheme which Thomas Hawksley and two other engineers submitted to Liverpool Corporation in 1846. The Health of Towns Commissioners had said that though the existing supply was good and pure – it ran through hygienic iron pipes – it was wholly inadequate for people in the town's poorer districts. There were no taps in their houses, only a communal stopcock in the courtyard. The water was only turned on for a quarter of an hour every other day, and that at eleven at night or six in the morning. The water company was refusing to lower its prices or improve the supply. If the people were too poor to pay the charges the water was cut off. As a result they went round begging for water.

Hawksley's scheme involved impounding the upper waters of the River Douglas and the River Roddlesworth. Parliament authorised the Rivington Pike Scheme, as it was known, in 1847, whereupon Liverpool Corporation purchased the two commercial water companies and took over Green Lane Works from the Highway Commissioners. The Rivington watershed consisted of 9,710 acres of hill and moorland lying between Bolton and Blackburn. Construction began in 1852, and water was being delivered to Liverpool five years later, in spite of a certain amount of public opposition. There were further murmurings when, compared with the crystal-clear well water to which most Liverpudlians had been used, the Rivington water was brown. The Corporation had expected to be able to close down the wells and save money, but it had to mix the new water with the old well water. It built another reservoir at Upper Roddlesworth in 1865, and ten years later a third at Yarrow. The three of them covered 598 acres and contained 4,105 million gallons. Total length along the top water line was five and a half miles. The embankment stretched for three miles. The water was filtered in eight slow sand filters at Horwich.

The Longdendale Valley through which the River Etherow ran was ten miles east of Manchester. When the supply, which the waterworks company (which Manchester

A Cornish beam engine built in 1876, with its counter-weighted pump-end in the foreground, in the Yorkshire Water Museum at Hull. Behind the left-hand support column can be seen the single-acting cylinder.

Corporation had purchased) was obtaining from the Manchester and Ashton Canal, proved insufficient, the Corporation acquired the valley where the annual rainfall was 54 inches. It covered 19,300 acres. Work on building five service reservoirs for the Longdendale Works, the first of their kind in Britain, began in 1848. The first instalment of the works at Longdendale was completed and brought into use in 1855, at a time when Manchester's consumption was eight million gallons of water a day.

In Wales fresh water was closer to hand. Mr Tucker and Mr Baker, who made a survey of Cardiff's water needs in 1849, found they could convey water from the River Ely to a reservoir only three miles away. There was plenty of water in Wales, and in 1867 John Bateman proposed sending some of it to London from Cader Idris and Plynlimmon, an area of 200 square miles which was the source of the River Severn. He could bring 230 million gallons of water a day along a 173-mile aqueduct to service reservoirs at Stanmore ten miles north of London. It would cost around £11,400,000. But the idea was considered too expensive and just too far.

In Northern Ireland the Water Commissioners found a new source of water for Belfast, with its population swollen to more than 70,000, at Carr's Glen River, now known as Antrim Road Waterworks. Under the Belfast Water Act of 1840, the Commissioners had taken over all existing waterworks, leases and rights owned by the Belfast Charitable Society.

In Scotland seven reservoirs were built between 1847 and 1856 to supply Edinburgh and make sure there was no recurrence of the disastrous emptying of the Glencorse Reservoir in the drought of 1836. When the Glasgow Waterworks Company failed to extend its supply or provide adequate filtration works, in the face of public agitation, in 1845, it promoted a scheme to bring in water from distant Loch Lubnaig. In the same year, however, two rival schemes were launched: one by a body of citizens proposing to form a company to abstract water from the even more distant Loch Katrine 34 miles away; the other by The Gorbals Gravitation Water Company who had a plan for supplying the southern parts of the town. Glasgow Waterworks persuaded the promoters of the Loch Katrine scheme to withdraw in favour of their own Loch Lubnaig scheme, but the Gorbals Company were not to be frightened off. The two remaining schemes were both approved by Parliament, but when the engineers of the Loch Lubnaig scheme started to work out the details, they found it was impracticable. The Glasgow Waterworks Company thought that in principle it was the best of the schemes and submitted an amended version of a Loch Lubnaig supply. Glasgow Town Council, however, preferred Loch Katrine, and in 1855 the Glasgow Corporation Water Works Act was passed which placed the city's water supply under municipal control. Loch Katrine waterworks, opened by Queen Victoria in 1859, was the earliest 'impounding' scheme in the British Isles. The loch was 364 feet above sea level, and 50 million gallons of water a day flowed from it to Glasgow, with more than 40 million coming in from Loch Vennachar as 'compensation water'. The water was drawn off from the loch's top seven feet. Engineers raised the natural water level by four feet, and then drew off water so that the surface dropped three feet.

Municipal control of the water supply of a much smaller town, Wrexham (population 7,500), was one of the main objectives of the town's application for incorporation in 1857. Up to then the Pearl of Denbighshire had been dependent on pumping water from shallow wells, the quality of which was deplorable. The people of Wrexham had to suffer for another six years. It was not until 1863 that a group of enterprising townsmen took matters into their own hands, in the light of municipal inactivity, and formed The Wrexham Waterworks Company with a capital of £15,000 to bring a piped supply from

Pentrebychan Stream. An abstraction reservoir with a storage reservoir and slow sand filters at Packsaddle were opened in 1867.

To make sure its water survived the five-hour 15-mile journey from a stream at Tottiford which ran into the River Teign on Dartmoor, in as pure a condition as possible, the Torquay Water Company had the pipes scraped in 1864 – the first town in the world where this was done according to water historian R C S Walters. There was a long journey, too, for the pipeline which Durham City Water Company laid to take water from its pumping station at Houghall in 1847 to its reservoir at Mount Joy, and thence to the centre of the city to meet its growing industrial and domestic needs.

One of the most striking urban expansions in Britain took place in Aberdeen, accompanied by an even greater increase in water consumption. In the 1830s only six hours' pumping a day was enough for Aberdeen's water needs. By 1855, however, it took 23 out of every 24 hours to force up the 1,125,000 gallons required. In 1861, with a population of 75,198, daily water consumption stood at 1,250,000 gallons or 16 gallons a head. Ten years later the population had risen to 89,554, but total consumption had more than doubled to 3,131,514 gallons of water a day.

**Building the brick invert on Aberdeen's Long Sea outfall in 1906.**

James Simpson, who had pioneered the slow sand filtration principle at the Chelsea Waterworks in 1829.

How to cope? The Commissioners of Police, who had the responsibility of supplying Aberdeen with water as well as preserving law and order, sought the advice of the leading London civil engineer, James Simpson, who put forward four possible schemes. They could build a 20-mile aqueduct from the River Don to the reservoir at Hilton; a 21½-mile aqueduct from Potarch Bridge on the Dee to Springbank reservoir; a 19-mile aqueduct from Cairnton on the Dee to Springbank; or supply direct from the Dee by high pressure condenser engines. They were all going to cost around £100,000, and the Commissioners decided they could not afford any of them. So in 1861 the Lord Provost called a meeting of citizens who voted for water to be brought in from Cairnton. The required Parliamentary Bill was passed the following year, authorising the taking of six million gallons a day and expenditure of £115,000. The scheme involved a 19-mile aqueduct to a reservoir at Mannofield. At Invercannie, a mile below Cairnton, was a settling reservoir. The works were opened by Queen Victoria on 16 October 1866.

Why had such an increased supply become so suddenly necessary? It was due, said Dr John Milne LL D in *Aberdeen* (1911), to the introduction of WCs and baths.

An Act of Parliament of 1862 gave Aberdeen Town Council power to require the owner of every house where there was water within ten yards to introduce, from the street, pipes into the house to fit up a sink and a WC with 'soil-pipes' leading to the nearest drain. Since that had to be done to the satisfaction of the town council, some architects had the pipes brought down the walls of the house close by the front door so everyone could see they had complied with the law. Recording this, John Milne said some people would not live in such houses even though they got them rent free 'nor even within sight of such suggestive pipes'. The town council, he said, should have a care in passing plans of new houses to see that they would not be offensive to the neighbourhood:

> The exercise of the powers conferred by section 300 [of the 1862 Act] has almost abolished dry closets, and though this is not to be regretted it has tended to augment the daily consumpt of water. It has also removed the need for pillar wells in the street, and they are no longer to be seen in Aberdeen; but some of the Aberdeen pillar wells may yet be seen in the streets of Fraserburgh.

James Simpson was also asked to sort out the water supply of that equally ancient university town, Cambridge. In the milder climate of East Anglia it was not a matter which the authorities considered of any great urgency. Although, from a petition presented to Parliament in 1788 asking for water from Hobson's Conduit to be made more widely available, it seems that the need to make the supply more plentiful was an ever-present problem, nearly a century passed before anyone took steps to do so. In 1852, however, the Vice-Chancellor of the University set up a committee of heads of colleges and leading citizens to promote the creation of an undertaking to supply the market/university town with water from the Paper Mills stream. They invited Simpson to put up a scheme for which the obligatory Act of Parliament received the royal assent in June 1853. The Cambridge University and Town Waterworks Company had an equal number of directors from town and gown. They sank a well 48 feet deep and installed pumping machinery powered by two 15 horsepower beam engines and constructed a covered service reservoir on the top of Lime Kiln Hill, Cherry Hinton, with a capacity of a million gallons of water. The water was carried around Cambridge along 26 miles of cast-iron pipes.

The opening ceremony on 23 October 1855 was attended by Revd William Whewell DD, Master of Trinity, who was the water company's chairman, the Vice Chancellor, the Deputy Mayor and the local MP. 'We do not know,' stated the *Cambridge Chronicle* reporter, 'that upon any former occasion we witnessed so satisfactory a union of the Town and University as in the celebration we are about to record. The two bodies were engaged in a good work calculated to benefit the inhabitants of this place for ages to come.' The discharging of jets of water from stand pipes on Market Hill and King's Parade inaugurated the arrival of water in the town, in the scheme engineered by James Simpson that thoroughly compensated for 200 years of neglect.

For most of the towns of the Black Country, the need to have a plentiful fresh water supply was less academic. Luckily they had natural sources near at hand. But by the time the water reached them, the 'trade effluent' of South Staffordshire's mining and iron industry had poisoned it. Thousands died of cholera in the 1848 epidemic. The tragedy spurred the authorities to form The South Staffordshire Waterworks Company (motto: 'Nothing Without Water') in 1853. Rejecting proposals to take water from the River Trent or the Smestow Brook, it went to springs west of Lichfield and conveyed it to a reservoir at Pones Mill. Ten years later it acquired The Dudley Waterworks and The Burton-upon-Trent Waterworks.

The population of the Potteries increased tenfold in the 19th century. In 1847 citizens of Hanley and Shelton formed The Staffordshire Potteries Water Works Company to draw water from St Caena's Well at Wall Grange on the estate of the Duke of Sutherland; and two years later it took a lease of the Duke's waterworks at Meir.

**The 17th-century conduit head that once stood in the market place at Cambridge.**

## Water for Firefighting

With the number of dwellings and public buildings increasing every year, the local authority who managed a town's water supply had to make it available for firefighting at every street corner, however far out. The Select Committee enquiring into the legislative provisions for protection of life and property against fire reported in 1866 that out of the 86 towns which had answered its questionnaire, private companies supplied water for firefighting in 38 of them and local authorities in 42:

> There are no particular regulations regarding the supply of water [stated paragraph 3 of their findings] but the private companies and local authorities are understood to be bound to give a full supply of water free of charge, and fire plugs are placed in all the mains. In the large towns turncocks are appointed to whom notice is sent when a fire occurs.

The Committee asked William Whiffen, secretary of the Middlesex Water Works, why London's water companies did not give a continuous supply. The Waterworks Clauses Act, said Whiffen, made it mandatory for a company to do so, but only if four-fifths of the inhabitants of a district laid a requisition on it. If householders wanted it in their street they had to set their house fittings to stand the constant pressure. When they had done so they felt able to coerce the remaining one-fifth to do the same. It would cost £2 million to bring all the house fittings in London up to standard to receive constant pressure. Moreover, before a constant supply could be given 'intrusive supervision would be necessary including an inquisitorial system of inspecting everyone's water closets'.

**Lichfield Cathedral overlooks Stowe Pool, the first reservoir of the South Staffordshire Water Company.**

Public utilities provided and managed by private companies and local authorities included street lighting. Since Frederick Winsor had obtained a charter in April 1812 for his Gas Light & Coke Company of London, street lighting progressively meant gaslighting. Preston was the first town to follow suit outside London in 1816.

In several towns entrepreneurs formed companies to provide water *and* gas. One of the earliest was The Canterbury Gas Light and Water Works Company. On its formation in 1822 its managers saw it merely as a gaslight company, but the next year they elected to be a water supplier as well. They abstracted water from the River Great Stour but, with few water customers, the company was kept in business by gas. Demand had increased by the 1860s and they abandoned the river supply in favour of raising groundwater from the chalk piped to a waterworks at Thanington.

The company which a group of gentlemen thought of forming in Lowestoft in 1852 was from the start intended to provide the town with both gas and water – and to establish a public market place. Under the powers they obtained by their Lowestoft Water, Gas and Market Act 1853, they set up The Great Yarmouth Waterworks Company which drew water from a well they sunk at St Margaret's Road in the north of the town. Professor Cooper, an eminent analyst, tested the water when they had reached a depth of 89 feet and pronounced it 'very thick from clayey matter suspended in it'. He had difficulty in filtering enough to make an analysis. By sufficiently long repose, however, he thought it would become very bright:

> It is however somewhat hard, i.e. it curdles soap rather more than our Thames Water, but in every other respect I esteem it to be a good and wholesome water.

It was sufficiently encouraging for them to authorise pipelaying which began in May 1854. At 15 shillings a week there was no rush to buy the service, but it was not long before the venturers' faith in the enterprise was justified. In 1857 they built a waterworks at Lound seven miles from Lowestoft to raise water from Hopton Basins – an operation still in being today. Through the Great Yarmouth distribution network and the supply works on the Ormesby group of Broads, they were able to supply water throughout the whole Great Yarmouth area.

The proposal which William Cash and Edward Woods put to the Bournemouth Commissioners was solely to supply gas. When they were told they would be allowed to do so provided they also supplied water, they agreed. So they formed the Bournemouth Gas and Water Company in 1863 whose water/gas works, as requested by the Commissioners, was at least two miles from the town, in the valley of the Bourne stream. The waterworks which opened in 1864 took water from the Kinson Brook. After being purified by slow sand filtration it was pumped to a 200,000 gallon reservoir on high ground at Parkstone, and from there flowed by gravity to the town. The company began by serving six customers, but within five years there were 185. With the passing of the first Bournemouth Gas and Water Act in 1873, the supplier became a statutory company. The 700 customers now wanted more water than the works could supply so the company built a second reservoir with four times the capacity of the first, and a 161,000 gallon elevated storage tank in Palmerston Road, Boscombe, still in use today. After failure of the well dug at Tuckton, the company found all the water it wanted in an extensive deposit of water-bearing gravel near Longham village, and leased an area of land at Alderney on which to put a water treatment plant, a reservoir and two filters, later connected to the whole area of supply by an 18-inch main.

This flurry of activity all over Britain to make up for lost time and give urban communities a sufficiently plentiful water supply, would have been more laudable if the statutory companies and local authorities (stimulated by the duties imposed on them by the Municipal Corporations Act of 1835) had given as much attention to making it pure, sweet, clean and wholesome. These were the adjectives they applied to what their water supply *should* be but, even after the shock of the cholera epidemics of 1831 and 1849, it was often foul, polluted, unhealthy and insanitary.

It was not for lack of public agitation. In the metropolis, Londoners like Charles Dickens thought it absurd and monstrous that the capital should be excluded from the Public Health Act on the grounds that it was being served by the Metropolitan Commission of Sewers, whose members were appointed by the government and to which one Joseph Bazalgette was made Assistant Surveyor in 1849. In the six years since 1847 some 30,000 cesspits had been removed, but the draining of foul sewers into the Thames at low tide meant heavy rain carried the sewage back up and into people's basements. Worse, it was carried by the rising tide up the river, to be brought back by the following ebb-tide. A pressure group called The Metropolitan Sanitary Association was formed to spur the eight water supply commissions and other official bodies to take action. At its first public meeting in February 1850 Dickens seconded a motion deploring the number of deaths from preventable disease in London. The existence of a Public Health Act with the metropolis excluded, he said, was like *Hamlet* with nothing in it but

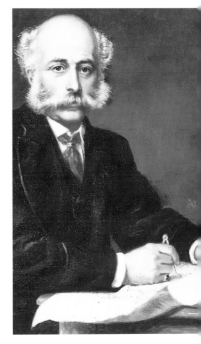

**Sir Joseph Bazalgette (1819–91), the father of London's sewerage system, who helped to make the Thames one of the cleanest metropolitan rivers in Europe.**

the gravedigger. Of the sanitary condition of London he solemnly believed it would be almost impossible to speak too ill. He knew many places in it unsurpassed in the accumulated horrors of their neglect by the dirtiest old spots in the dirtiest old towns under the worst old governments in Europe. There were classes of people who objected to taking action. There were the small owners of small tenements who pushed themselves forward on boards of guardians and parish vestries, and who were clamorous about the ratings of their property. And there were the gentlemen who had a weak leaning to the words 'self-government':

> Remembering how clearly they [the Board of Health] showed us the advantages of a continuous supply of soft water, and how they pointed out to us an abundant source of supply, I cannot cast upon them the blame of a measure which gives us only hard water. Remembering how they dwelt upon the necessity of a combination of waterworks I cannot charge them with the injury of perpetuated separation. Remembering how they demonstrated to us that disease *must* lurk in houses founded over cesspools and built upon foundations saturated with cesspool matter, I cannot hold them responsible for a system of drainage which does not remove these ills.

Papermaker John Dickinson FRS (his company became one half of the Dickinson Robinson Group) demonstrated to members of the Royal Institution in February 1855 'various novel contrivances for the deposit of everything of greater specific gravity than water and to intercept everything that would float, and to clear away the scum and guard the channel from leaves and vegetable refuse, also to aerate the water'. He proposed providing an additional supply of pure water from a second New River conveying water from four streams: the Colne, Ver, Gade and Chess. United at Rickmansworth they would give London 42 cubic feet of water a second. Delivery to Kilburn, purified and filtered, would cost no more than three farthings per thousand gallons. Dickinson thought all London south of Piccadilly could be supplied by a gravitation system at one-fourth the scale of the current rate of charges.

Of greater weight was Michael Faraday's protest, whose interest in analysing fresh water at the Royal Institution has already been seen. In *The Times* of 9 July 1855 the following letter appeared:

Royal Institution<br>July 7, 1855

SIR,

I traversed this day by steamboat the space between London and Hungerford Bridges, between half-past one and two o'clock. It was low water and, I think the tide must have been near the turn. The appearance and smell of the water forced themselves at once on my attention. The whole of the river was an opaque pale brown fluid. In order to test the degree of opacity, I tore up some white cards into pieces, and then moistened them, so as to make them sink easily below the surface, and then dropped some of these pieces into the water at every pier the boat came to. Before they had sunk an inch below the surface they were undistinguishable, though the sun shone brightly at the time, and when the pieces fell edgeways the lower part was hidden from sight before the upper part was under water.

This happened at St Paul's Wharf, Blackfriars Bridge, Temple Wharf, Southwark

Bridge, and Hungerford, and I have no doubt would have occurred further up and down the river. Near the bridges the feculence rolled up in clouds so dense that they were visible at the surface even in water of this kind.

The smell was very bad, and common to the whole of the water. It was the same as that which now comes up from the gully holes in the streets. The whole river was for the time a real sewer. Having just returned the country air, I was perhaps more affected by it than others; but I do not think that I could have gone on to Lambeth or Chelsea, and I was glad to enter the streets for an atmosphere which, except near the sink-holes, I found much sweeter than on the river.

I have thought it a duty to record these facts, that they may be brought to the attention of those who exercise power, or have responsibility in relation to the condition of our river. There is nothing figurative in the words I have employed, or any approach to exaggeration. They are the simple truth.

If there be sufficient authority to remove a putrescent pond from the neighbourhood of a few simple dwellings, surely the river which flows for so many miles through London ought not to be allowed to become a fermenting sewer. The condition in which I saw the Thames may perhaps be considered as exceptional, but it ought to be an impossible state; instead of which, I fear it is rapidly becoming the general condition. If we neglect this subject, we cannot expect to do so with impunity; nor ought we to be surprised if, ere many years are over, a season give us sad proof of the folly of our carelessness.

I am, Sir, your obedient servant,
M. FARADAY.

*Punch* printed a cartoon by John Leech showing Faraday giving his card to Father Thames, with the caption 'And we hope the Dirty Fellow will consult the learned Professor'. The facing article headed 'A Philosopher Afloat' told of Mr Punch's rejoicing that Faraday had enabled the public to form a correct idea of the constituents of the Thames which were something more than oxygen and hydrogen:

> Because we are losing brave men by war [in the Crimea], it is rather more desirable than otherwise that we should also not lose useful citizens by pestilence, as we certainly shall if the Thames continues much longer to be an open sewer.
>    We hope that Professor Faraday's publication which takes the shape of a concise letter to the *Times* will effect a saving of human life still greater than that which has resulted from his predecessor's [Sir Humphrey Davy's] safety lamp. Davy's invention prevents carburetted hydrogen from blowing up miners; may Faraday's epistle avert cholera and typhus by stirring up senatorial and municipal persons to prevent sulphuretted hydrogen from being disengaged.

When *Punch* heard that the organisers of the Great Exhibition in the Crystal Palace in Hyde Park in 1851 were obliged to offer visitors a glass of fresh water, they commented:

> Whoever can produce in London a glass of water fit to drink will contribute the rarest and most universally useful article in the whole exhibition.

At least the organisers had agreed to provide the retiring rooms with the 'monkey closets' invented by George Jennings, who became the champion of public conveniences all over Britain.

In this *Punch* cartoon (1855), John Leech showed Michael Faraday holding his nose while giving his card to Father Thames. Faraday's experiment demonstrated that a white card was no longer visible after it had sunk an inch below the surface, owing to the foul state of the water.

**Monster soup commonly called Thames Water, being a correct representation of that precious stuff doled out to us!!!**

A magnified drop of water is shown to contain grotesque aquatic creatures in this satire on the Metropolitan Water Supply Commission, which reported in 1828 but suggested no remedy for contamination.

### Florence Nightingale Joins the Agitation

Florence Nightingale, whose care of the sick and wounded in the Crimea made her a national heroine, added to the chorus of disapproval of conditions on the home front in the 1860s:

> Many have no idea in what good drainage consists. They think that a sewer in the street, and a pipe leading to it from the house is good drainage. All the while the sewer may be nothing but a laboratory from which epidemic disease and ill health is being distilled into the house. No house with any untrapped drain pipe communicating immediately with a sewer, whether it be from water closet, sink or gully-grate, can ever be healthy. . . . I have met just as strong a stream of sewer air coming up the back staircase of a grand London house from the sink as I have ever met at Scutari. (*Notes on Nursing: What it is, and what it is not*)

There had been progress, albeit meagre, but one had to be thankful for small mercies:

> Pure water is more generally introduced into houses than it used to be, thanks to the exertions of the sanitary reformers. Within the last few years a large part of London was in the daily habit of using water polluted by the drainage of its sewers and water closets. This has happily been remedied. But in many parts of the country, well water of a very impure kind is used for domestic purposes. And when epidemic disease shows itself persons using such water are almost sure to suffer.

Prince Albert, who conceived the Great Exhibition, designed upward flow filters of ashes and gravel for Osborne House on the Isle of Wight; but more importantly professionals were busy formulating a sanitary science. A Commissioner for Sewage Disposal was appointed whose first report of 1858 pulled no punches:

> The increasing pollution of the streams and rivers of the country is an evil of material importance which urgently demands the application of remedial measures, for the discharge of sewage and obnoxious refuse of factories into them is a source of nuisance and danger, and acts injuriously not only in the locality

George Cruickshank's attack (1832) on Southwark Water Works and its owner, John Edwards, depicted as an ancient Welsh chieftain crowned with a chamberpot. While the companies supplying the north bank of the Thames had introduced improvements, the 7,000 families living in Southwark were still served by water taken from the spot where the great common sewers discharged into the river.

where it occurs but on the population of the districts through which the polluted water flows. It poisons the water for drinking, and kills the fish.

His appointment was due to the growing uneasiness of some MPs about the danger arising from the insanitary conditions. Only in the 1850s was there any sign of any serious research being made into ways of treating sewage from towns – and now foul sewage was being deposited into rivers and not cesspits on land, the need to develop a science of sewage *treatment* before discharge became as urgent as perfecting the means of sewage disposal and water supply. Up to 1854 it was considered dangerous to spread foul sewage onto land except at a distance from dwellings. As a writer in *British Waterworks Association Proceedings* has observed, 'some of the early pioneers of sewage treatment were mostly concerned with any monetary value that sewage might possess rather than sewage treatment as a necessary health service.'

The first *works* for treating town sewage sludge were built by Thomas Wicksteed at Leicester in 1853. They consisted of a sizeable vertical plunger pump operated by a beam engine to lift sludge, which was de-watered and sold as manure. 'Cream of lime' was mixed with the sewage before admission to the tanks. Wicksteed's operation at Leicester was the forerunner of several works of this type, many of which were built and operated by statutory public companies. In some cases the sludge was converted into bricks and cement instead of manure. Chemical precipitation of sewage was mainly aimed at producing manure, however. In 1869 the Native Guano Company was treating sewage at Leamington and Hastings with centrifugal drying machines or hydro-extractors. Ten years later it opened a highly successful sewage treatment plant with 16 filter presses. But generally filter pressing met with little success until 1881 when S H Johnston installed two presses at Coventry. Previously Coventry had tried using a vacuum process – Milburn's continuous automatic filter patented in 1872.

## The Year of the Great Stink

Science did its best, but news of its achievements, in a country where communication between one part and another was then less common, travelled slowly. London was a more closely knit community, but by the time Michael Faraday exposed the condition of

**A Victorian folly – part of the water treatment works at Swithland reservoir in Leicestershire, now in Severn Trent's region.**

the Thames by his scientific chemical analyses, the water companies were not going to be pushed into precipitate action. In 1851 the light-hearted criticism of *Punch* was reinforced by the heavy hand of the Royal Chemical Commission who proclaimed that the abandonment of the Thames for water supply was only a matter of time unless an artificial means of purification could be devised and applied. The following year the first general Water Act for London confirmed the functions of the metropolitan water companies. All reservoirs and aqueducts within five miles had to be covered unless the water was subsequently filtered. All water for domestic use had to be filtered unless pumped direct from wells into covered reservoirs. Within five years a *constant* supply had to be available for four-fifths of those who asked for it. But the year 1858, by universal consent, was declared 'The Year of the Great Stink'. It was too much for the Chancellor of the Exchequer, Benjamin Disraeli, and he instructed the Chief Engineer of the Metropolitan Board of Works, which had superseded the Commission of Sewers in 1856, to solve the problem before Londoners were asphyxiated and the stink became political.

Joseph Bazalgette knew just what to do; he already had a plan up his sleeve – the one for intercepting and collecting all the wastewater from London and diverting it to a different location far downstream where the estuarial tide would carry it away. He conceived the 'interceptor' system of sewers, the building of which involved 318 million bricks and 880,000 cubic yards of concrete and mortar. Started in 1859 and completed in 1865, it changed the face of London. The giant water-borne sewer on the north side of the river lies under the Embankment. The idea of constructing interceptor sewers along each bank of the Thames had first been conceived in 1850, but the old Commission of Sewers lacked the power to execute it. The situation was changed by the Great Stink, and when the Prince of Wales opened the southern outfall works at Crossness on the lonely Belvedere Marshes, London started to become sanitary for the first time for centuries.

The main engine house at Crossness was built in the Italianate style with a chimney stack resembling a Tuscan *campanile*. The four James Watt & Co steam engines which lifted the sewage from the main sewer into a reservoir were named Victoria, Prince Consort, Alexandra and Albert Edward. These were of an advanced design insofar as one end of their beam was used in conjunction with a flywheel, a new way of increasing efficiency. A second innovation was to use the other end to power a smaller beam which in turn operated the air and water pumps. Each engine had two pumps; each stroke of a pump moved five and half tons of sewage. Thames Water, through the Crossness Engines Trust, has preserved the pumping station – The Sleeping Beauty – for public viewing.

A town councillor, or indeed an MP, did not need to be a scientist to grasp the fact that if fresh water came into contact with human excrement and chemical waste it was no longer fresh, no longer drinkable. Whether it could be contaminated by lead pipes was less clear. When Glasgow town councillors promoted a Bill to build waterworks to bring 50 million gallons of water a day from Loch Katrine, they were confronted, in the words of a civil engineer, 'with the startling assertion that the water of the loch could not be conveyed through lead pipes or stored in lead cisterns without the certainty of its becoming poisonous by reason of its great purity enabling it to dissolve lead rapidly and in large quantities'.

The Bill was already being opposed for a variety of reasons by an influential section in the town council, by the owners of houses on the north of the Clyde, ratepayers in the Gorbals, the Gorbals Water Company, owners of land bordering the lock, riparian owners of the Rivers Teith and Forth, the owners of salmon fishing rights, the Commissioners of the Forth Navigation, and the Admiralty. But the lead poisoning

The northern outfall of Bazalgette's interceptor sewers in London was unusual in being built above ground.

**The enormous disturbance caused by the building of the metropolitan main drainage system is well illustrated by this picture of work in hand at Crossness in 1864.**

scare was enough to have the Bill thrown out, however valid the other objections – and scare it proved to be. In a subsequent investigation the fear of lead poisoning was declared to be without foundation. The land, river and navigation proprietors were conciliated or compensated, and the Admiralty were convinced that no damage was likely to be inflicted on the navigation of the Forth or the anchorage of St Margaret's Hope at Queensferry. There was no opposition when the Bill was re-presented in the next sessions and it received the royal assent in July 1855.

In the event, cast-iron pipes replaced the tunnel conduit across deep ravines, and cast-iron pipes took the water the final eight miles of the 34-mile journey into Glasgow. Water from the Mugdock Reservoir, formed in a natural valley north of Milngavie, was strained through a copper wire cloth fixed in frames of wood to form an inner octagonal well – 'The Straining Well'. When Queen Victoria, the Prince Consort and the Princesses Alice and Helena opened the works in October 1859, it was not a question of the quality being too low but the quantity being too high – there was a surplus of discharging power and the pipes delivered more water than had been calculated.

### Choice of Water Pipe

Choice of water pipe was a scientific matter but still, as the Glasgow experience demonstrated, a grey area. For the lack of any hard and fast guidelines water engineers often played safe by choosing fireclay pipes closely jointed with cement, as was the choice of The Forres Water Company in the Scottish Highlands in 1879. These took

Edward, Prince of Wales,
opening the Crossness
works in April 1865.

water from springs on Edenvale and the Hill of Mulundy to a small reservoir on the Craigmill lands and thence into the town at a rate of 114,000 gallons a day or 33 gallons a head. Reporting the extension of the water supply the *Forres Gazette* stated:

> The quality of the water bears the highest character in suitableness for domestic and other useful purposes. It is indeed said to be unequalled for purity in the North.... The Town of Forres is now in possession of a supply of excellent water at a moderate cost – the greatest boon that can be conferred on any community.

Tree trunks began giving way to cast-iron trunk lines from the 1820s. As a pipe material for water mains, cast iron held sway until the end of the 19th century, when steel also came into use for large-diameter trunk mains. The early cast-iron pipes of irregular shape were cast horizontally with one plain and one socketed end, jointed with caulked yarn and run lead. Vertical casting gradually replaced horizontal casting in the 1870s. The engineer of the New River Company had no doubts about their superiority. 'In respect to the durability of cast iron pipes in the streets of London,' he stated in 1821, 'I am confident that they will be as perfect at the expiration of 100 years as they were in the first instance.' As John Neve has pointed out in the *Journal* of the Pipeline Industries Guild, the passage of time has proved how true this forecast was. 'There are many miles of cast iron mains under London's streets still [in 1992] giving good service after 100 years, some of which are as large as 36 inches diameter.'

The ability of iron pipes to carry water without leaking, and to do so for decade after decade, was little in doubt; but they never completely shrugged off the suspicion that in time deterioration might cause contamination. In the deliberations about the public water supply there was tacit understanding that 'water' meant *clean* water. The brief of the Royal Commission on Water Supply appointed under the presidency of the Duke of Richmond in 1866 was:

> what supply of *impolluted and wholesome* water can be obtained by collecting and storing water in the high grounds of England and Wales, either by the aid of natural lakes or by artificial reservoirs, at a sufficient elevation for the supply of large towns [our italics].

The main message of its report, issued in 1869, was that some form of central control of wholesome water resources was needed in place of the existing parochial administration.

**The public pump for drawing well water presented to Ringmer Parish in Sussex in 1883.**

No town or district, it said, should be allowed to appropriate a source which was nearer to another town, and any place beside a long pipeline should be provided with a supply from it.

Ten years later the future King Edward VII, as Prince of Wales, wrote to the Council of the Society of Arts and Commerce of which he was president, pointing out that while big cities like Manchester, Liverpool and Birmingham were taking steps to obtain an improved water supply, many smaller towns and villages were dependent on sources of supply which were inadequate for health and comfort:

> While the larger populations are striving, each independently and at enormous cost, to secure for themselves this article of prime necessity, the smaller localities must make the best shift they can, and in many instances are all but without any supply at all.

It was not a problem that was to go away for at least 100 years. In 1878 His Royal Highness suggested that the Society of Arts should consider how far the great natural resources of the kingdom might 'by some large and comprehensive scheme' be turned to account for the benefit not merely of a few large centres of population but for the advantage of the general body of the nation at large. At a congress convened by the Society the idea of dividing the country into watershed areas was discussed, but no government department saw fit to follow the idea up and the whole concept of the national control of water resources elicited no official interest from any quarter. Where Edwin Chadwick had failed, HRH encountered equal disdain.

There was nothing like a Great Stink infiltrating the corridors of power to prick the consciences of those who paced them. The Sewage Enquiry Committee, appointed at the request of Councillor Thomas Avery in 1870, revealed what Asa Briggs called 'a devastatingly candid account of the sanitary state of Birmingham':

> The overall city death rate concealed the great variations in mortality in the different parts of the city and the exceptionally high mortality in wards like St John's and St George's. . . . [Joseph] Chamberlain followed Chadwick in asking the question: 'Could any one doubt the evidence of the medical men that a large proportion of the death rate was distinctly due to the existence of pestiferous nuisances in the town?' *(Victorian Cities)*

The Sewer-Hunter. Valuables that disappeared down the plughole were netted in the sewers under London by scavengers.

Birmingham's Sewage Enquiry Committee was charged with reporting to the town council its opinion on the best mode of dealing with the Borough's sewage. Its 300-page report reviewed the day's conflicting theories of sewage disposal. One way, it said, was to get rid of the 14,000 open middens and ashpits which still existed in 1870 and drained directly into the sewers. After a very long debate this and other proposals of the Committee were accepted by the town council, but the voting was 33 to 23. A new plan for sewage disposal was put into operation which, in spite of resistance by private interests, succeeded in removing all the nuisances by 1875.

Birmingham not only lacked sanitation in 1870 but water. The poor people of Birmingham, according to the town's Mayor, Joseph Chamberlain, were so short of water that they were driven to steal it from others, or else had to draw it from unhealthy and contaminated wells. 'What do you think of the inhabitants being compelled to drink water which is as bad as sewage before clarification?' he asked as part of his campaign to have The Birmingham Water Works Company, founded in 1826, purchased by the council, the representatives of the people. The Royal Commission on Sanitary Reform of 1869 had declared that 'the power of life and death' should above all else not be left in

Flushing the sewers to keep the water on the move, and with it the waste that had to be carried as far away as possible.

Angle tip-up lavatory by Stidder and Co., recommended for billiard rooms or passages in Victorian country houses.

private hands. Another Sanitary Committee undertook a large-scale sanitary survey of Birmingham in 1874–5. Though the town council supported the Mayor in his bid for the water company, the House of Lords opposed the Bill as compulsory purchase unfair to shareholders, but failed to kill it. On the transfer of the private company to municipal control the *Birmingham Mail* commented:

> Without the additions which have been made, the town would have been a desert of Sahara, while the Edgbaston horticulturists would have been reduced to the necessity of moistening their lawns with beer.

It was all part of the general 'Improvement' campaign in which all local authorities were indulging at the time, of which the Artisans' Dwellings Act was part, providing for the compulsory acquisition of insanitary areas. Birmingham set up an Improvement Committee and a Health Committee charged, among other things, with the disposal of sewage. Additional inspectors were appointed – Birmingham had only one for every 30,000 inhabitants compared with Manchester's one for every 8,000. Within eight years the inspectors exposed 3,000 wells used by 60,000 people as dangerously contaminated. By 1881 the town council was able to report that as regards health, Birmingham was first among all the large towns of Great Britain which were fairly comparable with it.

### Control Water Resources!

Central government had in the meantime been busy in seeking out the root causes of the country's insanitary state, and appointed a Rivers Pollution Commission which sat from 1865 to 1867. They recommended legally controlling the management of rivers and their watersheds, which should be placed under supervision irrespective of county and other boundaries; and that 'all rivers and streams in England be placed under the superintendence of a central authority'. The Royal Sanitary Commission of 1869–71 advocated the setting up of Watershed Areas each controlled by a Watershed Authority. Though it passed the Public Health Act of 1875 embracing many of the recommendations of the Royal Sanitary Commission, the Rivers Pollution Prevention Act 1876, and the Public Health (Water) Act of 1878, which made it the duty of all rural authorities to provide a supply of water to houses in their area, Parliament took no steps to implement the recommendations of any of the commissions with regard to the control of water resources.

Adding to the pollution, though not as abrasively as WCs, were the fixed, plumbed baths. Taking a regular hot bath was a new fad: the Duke of Wellington, who took one every day, had been regarded as highly eccentric. There was no bath in Buckingham Palace in the 1860s. Richard Durtnell, the Brasted builder whose firm was established in 1591, put a bathroom into the house called Darenton for himself and his new wife in 1863, and claimed it was unique. Eardley Bailey-Denton who wrote a *Hand Book of House Sanitation* in 1882 obviously thought he had need to inform any reader who was not as yet in touch with latest developments:

> It is now generally acknowledged that a dwelling cannot be considered as complete without a bathroom, and that its adoption should not be limited to the superior mansions of the wealthy, but that all classes of our population should have it within their power to benefit by the comfort, cleanliness and healthfulness afforded by both hot and cold baths.

TOP AND BOTTOM: **The ornate bathrooms of Victorian middle-class households, which put a strain on the water companies' supply.**

In large mansions there should be one or more bathrooms on every floor, while in average-sized dwellings one place in a central position would be found to be all that might be positively necessary. Washbasins with hot and cold water might be readily adopted throughout bedrooms and dressing rooms on the upper floors 'in place of the jug and basin system which is now so universal, and by its adoption not only may time and trouble be saved to the occupants but a large amount of unnecessary labour to the servants'.

The running of taps to fill baths and washbasins, and the pulling of plugs to flush WCs, increased demand for fresh water in so sudden a way that many of the urban water suppliers found their waterworks quite unable to meet it, but at once took steps to bring in the greater volume required. In 1880 Liverpool authorised a scheme to impound the upper waters of the River Vyrnwy in a large reservoir in Montgomeryshire (now Powys). Holding 13,000 million gallons of water it was the largest artificial reservoir in Europe. The immense dam which closed the mouth of the broad flat valley was the first masonry dam – slatey stone – to be built in Britain. It was 1,172 feet long and 161 feet high. Some 18,250 acres of ground drained into the reservoir. Two of the river's tributaries were diverted into the lake in huge tunnels. A 65-mile aqueduct carrying two 42-inch pipes took the water through Oswestry, Malpas and under the Mersey near Widnes to Liverpool.

In 1881 Harwich Corporation found that of the town's daily need of 200,000 gallons of water, Peter Bruff's water company was only able to supply 50,000. Moreover, people were questioning the purity of the water from his Dovercourt works. So in 1884 Bruff formed The Tendring Hundred Waterworks Company to bring water from Bradfield Heath eight miles out of Harwich and two years later from Mistley where he made boreholes into the chalk. The first drinking water came through in 1887.

In Northern Ireland the town of Belfast had greatly expanded and buildings were being put up on land higher than the Oldpark service reservoir, so three years later further catchments were acquired at Stonyford and Leathemstown in County Antrim, each with a storage reservoir. A service reservoir was built at Lagmore, but still the supply was not enough. More catchments were acquired in the Kilkeel and Annalong valleys in the Mourne Mountains, and a main conduit built from the southern end of the Annalong Valley to a service reservoir at Knockbreckan near Belfast.

North London's demand for water never stopped growing. Bushey's inhabitants were glad to have the additional supply which came from the boreholes which Robert Stephenson drove in 1840, but no other source was added for another 30 years. When an analysis of the water in 1871 showed it to be 'grossly contaminated by sewage, surface drainage, oozings of house drainage etc', a group of local gentlemen put up a scheme for pumping water from a well near Bushey Heath. But the Parish Water Committee thought they could not afford the £10,000 cost which represented a one shilling and sixpence increase in the rates – despite the outbreak of typhoid which the existing water supply facilities had caused. So locals formed the Colne Valley Water Company in December 1872 to take water from 235-feet deep wells in the chalk, and pump it to a covered reservoir at Bushey Heath. They obtained their Act of Parliament, but not without the traditional opposition of owners and occupiers of lands and mills on the banks of the River Colne and its tributary the Ver, who feared the scheme would raise the water level and jeopardise amenities. The Bill gave powers to the company to prevent the water 'being polluted, wasted or improperly taken'. Its customers numbered around 7,000. To supply them the company built a pumping station with four Watt steam engines, later replaced by four beam engines each able to deliver two million gallons of water a day. The first of these remained in service from 1891 to 1941.

Up to 1884, the people of Rickmansworth were also dependent on wells for their water, or streams in the valley of the River Colne. But in that year Parliament, acknowledging, as they did in the cases of towns all over Britain, that the Hertfordshire village was 'imperfectly supplied with water', granted a group of locals an Act of Parliament to form The Rickmansworth Water Company with a capital of £24,000 to sink a well and build a pumping station at Drayton Ford, Mill End, and to lay pipes from there to a reservoir at Heronsgate. When it obtained another Act the following year, extending the limits of supply, the company changed its name to Rickmansworth and Uxbridge Valley Water Company. The sluices were opened in February 1889, but for some time village people, who for so long had got into the habit of drawing their water from wayside pumps, shied away and had to be coaxed to become customers by a press advertisement informing them 'Pure Water Can Now Be Obtained From Artesian Wells – Apply to Waterworks House'.

There were quite a few artesian wells in Britain at this time. They had a small-diameter bore of great depth to a water level lying between two impervious strata from which water, released from its confinement and given an adequate head, would rise to flow over the top of the bore. The 'artesian well' took its name from the French province of Artois where the idea is said to have been first tried out in 1126. In the 1850s there were wells in France driven to a depth of 1,800 feet, and many in the United States were more than 5,000 feet. In England it was not necessary to drill so far, and there were many cases of money spent on boring which never found water. Southampton wasted £20,000 in 1838 on an abandoned artesian bore on the common. In London many business houses sank artesian wells on their own premises to avoid paying water charges based on rateable value.

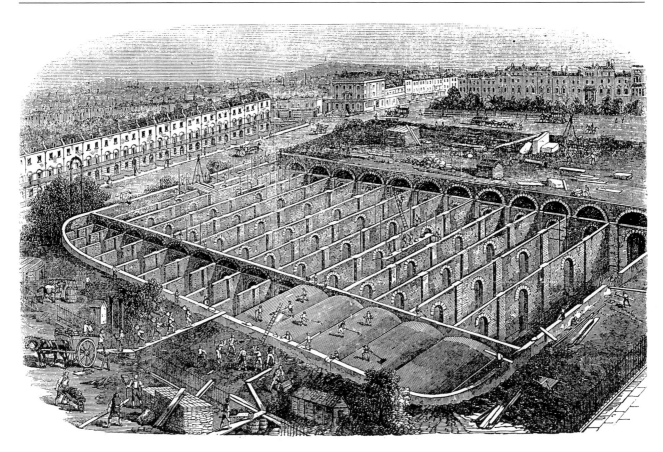

Outside London, the charges were lower and the supplier who had to develop a commercially viable business from a handful of customers found it hard to make ends meet. The Barnet District Gas and Water Company's earnings for the first quarter of 1872, when they were founded, were £520. It made them a profit of £177. And then the single source waterworks at New Barnet broke down, leaving their 1,000 customers without water while the plant was repaired. When the Herts and Essex Water Company was formed ten years later, it had 392 customers and an income of £678. By 1895, however, it was getting into its stride and turnover had risen to £2,289. These were the companies which gave the present-day Lee Valley Water Company its sure foundation.

The nine water companies of London, who were seen to be overcharging, were delivering 150 million gallons of water to the metropolis every day in 1886, of which 69 million came from the Thames and 59 million from the New River and from the River Lee. Herbert Fry told readers of his guidebook *London in 1886* that a statue of Sir Hugh Myddelton, the Welsh man from Denbigh who started building the New River in 1603, still stood at the southern entrance to Islington Green:

> The New River (an artificial stream 38 miles long) which nearly ruined its founder in making it, is now estimated to be worth over eleven millions sterling; its shares readily sell from three hundred to four hundred per cent over their nominal value.

Commercial companies such as The New River Company, which earned high dividends for their shareholders, may have been unpopular with those who had to pay high rates for their services, but they were the pace-setters, prepared to take the risks and to experiment, who paved the way for the developments of the 20th century.

**Putting a roof on the New River Company's service reservoir in Claremont Square, Pentonville.**

## Municipal Ownership of Water Supply

The 1867 Franchise Reform and the 1875 and 1878 Public Health Acts gave local authorities powers which hitherto they could only obtain through an Act of Parliament, so that whereas in the 1830s there were only 11 municipal water undertakings, in 1878 there were 78. The Local Government Acts of 1882, 1888 and 1894, together with the Gas and Waterworks Facilities Acts of 1870 and 1873; resulted in Britain's water supply being taken into municipal ownership at a greatly increased rate. But for the resistance put up by undertakings such as The Sheffield Water Company, it would have been even faster.

The Royal Commission on The Housing of the Working Classes of 1885 stated:

> Your Majesty's Commissioners are clearly of the opinion that there has been a failure in administration rather than in legislation. . . . What at the present time is specially required is some motive power, and probably there can be no stronger motive power than public opinion.
>
> Prolonged experience has proved that the Vestries could not be relied upon to enforce the laws, and it was manifest that some effective provision must be devised for preventing them perpetually thwarting the intentions, and defeating the imperative enactments, of Parliament designed for the welfare of the community at large.

For professionals such as Percy Blakelock, chairman and managing director of the Sheffield company, this was not to be tolerated and it was not a problem to be experienced even longer. Joseph Chamberlain had manoeuvred the heavy-handed machinery of local government to work wonders for the improvement of Birmingham, but there were not many with his patience and sense of mission – and, indeed, charisma. Besides, the people who needed water – plentiful and pure – were not confined to the big cities where the town council could count among its members businessmen and industrialists.

Blakelock and his like saw that stemming the tide of municipal acquisition would gain in momentum if individual resistance was seen as part of a movement.

In April 1885, 38 commercial water companies were persuaded to send representatives to a meeting in London's Westminster Palace Hotel to consider forming an association of provincial water companies, and coordinate opposition to the Water Companies (Regulation of Powers) Bill then before Parliament. There was no dearth of well-intentioned legislation – Disraeli's Public Health Act of 1875 had set up a nationwide system of sanitary authorities responsible for water supply *and* sewerage – but the professionals shared the doubts of the Housing Commissioners that the elected representatives of the people at local level had the will or the ability to carry it out. The Provincial Water Company Association they formed in 1885, with Percy Blakelock as its first chairman (the name was later changed to The Water Companies' Association), has been the efficient mouthpiece of the statutory 'water supply' companies ever since. When it was formed, as the author of the association's centenary history observed, the water industry was a small world:

> The companies employed the same consulting engineers – Newcastle's Yarnold in the 17th century, also involved in the scheme for Oxford, Windsor, Deptford and Greenwich, no less than the Hawksleys in the 19th century. Both engineers and chairmen followed family traditions of service. James Simpson, one of the great 19th-century water engineers, was born in a company house at The Chelsea Waterworks Company works, where his father Thomas was engineer. Percy

OPPOSITE: A comic strip from *Fun*, 10 January 1883, poking fun at popular fears and uncertainty about impurities in drinking water.

# THE WATER TORTURE.

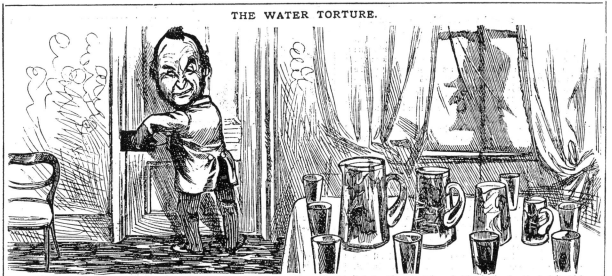

The London Water Consumer said, said he, "I will *not* bear it any longer. Doctor Frankland shall *not* burst in at the end of the month, after I've had my drink of water, and maliciously inform me that it was turbid and unfit for drinking, and held a large amount of matter in suspension." So he locked the door knowingly, and sat down to enjoy the drink he loved, unharrowed by fears of future horrible revelations.

But past reports *would* haunt his mind—he wrestled with them—they grassed him repeatedly—he felt a nausea—he banished the drink he loved. Then a triumphant thought came into his bosom. "Dr. Frankland *shall* come in with his horrible report. I haven't drunk the water. Who'll have the grin now?" said he.

At the end of the month Dr. F. *did* come in. "The water during the past month," said he, "has been particularly free from impurities of all kinds. The grin was with the Doctor as usual.

Blakelock was the great-great-grandson of Joshua Matthewman, who had founded the Sheffield works in 1737, and whose descendants managed the undertaking in unbroken succession for 150 years.

The corpus of knowledge and experience they built up has paid dividends in terms of ability, as operators in an industry which is no longer a small world, to give their customers the sophisticated service they take for granted a century later.

Not only the managers saw the wisdom of combining, but the engineers too – men who in many cases had been instrumental in forming a water company, like Arthur Pain. This railway engineer created The Frimley and Farnborough Water Company in 1893. Renamed the Mid Wessex, it joined with the Wey Valley, to become today's Mid Southern Water Company. Pain supplied his 20,000 customers with water he had come across when building the London to Basingstoke railway.

After Donald Gaskin, Engineer of Nottingham Corporation Waterworks, received a good response to his letter in *The Contract Journal*, following discussions in Manchester in 1894, a meeting took place in London in April 1896 approving the formation of a British Association of Water Works Engineers (which in 1911 was incorporated as The Institution of Water Engineers, amalgamating with The Society for Water Treatment Examination in 1975 as the Institution of Water Engineers and Scientists).

In his *Contract Journal* letter of 20 November 1895, Gaskin solicited support for an institution 'wholly given up to water engineering questions in England, although such questions are occasionally treated of by the Institution of Civil Engineers'. It was a mark of the importance now given to providing Britain with an efficient water supply system that water engineering was seen as a separate discipline of civil engineering and meriting its own professional body. The new body's main purpose was to provide a forum for the exchange of information and the discussion of developments in water supply technology. This aim was reinforced in 1899 by the launching of the industry's own trade journal *Water & Water Engineering*, which in 1918 became the Institution's official publication.

Water engineers saw their role increasingly from this time as dealing not only with the mechanics of supply, but also the means of protecting sources from pollution and determining the extent to which natural water had become polluted and needed treating to make it pure enough to drink. From 1885 dates the first attempts at bacteriological examination of water – in London. In that year Theodore Escherich identified the colon bacillus, and provided a criterion by which routine water samples could be judged. On 4 December 1885 a writer in *The Standard* said:

> bacteria are only detected after a process of cultivation has been adopted by the use of gelatine; and it would dispose of a considerable amount of anxiety if we say at once that by this mode of examination Thames water is made to appear purer than that which proceeds from the deep chalk wells.

### Sanitary Science

How pure was 'pure'? Dr Parkes, a noted authority on the subject, held that the purest water came from granite, clay-slate and chalk. 'It must be transparent, colourless, without odour and tasteless; it should be well aerated, cool and pleasant to drink; it must have no deposit; vegetables should be readily cooked in it.'

It was *drinking* water that had to be 'pure'; 'pure' in the sense of 'wholesome' or good for you. Water is naturally full of traces of minerals that make up its healthy balance; in

excess, some of these minerals would do us no good. Dr Parkes (quoted in an article on 'Sanitary Science' in *Chambers Encylopaedia* of 1880) reckoned that a ten-stone man consumed 70 to 90 ounces of water every day – 40 of them in food, 50 in liquid. He used four gallons a day on bathing, washing and what Dr Parkes called 'habitations'.

Since thousands of water closets were emptying ordure into water-borne sewers, which in their turn were discharging into rivers from which fresh water was extracted, discovering an efficient way of purifying *sewage* was now a prime objective of sanitary science. And from the 1880s sanitary engineers/water engineers began to realise that its *complete* purification was only possible by the action of bacteria.

In the early 1890s W J Dibden developed the contact bed at Barking. The first full-scale works of this type was built at Sutton in 1896. The septic tank process was developed by Donald Cameron at Exeter, and the first installation (at St Leonard's) was brought into use in 1896, the effluent being treated on contact beds. But these two processes did not destroy all organic matter, as anticipated. It was thought that no sludge would be produced, but that was not the case. More successful was the biological filter which remained unchanged for a quarter of a century. The introduction of biological filters and (later) the activated-sludge process necessitated the design of specialised machines. Of all the processes, says J D Cargill:

> possibly sludge treatment has undergone the greatest changes over the last 120 years. Filter presses, vacuum filters, centrifugal machines and various drying machines were used prior to 1900, but in most cases these were abandoned due to either high running costs or the difficulties experienced in dewatering sludge when bacterial processes were introduced.
> ('A History of Sewage Works Machinery', *Water Pollution Control*, 1975)

At the end of the 19th century, built firmly into the business of providing fresh water – no longer a boon but a prime necessity – was sanitary science. Progress was now engineering-led, though of course it still required the willingness of the administrators, commercial or municipal, to finance it. A prime significance of the formation of the British Association of Water Works Engineers and the Association of Sewage Managers was that the legislation of the 20th century would be drafted with the advice of a professional body which understood the increasingly sophisticated technical issues.

'Such a row going on! The Ratepayer came out of his door to see what was the matter, and received a dab of mud on each eye. It was the Metropolitan Board and the Commissioners of Sewers pelting each other with mud which they couldn't agree what to do with.' Cartoon from *Fun*, 30 May 1883.

OVERLEAF: **Rainbow over Loch Leven, Tayside, Scotland.**

# CHAPTER FIVE

# Towards a national water policy

WELSH WATER SCHEME · MORE WATER FOR SCOTLAND · TOWN AND COUNTRY · USE OF
CHLORINE · ORGANISING FOR PLENTY · SEVERE DROUGHT IN 1934 · CLEANING WATER BUT
NOT SEWAGE · PLANNING FOR POST-WAR REORGANISATION · WATER FROM LOCH LOMOND
AND THE SILENT VALLEY · RIVER AUTHORITIES COORDINATE RESOURCES

**One of the three Elan dams which formed part of James Mansergh's Welsh Water Scheme to supply Birmingham in the 1890s.**

Civil engineer and Fellow of the Royal Society James Mansergh employed all the latest technology in his Welsh Water Scheme throughout the 13 years it took to build it. He first saw the Elan and Claerwen valleys in 1862 when he was building the Mid Wales Railway. They struck him then as an ideal source of fresh water for Birmingham. Average rainfall in the watershed was 70 inches a year. The water of the Elan and Claerwen rivers (tributaries of the Wye) which ran in narrow downstream valleys, easy to impound, was of remarkably good quality. The valleys' impermeable bedrock would give good retention of stored water if enclosed by dams. Moreover they were high enough above Birmingham for the water to flow to the city by gravity without having to be pumped.

It was not for another 30 years, however, that Mansergh had the satisfaction of hearing that, with the aid of Joseph Chamberlain, the city's MP, the Birmingham Water Act 1892, promoted by the corporation, had received the royal assent. By then the city's population of 648,000 was already consuming 15 million of the existing 20 million gallons which came from five local rivers and six large wells, and at the rate the area was expanding supply would soon be wholly inadequate.

The Act allowed the compulsory purchase of 45,560 acres of the Welsh valleys, with generous compensation for landowners like the Lloyds of Nantgwyllt, but none for the tenant farmers and smallholders, many of whom emigrated to the colonies. The first task was to build the Elan Village to house 1,500 people; for permanent employees there were detached houses, and for married labourers small terraced houses. Single men were housed in groups of eight. The buildings were of rough, tarred wood with occasional brick walls to prevent the spread of fire. There was a school for children who could attend up to the age of 11, when they became eligible to work for their living. There was a village shop, a mission hall and a building which acted as a library and recreation room. There was a bath-house; a hospital for anyone injured in an accident and another, further away, for anyone who contracted an infectious disease such as smallpox; a canteen for men only, where beer was served during strictly enforced opening hours, the profits from which were invested in educational and recreational facilities. The village had running water and electric lighting. Birmingham Corporation ran the village on a tight rein with regulations in conformity with its belief

**Elan Valley Visitor Centre – originally the main workshop for dam construction – was opened by Welsh Water in 1985 to house displays and organise guided walks.**

**Pen-y-garreg dam, 123 feet high, in the Elan Valley, which impounds water in a 24-acre reservoir for pumping to Birmingham.**

that 'the bulk of men were of the tramp class and could not be dealt with on ordinary principles'. The huge exercise did indeed attract men of the road whose suitability was vetted in the doss house on the opposite bank of the Elan where they had to spend several days to prove they were healthy and well behaved. Only when they had done so would they be moved to the Elan Village proper and be given a job. Over the 13 years some 50,000 men passed through the books.

Early on, the men built a 33-mile single-track railway line to link the site with the Mid Wales line at Rhayader. Starting in 1893, it took them three years. They blasted the foundations of the dams out of the rocky river beds and laid the massive masonry blocks of the reservoir embankments. They used steam-powered cranes, drills and crushers, but mostly picks and shovels. Many injured themselves falling from cranes and rocks; several were drowned when the reservoirs started filling up.

Mansergh's original plan was to build six reservoirs, three each on the Rivers Elan and Claerwen, capable of providing 74,800,000 gallons a day for supply, and 27,060,000 gallons for compensation to top up river levels below the dam. In the event, however, he only built the three Elan dams and the base of one in the Claerwen valley. The lowest in the chain of reservoirs impounding the Elan was Caban Coch. Under it is the site of Nantgwyllt, the house where the poet Shelley lived with his first wife Harriet Westbrook. Only the garden walls remain and they can still be seen when the water level is low. The house is believed to be the inspiration for Francis Brett Young's novel

*The House Under the Water*. The building of the Elan Valley waterworks is certainly the background to the novel *Undergrowth* by Francis Brett Young and Eric Brett Young, published in 1913.

The other two reservoirs in the Elan Valley were the Pen-y-garreg and the Craig Goch. The original design did not include filter beds but, as a result of the experience on the Liverpool aqueduct, they were added later to prevent peat deposits building up in the pipelines. The water was taken from the reservoirs to Birmingham along a 73½-mile aqueduct of conduits and pipes by gravitation, the total fall from Wales being 169 feet.

The Welsh Water Scheme was opened by King Edward VII on 21 July 1904 and Elan water reached Birmingham a week later. It took another two years for the village to be cleared away and the railway line dismantled. To house those re-employed to maintain the dams and filter system, Birmingham Corporation built another 'model village'.

## More Water for Scotland

Glasgow's supply was increased in 1903 by raising the storage of Loch Katrine from 7 to 12 feet, and adding to the input from Loch Vennacar. They had to withdraw the restriction of drawing only 50 million gallons a day – raised to 70 million in 1919 when storage was again raised, to 17 feet, in spite of the construction four years earlier of the Arklet Works. Likewise Aberdeen's supply was found to be lagging well behind. In 1909 the town council brought a Bill into Parliament to bring water in from Glen Avon. It was reckoned this would provide 20 million gallons of water a day and cost £1,400,000. The scheme was opposed by the railway companies, land and property associations and manufacturers and many private householders. The railway companies insisted on a guarantee that they would not be charged more than a shilling a thousand gallons. Some of the people of Aberdeen said they would not agree to the increased supply unless the census of 1911 showed a marked increase in the town's population since 1901. So great was the opposition that, though a majority of Aberdonians favoured the Glen Avon Scheme, Parliament rejected the Bill mainly on the grounds that it had not been fully put before the ratepayers or adopted by them. So the town council appointed a committee to ascertain from eminent engineers how much it would cost to take 10 million gallons from the River Dee. Messrs H Fox, Yourdi & Bateman quoted £777,000, but Sir Alexander Binnie, who had advocated adopting the Glen Avon Scheme, reckoned it would cost £850,000.

## Town and Country

The big towns where there was a good prospect of recovering the huge financial outlay, and then a profit, were well looked after, as were places where nature had endowed a not-too-distant gathering ground with a steady, reliable rainfall, like the St John valley with its average of 90 inches and a maximum of 243 inches a year. But the water supply from Manchester's Longdendale Waterworks, involving five service reservoirs at Denton and Audenshaw impounding the River Etherow (which became the Mersey after Stockport), was soon going to be incapable of meeting that great industrial city's growing demand. To supplement it the corporation acquired the 10,120 acres of the St John Valley in Cumberland's Lake District for the Thirlmere Scheme. They increased the capacity of Lake Thirlmere by 8,900 million gallons, so it would be able to supply 36 million gallons of water a day. They built a masonry dam across the valley and led the water in an aqueduct 106 miles long to the Audenshaw

'Lutyens' Folly' on top of
Whitchurch Down
reservoir in South West
Water's region houses an
access manhole. Built in
1914 to the design of Sir
Edwin Lutyens, architect
of the Cenotaph in
Whitehall, The Pimple
was originally part of the
water supply to a nearby
private house.

reservoirs through a tunnel, a covered channel and pipes. The journey to Manchester took three days. It cost Manchester Corporation £7 million. Unfortunately the soft water dissolved a part of the aqueduct made with mountain limestone, creating holes and fissures. To stop the water leaking, the section was relined with blue brick.

People living in the country at this time were less well served. Flora Thompson described how:

> In dry summers, when the hamlet wells failed, water had to be fetched from a pump at some farm buildings half a mile distant. Those who had wells in their gardens would not give away a spot, as they feared if they did theirs would run dry, so they fastened down the lids with padlocks and disregarded all hints.

And the receptacle for ordure could hardly be called a convenience:

> The only sanitary arrangement known in the hamlet was housed either in a little beehive-shaped building at the bottom of the garden or in a corner of the wood and tool shed known as 'the hovel'. It was not even an earth closet; but merely a deep pit with a seat set over it, the half-yearly emptying of which caused every door and window in the vicinity to be sealed. Unfortunately there was no means of sealing the chimneys! (*Lark Rise to Candleford*, 1945)

The need for piped water supplies to rural areas had been recognised as early as 1878, but the water suppliers, private and municipal, were reluctant to embark on laying long lengths of main water pipes in view of the relatively heavy cost. In 1897, however, the Medical Officer of Health was glad to note that 'the Tendring Hundred Waterworks Company's main ramifies through many parishes of the district'. At the Parliamentary Inquiry into his original Bill, Peter Bruff had promised that 'the supply would be conveyed to the villages which had hitherto been solely dependent upon impure wells and even the ditches on the roadside'. The villages of Beaumont, Bradfield, Great Holland, Great and Little Oakley, Kirby, Ramsey, Thorpe and Wix were placed in the company's area, and by 1901 Ardleigh, Lawford, Little Bromley, Little Clacton, Tendring and Weeley had been added to their number. Even more were included before 1905, but in all these cases it was only a few houses and by no means whole villages. With the agricultural depression and local workshops closing in face of factory competition, village populations were falling, and the water company hesitated to risk its profitability by extending its service into places where the revenue seemed unlikely to justify the expenditure. As a result, most of Ardleigh and Weeley remained dependent in 1911 on local supplies 'from shallow wells, usually made of dry bricks which created openings for all kinds of soakage getting into the water'. The company asked for a minimum return on its expenditure and, where ratepayers and local authorities declined to give any such guarantee, all idea of laying a water pipe to a village was abandoned. Having the luxury of piped water was a low priority. When in 1910 the Tendring Hundred company was considering supplying the whole village of Weeley, a questionnaire to householders revealed that only three of them had any intention of using the service if it was provided. Attitudes gradually changed however. By 1914, the company 'could claim to have created a system which already met the needs of the area's urban communities and was capable of extending its mains to the relatively few rural places where they had yet to be laid'.

The Rickmansworth Water Company obtained an Act of Parliament in 1900 to extend its area to include Horton, Iver, Denham, Chalfont St Peter, Hedgerley, Woburn, Hedsor, Great Missenden, Little Missenden and many neighbouring parishes. Since the

The majestic Gothic
water tower at
Swynnerton, near
Stone in Staffordshire,
built in 1892.

Missenden area covered some 30 square miles and was one mile distant from the other areas of supply, the company built a pumping station at Great Missenden capable of yielding 1¼ million gallons of water a day. With the aid of water towers at Prestwood and Lee, this kept the area self-supporting until 1970.

**The ten-mile conduit and aqueduct which carries Mendip water across Avon – part of the Line of Works, Watery Lane, Winford – a triumph of Victorian engineering still in use by Bristol Water today.**

## Use of Chlorine

The lot of remote country mansions like Petworth House in Sussex, still relying on the Coultershaw Beam Pump, was greatly improved by the application of the latest advances in technology. In 1909 they installed an electric water level indicator. Pumping had to be intermittent during the dry summer of 1911 because the spring was low, and water was needed to work the hydraulic blower which someone devised to operate the organ in the parish church. The bacteria count taken in 1911 – their first – was abnormally high, but fears of an epidemic were allayed when the bacteria in question were pronounced harmless.

The Cambridge Water Company feared pollution of the Fulbourn Well when, in 1903, cases of typhoid fever occurred at the Fulbourn Asylum where the sewage disposal works were on the primitive side. It therefore sought statutory powers to sterilise the water by treating it with chlorine or ozone – was this perhaps the first attempt by a water company in Britain to do so? When the House of Lords' Committee refused to give its consent, despite much expert evidence in favour, the company was allowed to raise water from a new source away from houses at Fleam Dyke. In 1911 work began on a well with two adits, a pumping station driven by 180 horsepower compound horizontal steam engines, and another million gallon reservoir at Lime Kiln Hill.

The ignorance of the amateurs of the Upper House who rejected the Cambridge application to use chlorine was soon exposed. In 1904 Lincoln applied chlorine in

Built in 1901, Blagdon Lake is Bristol Water's second largest reservoir, covering 440 acres, and holds water from the Mendips.

order to sterilise river water which had been contaminated – the first town in Britain to use it continuously. Soon afterwards Shrewsbury used it for Severn water. Within years the chemical gained the reputation of making the greatest impact on the purity of water supply in Britain, both acting as a disinfecting agent on its own and in combination with other elements. Together with filtration, the effect it had on the incidence of water-borne disease was dramatic. On the outbreak of war in 1939, the government quietly organised chlorination of all the nation's drinking water.

Compared with today, there was less need for sterilisation in an era of immobile communities when upland reservoirs produced bacteriologically satisfactory water. Then the water company could purchase the catchment area and control the farming practices. A 'keep out' philosophy prevailed, enforced by strong fences which separated the public from contact with its water supply.

## Organising for Plenty

Between 1900 and 1910 three Royal Commissions considered and reported on the matter of sewage disposal, along with associated problems. All their recommendations pointed to the need for a central authority to control Britain's rivers for all water conservancy purposes, as had been suggested 40 years previously. All of them were ignored. The message was that the amount of rainfall over Britain – 'precipitation' – had been reasonably constant from decade to decade since the end of the Ice Age, but the number of the island's inhabitants who wanted to use it, before it ran into the sea, had never stopped growing. Britain could no longer afford the luxury of not caring whether or not water was wasted. And of course there were claimants on Britain's meagre water resources other than the fresh water suppliers: the 'rival interests' who wanted water to drive their watermills and navigate their barges on. Who should have priority? The Joint Select Committee who considered Lord Desborough's Water Supplies Protection Bill in 1910 reported that the moment had come for the government to apply itself seriously to the whole matter of the nation's water supply. Once again came the recommendation to establish a central water authority. Herbert Asquith, the Prime Minister, told the House that the President of the Local Government Board would introduce a Bill giving effect to this recommendation and those of the Royal Commission of Sewage Disposal; but sadly Parliament was dissolved before the Bill could be introduced. Before the dissolution Parliament called for a return from every water undertaking in England and Wales. This showed that there were 2,160 water suppliers, the largest local authority supplier being Manchester. with 14 million gallons a day. The London Metropolitan Water Board supplied 244 million gallons a day and Tees Valley 15 million. There were 152 statutory companies established by Act of Parliament. Of the 1,130 borough and urban districts, 1,101 had piped supplies, of which 822 were by municipal authorities. Out of the 12,869 rural district parishes only 4,784 had a piped water supply in 1910 – 64 per cent of them had none. Thus three-quarters of England and Wales had a piped water supply, of which two-thirds was provided by municipal authorities, a state of affairs that prompted the formation in 1911 of the Municipal Waterworks Association.

With the outbreak of the Great War in 1914 all schemes for new water supply legislation were halted. The Water Power Resources Committee, appointed as soon as the war ended, recommended setting up a Water Commission, responsible to the newly instituted Minister of Health, to consider how best to conserve the nation's water supply. The minister thought a better idea was to give such problems to the professionals, and constituted an advisory committee of engineers who were members of the British Waterworks Association, the Water Companies Association and the Institution of Water Engineers. From 1922 this body became the driving force behind the formulation, in the face of political indifference, of a National Water Policy. Their report of 1925 outlined *Measures for the Protection of Underground Water*. New legislation, they said, was needed to safeguard underground supplies and prevent their pollution. The Advisory Committee on Water was suspended at the time of the economic crisis of 1931; Parliament was much too preoccupied in taking measures to retain financial stability to give any thought to the water supply.

On the matter of pollution of underground sources the Committee recommended enlarging the appropriate sections of the Waterworks Clauses Act of 1847 to make them apply to underground water. To deal with the important question of water pollution in general the government established the Water Pollution Research Laboratory at Watford in 1927.

Water engineers looked to the manufacturers to come up with pipes made of the material most likely to deliver all, or at least most of, the limited amount of water raised from its source, to its final destination, and in an acceptable state of purity. Where corrosive ground conditions were known to exist water engineers began laying asbestos-cement pressure pipes in the 1920s, though they were never entirely confident that they would survive under roads subject to heavy traffic. Pre-stressed concrete pipes were even less prone to corrosion than steel pipes and in larger diameters were cheaper. Iron, however, remained the most reliable material, though since the 1930s straight pipes in the lower and medium diameters have not been cast but centrifugally spun, only giving way to ductile iron in the 1980s. Writing in the *Pipeline Industries Guild Journal*, John Neve commented:

> Despite the advent of other types of pipe, iron is still [in the 1990s] the most versatile pipeline material, and it is probably true to say that on balance it suits the requirements of the water supply industry better than any alternative available. This is particularly so in densely populated areas with their multiplicity of services connections and where heavy traffic conditions prevail.

It was mostly iron pipework too in pumping stations, filtration plants and in most installations where water was conveyed under pressure.

### Severe Drought in 1934

In the 1930s, however, the concern was not so much the means of delivering water as having enough to deliver. A severe drought in 1934 induced the government to pass the emergency Supply of Water in Bulk Act by which one statutory company could give water to another. The three water engineering associations called a joint conference to consider, yet again, the merit of a 'national water policy' and what it should be. Their report, issued in 1935, called for a water grid on the lines of the electricity grid, which savoured of 'nationalisation' and was unpopular. They suggested that the country's water supply should be controlled by a department of the Ministry of Health, thus preserving the autonomy of each undertaking. They proposed setting up Regional Advisory Water Committees under the jurisdiction of the Ministry's Water Department and recommended implementing their report on protecting underground sources.

The government was moved to appoint a Select Committee of both Houses to

**Tearing apart the roads to lay water pipes in Union Street, Birmingham, in 1928.**

enquire into the water resources and supplies of England and Wales. It reported there was no crisis – 'the aggregate available supply of water was ample for all anticipated requirements of the country'. The committee was worried, though, that the requirements of the fresh water suppliers would be paramount over those of manufacturers, farmers and fishermen – although they, as the law stood, were entitled to deplete the wells of any fresh water undertaking with impunity. Courtaulds were pumping two million gallons of water a day from one of the wells of Wolverhampton Corporation, one and a half miles away, which reduced the well's yield from 1¾ million gallons a day to half a million. The Sutton District Water Company had to obtain powers to stop the Southern Railway Company from boring for water at a spot within a thousand yards of its well. Elsewhere a coal-mining company ruined the fresh water supply because the waterworks were situated between the sea and the colliery, and salt water was drawn in. In the end the water company had to buy water from the colliery company. When potable water was pumped from a colliery, in many instances Parliament compelled the water undertaking to make use of that water rather than sink its own well. Noxious water pumped from East Kent coal mines entered the chalk and polluted wells. At the beginning of the century the South Staffordshire Water Works Company was prohibited by its Act of Parliament from sinking a well within seven miles of the parish church of Burton upon Trent, so that the water, which had peculiar properties for brewing, should not be abstracted.

Who should determine priority over Britain's water supply? The Joint Select Committee was not at all sure that the Minister of Health was the proper person to find an equitable answer to 'the question of competitive claims to an essential commodity in limited supply'. To help the government reach decisions which were seen to be 'fair', the Water Advisory Committee was resurrected in 1936 under the chairmanship this time of Field Marshal Lord Milne. When the Public Health Act of 1936 enabled the minister to constitute a Joint Board to control the water supply of a district, Milne's committee advised that these powers should be extended to enable the minister to authorise the amalgamation and acquisition (following a public enquiry) of water undertakings, whether local authority or private.

They used a strong steam crane to lay a 46-inch water main in Garthdee Road, Cults, outside Aberdeen in 1936.

In 1936 there were about 1,000 water undertakings in England and Wales. They included 50 county councils, 150 borough councils, 300 urban district councils, 300 rural district councils, 33 joint water boards and some 173 companies with statutory powers. A population of 27 million was supplied by local authorities and boards; a population of six million customers was supplied by private water companies; Manchester Corporation supplied one and a half million and The South Staffordshire Water Works Company supplied a million inhabitants spread over the area of 30 different local authorities; the Newcastle & Gateshead Company served 700,000, and the Sunderland & South Shields Company 500,000.

Writing on *The Nation's Water Supply* in 1936, R C S Walters concluded:

> The result of the Waterworks Clauses Acts and the Public Health Acts of the 19th Century has been a great increase in piped supplies of water in this country in the last 80 years, and it is probable that there are only a few places at all populous that have water that is deficient in quantity or quality all the year round and year in and year out.

It was true that this legislation had revolutionised the water supply industry in England and Wales, but it needed updating. A Parliamentary Joint Committee recommended that there should be a complete revision of all general law regarding water supply, which had never been changed since the Waterworks Clauses Acts of 1847 and 1863.

For one thing, since then the demands on the limited supply had been stepped up to an inconceivable extent by the huge rise in the numbers of houses built, all of which were fitted with WCs. In the 1920s it was reckoned that in Hull some 50,000 new houses had been built, in each of which four and a half people (considered the average occupancy) each made two flushes a day – 450,000 flushes a day. There were still places where too little attention was being given to quality. A disastrous water-borne outbreak of typhoid fever occurred in Croydon in 1937. The smaller water undertakings were slow to appoint a full-time waterworks chemist, but the Croydon epidemic gave rise to a major reappraisal of both the problems of safeguarding water quality and the importance of employing qualified scientific staff.

### Cleaning Water but not Sewage

In the 1930s the routine method of water purification was to pass it through screens to catch tree trunks, dead animals, and other solids; allow the sediment to settle at the bottom of a large reservoir; treat it with sulphate of alumina to coagulate any remaining solid particles; draw it through sand filters; and finally chlorinate it as a safeguard against bacterial infection. But little was done at this time to purify *sewage*. It would be quite possible to purify London's sewage at Barking by a suitable purification plant, admittedly elaborate, and use the water again, as suggested by Walters in 1936, but that was not done:

> The basic principle involving river schemes is to get the river as clean and pure as possible, and to abstract the water at such points on the banks away from sewage works of large towns higher up on the river. The effluent of most sewage works has a high degree of purity (from the sewage point of view) and is often only a very small proportion in volume to the whole flow of the river.

**Filter beds and a sand handling bridge in the 1930s.**

The flow of advice, in print and spoken word, showed no sign of abating. Disinclination to take it or even consider it was given new justification in September 1939 when the minds of all were diverted to the more pressing matter of how to prevent the German Führer imposing his idea of a 'new order' for Europe. The outbreak of World War 2 killed the Water Undertakings Bill, designed to revise the Waterworks Code, which had just reached its final stage in the House of Commons.

The call not to waste water acquired new significance. It needed little imagination to picture the conflagrations that could be caused by an enemy's persistent aerial attack on Britain's cities, particularly seaports. The firefighting aspect of air raid precautions needed longer preparation than most and in Portsmouth it began in 1934. At a confidential conference called by the Mayor of Portsmouth in that year a Home Office representative told them of future contingencies, of the fires that could be caused by high explosive and incendiary bombs and the destruction of water pipes and waterworks. Measures to protect Portsmouth's water supply were put in hand at once. The water from Farlington Reservoir to the densely populated area around Portsea Island was taken by six trunk mains lying side by side along a main road into the city, and could be cut off by a single hit. So they laid a 36-inch gravitation main from Farlington two and a half miles long. As a general precaution cross-connecting mains 3,300 yards long were laid on Portsea Island.

For most people, however, the first awareness of air raid precautions came with the Munich Crisis of 1938 or perhaps not till the following summer:

### Advice to Water Consumers

The Metropolitan Water Board has issued a statement on the precautions to be taken with regard to water supplies in case of war:

### METROPOLITAN WATER BOARD

*Air Raid Precautions: Advice to Consumers*

1. In the event of an air raid, damage may be caused to water mains, supply pipes and fittings, and while every effort will be made to isolate and repair the damage to mains as quickly as possible, there may be considerable waste of water and some interference with supplies.

2. Consumers are reminded that the water supply system within their property, including all pipes, tanks, fittings, etc., is the responsibility of the owner or occupier of the premises. The Board's responsibility is limited to the mains and pipes in the street, including the outside stop-valve, if one exists, on the communication pipe in the street.

3. In order to avoid waste of water and damage to property, consumers are advised to make themselves familiar with the position of the stopcock on the service pipe inside their own premises so that they can shut off the supply to prevent flooding should the internal pipes and fittings be damaged.

4. The Board's Bye-laws require all premises to be equipped with a storage cistern of adequate capacity which should be covered as a protection against frost and contamination. In the event of the temporary suspension of the water supply, the water in this cistern should be sufficient for the careful use of the occupiers of the premises and, so long as the cistern is kept in a clean condition (as should always be the case), the water can safely be used for drinking purposes. As an extra precaution, boiling is recommended.

5. Hot water systems which are properly designed are so arranged that there is no immediate danger of a boiler bursting if the water supply fails when a fire is burning, but in such an event it is advisable to put out the fire as soon as possible.

6. It is of the greatest importance that consumers should do their utmost to economise in the use of water as large quantities will probably be required for fire fighting, essential supplies, and decontamination purposes.

7. It is anticipated that all telephone lines to the Head Offices of the Metropolitan Water Board will be needed to deal with major problems during and after an air raid. Consumers are therefore requested to refrain from making telephone calls there.

8. Consumers should ascertain the addresses and telephone numbers of the local officials of the Board immediately responsible for the area in which their houses are situated. These particulars are in possession of local authorities and are available at Fire Stations, Police Stations, Public Libraries and local offices of the Metropolitan Water Board.

R P Morgan
Clerk of Works

Offices of the Board
173, Rosebery Avenue, EC1
30th June 1939.

*(from British Waterworks Association Official Circular vol. XXI, no. 169, Oct.-Nov. 1939)*

In 1938 HM Treasury gave the London County Council a grant of £500,000 to improve London's water supply. By the summer of 1939 work was already in hand to lay additional 24-inch steel mains to carry water for firefighting only. Existing mains were cast iron piping laid only a few feet under the ground to firefighting hydrants. But when the Luftwaffe flew over the metropolis in waves in September 1940 and April 1941 the demands on the water supply for firefighting very soon exhausted that supply. When an employee of Maple & Co, the furniture store in Tottenham Court Road, who was on night duty as a roof spotter, heard a colleague shout 'Incendiaries everywhere!', he rushed to the delivery yard in Gower Street and found them burning all over. Where to start?

> We started on those nearest to us, clearing them as we went. Within a matter of minutes however it was obvious we were going to have a major fire. The main water supplies had been hit, and we were unable to make use of the hydrants. We manned the motor pump but it emptied the 5,000 gallon emergency tank in minutes – and to no effect.

The fire that started on 16 April 1941 burned for 11 days. It was 100 years to the day since John Maple had opened his shop on that very site.

Six hundred and five of the Metropolitan Water Board's mains were broken that spring of 1941, including 98 large pipes 12 inches in diameter. The several fires which linked up at Elephant and Castle in south London exhausted all the static water sources including the whole of Manor House swimming pool, so water was piped through nine miles of hose from the Thames and Surrey Canal to fight the conflagration.

The bombs the Germans dropped on Portsmouth on the night of 11 January 1941 broke 63 water mains. Two additional water mains, widely spaced at the point of entry, were laid to HM Dockyard. When two of the three pipes were hit in a raid, the water

**Listening for leaks.**

**'O for the water they waste in Britain!' cries the soldier in the Western Desert on the poster in the foreground in the Wartime Fuel Exhibition held at Sutton Public Hall in November 1942.**

through the third met the demand. When much of southern Portsmouth was without water after raids, soldiers delivered water in watercarts and householders collected water from standpipes and hydrants which had been connected to water company mains from four of the city's private wells.

Queuing for water at Higham's Park, Essex where emergency water wagons and a mobile filtration plant were called in.

## Planning for Post-war Reorganisation

While Britain, her Commonwealth and her Allies were managing to survive and win the war, there were those who were already setting their sights on what would be needed when peace returned and began to plan for post-war reorganisation.

The Central Advisory Water Committee issued a third report in 1943 recommending the formation of River Boards; and the resulting River Boards Act (1948) created 32 of them covering the whole of England and Wales except the Thames and Lea catchments. They controlled the management of rivers from source to mouth in the way suggested by the 1865 Rivers Pollution Prevention Commission. Their duties were increased by the Rivers (Prevention of Pollution) Act of 1951, which made it an offence to allow any poisonous, noxious or polluting matter to enter a stream. Anyone wishing to discharge new or increased trade or sewage effluent had to obtain the consent of a River Board.

In 1944 the wartime coalition government issued a White Paper on A National Water Policy; and the Labour Party published their plans for a post-war National Water Commission vested with central control, but local water supply undertaken by publicly owned and controlled Water Boards. It seemed that Lark Rise and Candleford would be in for a better service with the passing of the Rural Water Supplies and Sewerage Act 1944 under which £15 million was set aside for bringing piped water to remote villages and hamlets, which so far had been deemed uneconomic. It certainly put such places on the water map; but when peace came the lack of labour and materials postponed any implementation of the schemes – an early example of public sector funds becoming inadequate to provide what the customer wanted.

A step in the right direction was the grouping of smaller water undertakings into Joint Water Boards, like the Thames Water Board (the biggest), under the political control of the Minister of Housing and Local Government, made possible by the Water Act of 1945. This replaced the 1847 Waterworks Clauses Act and, in the words of S B Dracup, 'laid the foundations of a new phase in the history of water supply, the keynote of which is

In normal conditions Britain has enough water resources not only for domestic and industrial use but also for ornamental grottoes, so popular in the 18th century, such as this one at Goldney House at Clifton in Bristol, built in 1764.

planning and coordination'. It put the government's National Water Policy on the statute book. The formation of the water boards took time, however, and continued well into the 1950s.

The concept of water boards greatly facilitated administration for large industrial centres such as Leicester; whose city water undertaking was able to take water, apart from the usual local sources, from a River Dove Water Board and a Derwent Valley Water Board. The concentration of supply available to the Tees Valley and Cleveland Water Board based on Middlesbrough, one of the six biggest water suppliers in Britain at the time, enabled it to deliver to Teesside around 80 million gallons of water a day. Eighty per cent of this was used by industry. Most of it came from five impounding reservoirs in the Pennines 45 miles away in Upper Teesdale. Darlington's supply came from the 7 million gallon service reservoir at Harrowgate Hill.

Coordinating water supply under local water boards was a first step in implementing a National Water Policy, and of course the systems they instituted have necessarily changed since those days in accord with new technology. The government of the immediate post-war period took the advice of the Central Advisory Water Committee and passed the River Boards Act 1948 to administer the River Pollution Prevention Acts of 1876 and 1893; it also assumed responsibility for controlling abstraction from underground sources. It was encouraging that the legislators were allowing themselves to be guided by the engineers. To promote the advancement of technical and administrative knowledge as applied to the water industry, a number of supervisors, foremen and inspectors in 1945 formed the Association of Water Officers (now the Institution of Water Officers).

The British water industry was putting its house in order. But, with the post-war shortages and restrictions, it could only be done piecemeal. 'With all the manifold modern improvements and developments,' wrote F W Robins at the end of his comprehensive *Story of Water Supply* in 1946, 'much remained to be done.'

> Britain is possibly the best 'watered' country in the world, but there are still villages without a modern supply and others where a joint tap outside has to serve two or several cottages. In 1943 a tenant in the Bridgwater Rural District, whose well had gone dry, was being provided with water in churns by his landlord.

Inspired by the 1945 Water Act the water undertakings lost no time in seeking suitable partners with whom to amalgamate, or were ordered to do so. The 'Harwich Peninsula' had no less than five separate water undertakings, three of which were very small indeed. So the Minister of Housing and Local Government required that a single undertaking should be established by The Tendring Hundred Waterworks Company absorbing the waterworks of the Clacton and Wivenhoe Urban District Council and of the Tendring RDC. When, later, the Brightlingsea UDC's waterworks also joined them, the new company's authorised area of supply covered 136 square miles.

A statutory order to re-group became necessary when none of the potential partners of a new bigger company wanted it that way. Unable to find agreement among any of the undertakings in the Cambridge area, the Minister organised the compulsory amalgamation of the undertakings of five local authorities and two bulk supply joint water boards. As a result the Cambridge Water Company found its area of supply expanded from 60 to 453 square miles and its consumers increased from 116,000 to 195,000. Two of the very small acquisitions, at Willingham and Over, were shut down immediately.

Water had always been scarce in the Sussex Weald to the north of the South Downs. As a leading landowner was heard to say, cows are better off for water than human beings. But the Mid-Sussex Water Company had surplus water at Poverty Bottom, the adit having been extended for the second time, and they devised a scheme to pump 500,000 gallons of water a day to a reservoir near Firle Beacon. After considerable wrangling over parties and terms, it was agreed to extend the scheme to Burgess Hill, and that led to the complete acquisition of the water undertaking of the Chailey RDC and of the Burgess Hill Water Company. It was not long before they added the waterworks of the Mid-Sussex Joint Water Board, of the RDCs of Uckfield and Cuckfield, the Crowborough Water Company and the East Grinstead Water undertaking which was part of the South Eastern Gas Board. The negotiations were held up at one point for six months while a resident of Newhaven petitioned Parliament to stop the amalgamation. She pleaded her case in person before a Joint Committee of the Lords and Commons who firmly but courteously told her her plea was over-ruled. The details of parcelling out the assets of the Weir Wood Reservoir jointly owned by the North West Sussex Board were finally settled on the pavement outside the Café Royal in Regent Street after the British Waterworks Association's annual dinner, and were hastened by the appearance of a policeman who ordered the negotiators to move along.

## Water from Loch Lomond and the Silent Valley

In 1960 the Scottish Development Department set up a working party of authorities who might wish to participate in a central water supply scheme. It consisted of the county councils of Lanark, Dunbarton, Renfrew and Stirling, together with the town council of Stirling and the Stirlingshire & Falkirk and West Lothian water boards. They recommended Loch Lomond as the most suitable source, and in 1961 formed the Loch Lomond Interim Water Committee. Four years later they promoted a water order for the abstraction from the loch of 100 million gallons of water a day for houses and factories in Central Scotland and compensation water for the loch's sole outlet, the River Leven. The order came into operation in February 1967.

Loch Lomond is some 26 feet above sea level and covers 17,600 acres. One foot of depth contains 4,780 million gallons. With an average annual rainfall of 80 inches, the loch has no difficulty in yielding the required 260 million gallons a day, assured moreover by the construction of the River Leven Barrage which gives at least four feet depth of storage. Water is pumped from the loch at Ross Priory through two pumping mains to Balmore Treatment Works for distribution to Grangemouth and to Blairlinnans Treatment Works and from there by gravity to the north bank of the River Clyde and via the Erskine Bridge to the Renfrewshire area. Treated water from Balmore is pumped to a service reservoir at Glenhove near Cumbernauld and to another at Muirhead near Lennoxtown. Other parts of the region are supplied from service reservoirs at Dalmacouter, Gowanbank and Eastcraigs. A third pumping main from Glenhove takes water to the service reservoir at Garbethill. As conceived in the 1960s the whole Loch Lomond Water Supply Scheme is controlled from the Balmore headquarters of the Central Scotland Water Development Board created by the 1967 Water (Scotland) Act and operational from May 1968.

As well as the Central Scotland Water Development Board, the Water (Scotland) Act of 1967 created 13 regional water boards to give Scotland its public water supply. Sewerage and sewage disposal were undertaken by 234 local drainage authorities. Nine boards were set up to ensure river purification in well-populated areas; local authorities, county councils and burghs were responsible for it in other parts of Scotland.

By the 1950s the Belfast City & District Water Commissioners had spent some £7 million on building waterworks and buying land to supply what had become Greater Belfast. The increase in demand had been foreseen in 1891 when their consulting engineer L L Macassey had advised them that the two deep valleys in the southern section of the Mourne Mountains would be the best source. The water of their rivers had the quantity and the quality needed. Acts passed by the Imperial Parliament in London in 1893, 1897 and 1899 gave them powers of compulsory purchase of the valleys' land and water. Macassey began by constructing a main conduit from the so-called Silent Valley, the more distant of the two, through the mountain slope in the townland of Brackney by a three-quarter mile tunnel, and thence by syphon to the entrance of the Annalong Valley to a service reservoir at Knockbreckan. When completed in 1901 the whole system could carry 30 million gallons of water to Greater Belfast every day. Nine years later plans were made to turn the Silent Valley into a reservoir holding 3,000 million gallons by impounding the water of the river, but for a variety of reasons the work was not completed until 1932. They then decided it was going to be too expensive to make Annalong Valley a reservoir as well, and opted for a scheme they could afford which was to divert the water of the River Annalong into the Silent Valley reservoir by means of a 3,700 yard tunnel 7½ feet high through Slieve Bignian. Designed to take a maximum of 90 million gallons a day, they estimated that even in the driest of years an average of five million gallons would flow through the tunnel from the Annalong Valley catchment to add to the 17 million gallons available from the Silent Valley reservoir. It was opened in August 1952. Four years later the syphon pipe sections of the Mourne Conduit were triplicated, and in 1957, to take advantage of the full yield of the Silent and Annalong Valley catchments and in place of the abandoned Annalong Valley reservoir, they built the Ben Crom reservoir, holding 1,700 gallons, which increased the yield of the Mourne scheme by some five million gallons a day. The total average supply to Greater Belfast throughout the year was in the region of 30 million gallons a day. The scheme involved the purchase of around 9,000 acres of land, and the total cost including construction and pipe laying and compensation came to approximately £4 million.

### River Authorities Coordinate Resources

Radical change came south of the border with the passing of the Water Resources Act of 1963. This, for the first time, coordinated water resources in England and Wales on a regional basis by creating 27 River Authorities with areas related to the basins of the main rivers, including those of the Conservators of the River Thames and the Lee Conservancy Board, to take the place of the River Boards. Their duty was to conserve, redistribute and augment the water resources of their areas. The President of the Water Companies' Association described the Act as 'the most important piece of legislation affecting the water supply since the Water Act of 1945'. Some saw it as a defence against nationalisation. Jack Jeffery, Managing Director of North Surrey Water Company, observed in the 1980s that lack of financial accountability had perhaps encouraged the planners to make assumptions about the rate of growth of demand, which had turned out to be exaggerated. He also thought, however, that they might be praised by future generations for their far-sightedness.

In 1963 too the government established at Reading a Water Resources Board to investigate and plan on a national scale the country's future requirements. The Board's role was to advise the River Authorities and the Minister who, under the 1963 Act, created a licensing system to control the abstraction of water, operated by the River Authorities.

The benefits which these changes brought to the statutory companies, hard pressed to find increased sources of supply to meet demand, such as the Cambridge Water Company, were considerable. In 1964 the company was supplying just under 8 million gallons of water a day. In the course of the next 16 years it had to find more than 14 million gallons a day. In that time the population it served increased by 51,500 (26 per cent); and consumption per head rose from just under 40 gallons a day to more than 57 gallons a day, a rise of 45 per cent. The local River Authority gave it a licence to take 3 million gallons a day from a source near the village of Melbourn and 2½ million gallons a day from another in the parish of Westley Waterless – a corruption of 'Water Leas'. In 1966 the Water Resources Board advised action on the company's consulting engineer's proposal for a groundwater low-level storage scheme in the Great Ouse basin to make room for additional storage of water which would otherwise have run to waste. Following a pilot scheme in the Thetford area the River Authority prepared a scheme for the river Rhee involving 18 boreholes, of which six were to be for the public supply with an estimated yield of 3.3 million gallons a day.

The question of how best to solve the problem of increasing supplies and treating them so as to make them acceptably wholesome, shared by all Britain's suppliers, was widely discussed. At a symposium held by the Institution of Public Health Engineers and The Institute of Water Pollution Control, its Chairman, C H Spens, Chief Engineer to the Ministry of Housing and Local Government, proposed the novel idea of multi-purpose Regional Water Authorities for England and Wales independent of local government.

The 1969 Royal Commission on Local Government recommended reorganising

**The River Tyne's unpleasant colour and smell have been eradicated under a multi-million pound scheme which revitalised the river banks.**

municipal bodies and their water supply service, which they saw as inadequate to cope with the increasing water pollution. Apart from the 29 independent statutory companies which provided about a quarter of the water supply in England and Wales, most of the 160 undertakings were based on local authorities, several hundred of which were responsible for sewage disposal. If Newcastle upon Tyne were representative of the state of affairs in other towns in England and Wales, it would seem that the insanitary conditions of the 1830s were still around. The town's Official Commercial & Industrial Guide of 1970 stated:

> The Tyne, whatever praises are sung in its favour, is very much an open sewer at present.

They hoped a multi-million pound scheme 'now being dealt with through a committee of engineers' would rid the river of its unpleasant colour and smell. Several miles of new sewers would be laid linking the drains of the city and other parts of the Tyne bank carrying sewage out to the North Sea and by-passing the Tyne. That would give an opportunity to revitalise the river banks.

It would seem that if the presumed growth in demand had been exaggerated, the reality of the state of pollution had not. Reporting on *The Future Management of Water in England and Wales* in 1971, the Central Advisory Water Committee stated that between 1955 and 1960 consumption of water was increasing at an average rate of 2.4 per cent a year; and that the average amount available per head of population was about 850 gallons a day, among the lowest in Europe.

Effective conservation of existing water needed discipline; effective treatment of sewage needed money. Both needed the intervention of central government. The reasons for local government's reluctance to use compulsion for, or spend money on, either of these was spelt out by the Advisory Water Committee in the 'Importance of Water Quality' section of their 1971 report:

> It has now been realised that the fast increasing consumption of water, domestic and industrial, will make imperative a much greater re-use of water in nearly all parts of the country.

Most water suppliers, given a free choice regardless of cost, said they would probably prefer to go to the upper parts of catchments where water was unpolluted. They usually developed the cheapest and nearest sources first, since the cost of exploiting upland sources and transporting the water had risen. Moreover, much public opinion was hostile to having a reservoir in an upland area. An extreme instance of the question of what to do about pollution was provided by the River Trent, the third largest in England and Wales with a potential yield comparable to that of a major barrage scheme:

> But at present it is heavily polluted by sewage and industrial effluent and therefore unsuitable for public water supply. Indeed there is a fundamental conflict between the existing and potential users of this major river. Some wish to see it carry away their effluent; others wish to develop it as a major source of supply.

It was one of the neglected sources which the Department of the Environment presumably had in mind when, in their Circular 92/71 of December 1971, they declared:

> Unless further sources are developed on a large scale, a dry year could lead to widespread restrictions on the use of water with potentially serious effects on public health and industry.

The conclusion of the Advisory Committee in their 1971 report was that the remedy lay in a much greater re-use of water and therefore much greater concern with the treatment given to water after use. That depended on the existence of a single comprehensive water management plan for every river basin. It was technically possible to cope with the increased use of water, but the solutions had also to be publicly acceptable and make the minimum demand on resources. There was a need for a sweeping reduction in the number of separate units in sewage disposal and in water supply.

**Where the River Derwent flows into Derwent Water.**

OVERLEAF: **Icicles hanging from alder boughs.**

## CHAPTER SIX

# *All change*

REORGANISATION IN ENGLAND AND WALES • IN NORTHERN IRELAND AND SCOTLAND • AN END TO WASTEFUL RIVALRY • PUBLIC LIMITED COMPANIES FOR WATER AND SEWERAGE SERVICES • PROTECTING THE CUSTOMER AND THE ENVIRONMENT • MOST CONTROVERSIAL, LEAST ADMIRED

The Conservative government promised action. Its plan was to replace the 29 river authorities, 160 water undertakings and 1,300 sewerage authorities in England with ten Regional Water Authorities. In moving the second reading of the Water Bill in February 1973, Geoffrey Rippon, Secretary of State for the Environment, said the proposed structure avoided 'heavy centralisation', and was radically different from the one set up by the Water Resources Act of 1963. He emphasised that local authority members would be in a majority in each regional water authority, thus meeting objections that local government would not be sufficiently associated with services of great concern to local people. The private statutory companies did a good job, he said, and were ready to be agents of a Water Authority. There was no good reason to abolish them and transfer their assets to one. 'There is little point,' he said, 'in paying compensation to them for doing what they are prepared to do in any event.' The Labour opposition spokesman, Denis Howell, said his party was concerned that a local authority would lose its water undertaking, but the independent companies would remain in private hands. A future Labour administration, he said, would reserve the right to bring them into public ownership.

The Bill was passed by a majority of ten – 220 to 210 – and became operative from April 1974. In the same month the new local government structure and the reorganisation of the National Health Service took effect. The Secretary of State for the Environment and the Secretary of State for Wales appointed the chairmen of the Regional Water Authorities; and they were joined by the Minister of Agriculture and local authorities in appointing the members. The Water Resources Board was abolished, and a statutory National Water Council created, consisting of the ten water authority chairmen, with its own chairman and some other members appointed by the government. It was a consultative and advisory body with statutory responsibilities for national pay negotiations, training and pensions, and an informal role in coordinating the water authorities, whose ten regions constituted the whole area of England and Wales. Otherwise each autonomous multi-purpose water authority was responsible for the whole of the water cycle in its region including pollution control, river and groundwater management, water resources, sewage treatment and disposal, water supply, drainage, recreation, navigation and fisheries.

Under their powers the water authorities were able to focus on the various roles of a river as a source of water, as an amenity and as a recipient of discharges from sewage works and factories. Each balanced these requirements in the best overall

## WATER SERVICE COMPANIES OF ENGLAND AND WALES

### (supplying clean water and treating wastewater)

Northumbrian
Water

North West
Water

Yorkshire
Water

Severn Trent
Water

Anglian
Water

Dŵr Cymru
Welsh Water

Thames Water

Wessex Water

Southern Water

South West
Water

interest, in the knowledge that river water quality, standards of sewage treatment and potential for water resource use were linked. The resources of rivers like the Thames, the Severn, the Tyne and the Dee could be managed as a whole over wide areas, which could be invaluable in times of drought. The new framework was severely tested only a couple of years after it was created when, in 1976, the country faced one of the worst recorded droughts, and again in 1984, when the western half of the country faced even drier conditions. The relevant autonomous authorities coped with the emergency in a way that would have been impossible under the old fragmented system.

They could also plan their capital investment in a far more effective way than was possible with small separate units. In the Black Country rationalisation and new investment under the authority's strategic sewage scheme, for instance, enabled 12

## WATER SUPPLY COMPANIES OF ENGLAND AND WALES
### (supplying clean water)

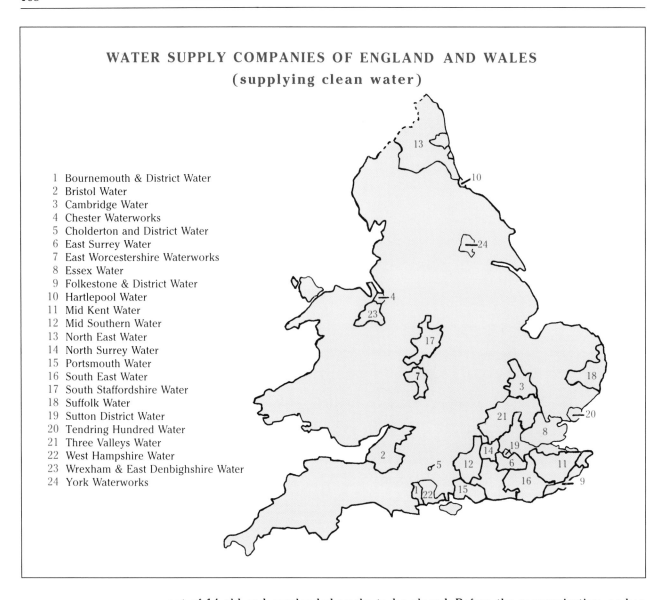

1   Bournemouth & District Water
2   Bristol Water
3   Cambridge Water
4   Chester Waterworks
5   Cholderton and District Water
6   East Surrey Water
7   East Worcestershire Waterworks
8   Essex Water
9   Folkestone & District Water
10  Hartlepool Water
11  Mid Kent Water
12  Mid Southern Water
13  North East Water
14  North Surrey Water
15  Portsmouth Water
16  South East Water
17  South Staffordshire Water
18  Suffolk Water
19  Sutton District Water
20  Tendring Hundred Water
21  Three Valleys Water
22  West Hampshire Water
23  Wrexham & East Denbighshire Water
24  York Waterworks

out of 14 old and overloaded works to be closed. Before the reorganisation, as has been seen, sewerage and sewage disposal were undertaken by local authorities. Thus 'the water rate' was for water supply only. The sewage charges, which attracted rate support grant from central government, were a minor part of the much larger local authority rate demand. It seemed that the sewage services were 'free'. After 1974 the water authorities received no rate support grant and had to cover all their costs from charges. Between 1974 and 1978 local authorities continued to collect the sewage charges, but paid them over to the water authorities. When the sewage charges were finally included in the overall bill for water services, they caused that bill to double overnight. In neither case, however, was there any real increase in income to the water authorities. Parliament required the water authorities to eliminate the subsidy which domestic customers had enjoyed at the expense of commercial and industrial customers, which again caused some domestic bills to rise sharply. In 1981 the government decided that the water industry should borrow less and less until they financed each year's capital expenditure out of that year's income and repay existing debts before their due repayment date. All such financial restructuring led to larger water bills. In view of

that, it was essential that the water authorities should be seen by their customers to be giving value for money, both with regard to the quantity and quality of what they were being asked to pay for. When the government abolished the statutory National Water Council in 1983, the water authorities set up their own non-statutory Water Authorities Association with headquarters in Lord Grey of Falloden's old house in Queen Anne's Gate, Westminster, to promote their interests nationally and tell the water-consuming public what they were doing and why. The Water Companies Association continued to represent the independent private statutory water companies.

More difficult than providing sufficient quantities of water was ensuring that it was clean enough. Under the Control of Pollution Act 1974 a Regional Water Authority had

**How drought can affect Britain's water resources – Taf Fechan reservoir, Brecon Beacons National Park in Wales, in August 1976.**

to keep a register of applications to discharge sewage and industrial waste into inland, coastal and underground waters. The National Water Council reviewed the classification system for 'water quality' in an attempt to bring consistency and to balance the rival claims. Water abstraction for agricultural irrigation, industrial cooling, steam raising, navigation and leisure amenities such as swimming, boating and fishing, did not need as pure water as that required for the other main contender, domestic use for drinking, cooking and washing. Creating 'use-related standards' that satisfied every category of user was a formidable task. It was eased by the establishment in 1974 of the Water Research Centre which brought together in one organisation the activities of the private Water Research Association, the government's Water Pollution Research Laboratory and part of the operations of what had been the Water Resources Board.

Assessment of what could be said to constitute 'wholesome' water, the adjective used in the 1945 Water Act, was made more difficult in 1980 by the government agreeing that the Drinking Water Directive issued by the European Economic Community – and which the British government had helped to formulate – should apply to the United Kingdom.

### In Northern Ireland and Scotland

In 1973 the Water Service of Northern Ireland's Department of the Environment provided half a ton of pure fresh water to each of 456,300 households every day, plus a roughly equal amount to thousands of industries and businesses. There were more than 70 local authorities in Northern Ireland responsible for the supply and distribution of water. With local government reorganisation the responsibility for both water supply and sewage services was assumed by government. The Water Service had its headquarters in Parliament Buildings at Stormont with a directorate for policy and overall control. Its staff coordinated operations and capital works programmes. A water resources section developed water resources, controlled water pollution and co-ordinated research and development.

By the Water and Sewerage Services (Northern Ireland) Order 1973, the people of the province have greatly benefited from having a single water authority committed to improving standards, increasing cost effectiveness and value for money, improving the physical environment and 'the health, prosperity and well-being of the community'. The people of Scotland have similarly benefited from the somewhat different arrangement introduced by the Local Government (Scotland) Act 1973, which gave locally elected authorities control, among other things, of water supply, sewerage and sewage disposal.

In Scotland before the reorganisation of local government under this Act, which came into effect in May 1975, public water supply had been undertaken since 1968 by 13 regional water boards and the Central Scotland Water Development Board. The regional water boards were the successors of the 20 water supply authorities which did the job until the coming into force of the Water (Scotland) Act 1967. Sewerage and sewage disposal were carried out by 234 drainage authorities; river purification by nine boards plus 12 local authorities, ten county councils and two large burghs. From 1975 the nine new Scottish Regional Councils had functions for public water supply, sewerage and sewage disposal broadly similar to those of the Regional Water Authorities in England and Wales. There was no general licensing of abstraction of water in Scotland. A regional council acquired water rights by means of a Water Order made by the Secretary of State for Scotland. The financing of Scottish water services was

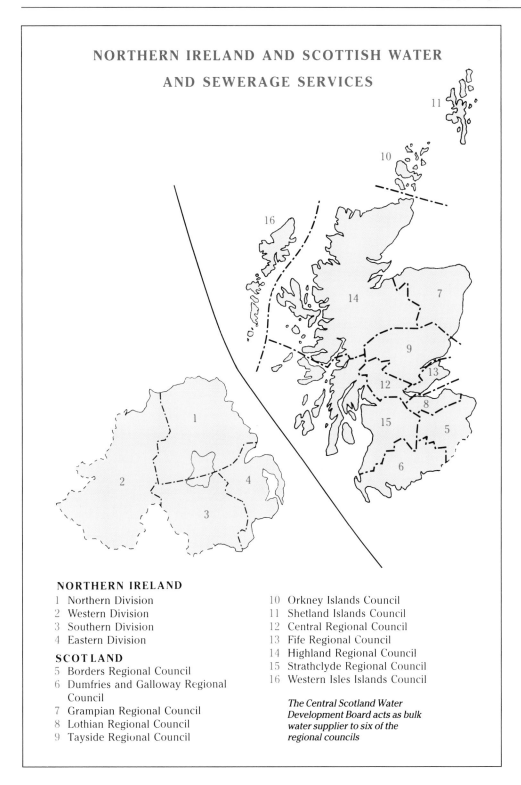

NORTHERN IRELAND AND SCOTTISH WATER
AND SEWERAGE SERVICES

**NORTHERN IRELAND**

1  Northern Division
2  Western Division
3  Southern Division
4  Eastern Division

**SCOTLAND**

5  Borders Regional Council
6  Dumfries and Galloway Regional
   Council
7  Grampian Regional Council
8  Lothian Regional Council
9  Tayside Regional Council

10  Orkney Islands Council
11  Shetland Islands Council
12  Central Regional Council
13  Fife Regional Council
14  Highland Regional Council
15  Strathclyde Regional Council
16  Western Isles Islands Council

*The Central Scotland Water
Development Board acts as bulk
water supplier to six of the
regional councils*

integrated with the regional council's other services and funded from rates as well as
water charges.

The Local Government (Scotland) Act of 1973 preserved the independent bulk supply
of the Central Scotland Water Development Board which serves an area in which live 80
per cent of Scotland's population. Its main sources are Loch Turret and Loch Lomond.

The nine river purification boards were disbanded in 1975 and replaced by seven new boards serving the whole of Scotland except the Western Isles, Orkney and Shetland. A third of each river purification board came from a regional council, another third from a district council and a third was appointed by the Secretary of State to represent agricultural, industrial and environmental interests. The boards were financed by the regional councils.

### An End to Wasteful Rivalry

At last the wasteful rivalry and lack of coordination that dominated Britain's water supply service had been remedied, and the nation's water consumers could look forward to enjoying a service of a kind that their ancestors had only been able to dream about.

Few, however, saw the structure imposed in 1973 as definitive. Over the following ten years came the expected fine-tuning in the light of experience. As a concession to local authorities for the transfer of their assets without compensation, the board of each water authority had to have a majority of local government representatives. This made for over-large boards – in one case, 80. In 1983, therefore, to make the boards of the water authorities more business orientated and more manageable, the Government passed legislation to end the built-in local authority majority.

The pattern of investment under the 1973 regime was highly unsatisfactory. At first there had been an increase, but it had been cut in the late 1970s as part of general public sector reductions under pressure from the IMF. This stop-go pattern of investment made the planning of major projects very difficult.

However, there was no halting work on a number of ambitious schemes that had already started: the 771-acre Bewl Water reservoir at Lamberhurst in East Sussex; the £190 million improvement programme in Wales involving water treatment works at Eithynfynydd, Alwen, Coslech and Mold, and the Glyncorrug trunk sewer for the Afan Valley; the South Devon Spine Main from St Ives to Penzance and the reservoirs at Wimbleball on Exmoor and at Colliford on Bodmin Moor designed to quadruple the region's 1974 water storage; the Alton Water reservoir in East Anglia taking water from the River Gipping at Sproughton; the Kielder Water reservoir opened in Northumberland in 1982; and the Wye Transfer Scheme, the first phase of which was opened in 1985.

Between 1961 and 1984 total public water supply in England and Wales rose from 2,400 million gallons a day to 3,600 million. Water for washing machines, dishwashers, showers, swimming pools and car washing now joined the still burgeoning use of it for WCs, baths, sinks, wash basins and garden sprays. The strain imposed on the inelastic sources of fresh water would have been even greater had it not been for the decline of Britain's manufacturing and mining industries which reduced industrial demand.

Was the 1973 structure capable of taking the strain? Was HM Treasury, obliged to treat water services as one of the many competing claims on the public purse, capable of allocating funds to it on the scale which the industry believed to be sufficient? By 1985 the government was beginning to have its doubts. As much as 25 per cent of clean water supply was already in the private sector in the form of the 29 statutory water companies which were owned by shareholders who received dividends.

In January 1985 the House of Lords questioned that water price increases above the rate of inflation were required by government in 1985/6. This followed from the then water authority chiefs reminding customers that the government carried the blame for the size of the increases. Sir Roy Watts, Chairman of Thames Water, stated that his authority – the largest in the country – was unwilling to act as an income tax collector:

> It is a matter for parliamentary debate. We wish the targets to have the force of law; and until such rules of return are approved we will if necessary, issue our own charging policy to reflect our own figures. The targets imposed are excessive.

The *Water Bulletin* reported that Thames Water were taking on the government. Sir Roy Watts used the charging debate to press for serious consideration of the privatisation of the water authorities. That is seen to be the beginning of the privatisation programme

**Another 'ornamental' use of water – the pagoda fountain at Alton Towers in Staffordshire was built by Robert Abraham in 1827 for the 19th Earl of Shrewsbury. As the water from the jet splashes onto a series of green roofs, the bells tinkle.**

**River management now in the hands of a National Rivers Authority – the River Hull tidal surge barrier.**

that was completed in December 1989. At the end of January 1985, the Prime Minister, Margaret Thatcher, told the House of Commons:

> The government would welcome new ideas on privatisation. However, the water authorities are natural monopolies for many of their functions and we need to be particularly careful when considering replacing a public monopoly with a private one.

In February 1985 Ian Gow, the Minister for Water, announced that he was to examine the possibility of finding a solution by a measure of privatisation in the industry opening it up to the long-term, stable funding which could never come from the taxpayer.

The debate that followed on the pros and cons of privatising the water service in England and Wales was as vigorous as that which took place 100 years before on Joseph Chamberlain's conviction that it was best placed in the hands of the people's elected representatives. Much of the controversy of the 1980s reflected concern about placing in private hands a natural monopoly responsible for services so essential to public health and well being. As with the 19th century debate on municipal versus private enterprise, the facts were often subsidiary to the politics. It was difficult for the politicians to admit that they had failed to maintain the great Victorian water legacy because investment in underground water pipes and sewers had always been less politically attractive than roads and houses, schools and hospitals. That underground network was now in need of repair and renewal.

Victorian outfalls to the sea, which in their day were a significant advance in public amenity and health, were no longer acceptable to a generation with higher expectations of what should be a 'clean' environment. Neither was it any longer enough for drinking water to be merely safe. It had to comply with European requirements sensitive to the increasing penetration of water supplies by new chemical substances, and concerned with colour and taste as well. Britain's water service was behind the times. To bring it up to date needed a massive increase in investment.

## Public Limited Companies for Water and Sewerage Services

The government believed that the best way to make this possible was to turn the ten regional water authorities into regulated, licensed public limited companies, stripped of their own regulatory powers and their responsibility for managing Britain's rivers. It wanted the companies' job to be confined to providing water and sewage services. It planned to separate regulation from operation with the management of the river basin delegated to a separate body, a government department with some such name as the National Rivers Authority.

There was a delay in introducing privatisation, mostly because of the backlog of other Parliamentary business, but there was no stopping the Water Act of 1989 becoming the law of the land. Provided they were efficient, the plcs could finance all the requirements placed upon them. A director-general of water services would regulate water charges and had the duty of ensuring companies *could* finance their water supply and sewage operations. Price regulation there would be, not profit regulation, and there would be published league tables to provide comparative competition. It would no longer be a matter of having to agree investment programmes within a Government Public Sector Borrowing Requirement. Moreover, to give them enough funds to pay for the enormous capital programme, most of the water authorities' current debts would be written off – a feature of the new arrangements which some on both sides of the House found less than pleasing. But the necessary debt write-off was balanced by the £5,225 million received by the Exchequer for the sale of the ten companies.

When he heard that planned investment by the water companies over the next ten years amounted to some £28,000 million, Sir David Trippier, the minister appointed to take charge of water in 1990 after privatisation, said he believed it was a sum which 'would never have been extracted from the Treasury'. But more importantly perhaps, the Water Act of 1989 meant the separation of regulation from operation; and separation of water supply and sewage services from all the other responsibilities of the water 'authorities', including river basin management which was hived off to a new body, the National Rivers Authority. For these monopoly suppliers of a commodity vital to health, there was environmental as well as economic regulation. It all involved, as Nicholas Hood, Chairman of Wessex Water observed, a cultural change – one that helped to ensure proper investment, high quality water and concern for the environment:

> A regulator appointed by the government is much more likely to be effective in dealing with a monopoly owned by shareholders who want profits (which the regulator can reduce if the company's service to customers is poor) than with a monopoly owned and financed by the government.

Under the 1989 Act the statutory companies, which were not publicly owned and provided a quarter of the fresh water of England and Wales, were subject to the same regulatory requirements for price and product and service quality as the ten new regional plcs. The Act enabled them, 29 in number at that time, to convert themselves to public limited companies, if they wished.

The organisation of public water supply and sewage disposal in Scotland and Northern Ireland was not affected by the 1989 Water Act which, however, empowered the Secretary of State for Scotland to make regulations on water quality – the Water Supply (Water Quality) Scotland Regulations 1990. The Act received the royal assent in July.

On 1 September 1989 each of the ten water authorities was created a public limited company wholly owned by government, and each ceased to have responsibility for river management. On 22 November the Government put their shares in these ten plcs for sale on the stock market. A nationwide marketing campaign was launched in the press and on television with the slogan 'You Too Can Be An $H_2$ Owner'. Members of the public and institutions would be investing in a business whose turnover for the year ending 31 March 1989 was £3.2 billion and with aggregate operating profits of almost £1.2 billion. The capital expenditure of the ten regional bodies and their sewage businesses amounted that year to £1.1 billion and would rise to £3 billion a year. It seemed that the investors would include the three largest private water companies in France: Lyonnaise des Eaux which had set up an office round the corner from the Water Services Association in Queen Anne's Gate; Générale des Eaux which had set up an office in Wimbledon, subsequently transferred to Knightsbridge, and anglicised its name to General Utilities; and the smallest of the three, Société d'Aménagement Urbain et Rural (SAUR). These French companies had already taken significant stakes in some of the statutory water companies.

It was the first time anywhere that ten separate independent companies were to be floated together on one day. There was a need, therefore, for a common approach, though, once in 'the private sector', each one would indeed establish a strong individual corporate identity. The flotation process involved offering a common share price of 240p with a different number of shares issued for each company, ranging from 65,490 for Northumbrian Water, capitalising the company at £157 million, to 384,208 shares for Thames Water, capitalising it at £922 million. Individuals could apply for shares in one or more of the companies, but institutions had to buy a package of all ten. In the event the public retail offer, after clawback, was 2.8 times subscribed overall, ranging from North West Water, 1.6 times subscribed, to Northumbrian Water, 9 times subscribed. A total of 46.87 per cent of the shares went to the public, 39.26 per cent to institutions and 13.87 per cent to overseas investors. With 2.7 million applications for the £2.9 billion shares, it was the second highest response ever for a government privatisation. The total amount raised for the Treasury was £5,225 million.

Many deplored the transfer to 'businessmen' of a public service such as water supply which had no competitors. Michael Carney, Secretary of the Water Services Association, saw the move as offering an escape from political interference and the stop-go investment policies inherent in the UK nationalisation model. In theory, nationalisation does not have to be synonymous with political interference and under-investment, but in practice the connection seemed to be immutable.

## Protecting the Customer and the Environment

In surrendering ownership, the government did not abandon responsibility. Far from withdrawing from the scene it remained as the watchdog, through regulators, overlooking the activities of the private commercial operators, to whom it had delegated the role of running so vital a public service, with few 'pure' market pressures on them. The government maintained its continued interest through the National Rivers Authority (NRA), Her Majesty's Inspectorate of Pollution (HMIP), the Office of Water Services (OFWAT) and the Drinking Water Inspectorate (DWI).

The NRA was established as an independent body to look after the water environment – the 'controlled waters' of rivers, lakes, reservoirs, aquifers and the sea around the coast for a distance of three miles. It was given responsibility for river basin regulation,

including setting river water quality standards, consenting to discharges, monitoring compliance and for licensing water abstraction from any source. It also had the difficult task of deciding between the competing claims of navigation, fishing, conservation and water abstraction. The creation of the NRA represented a return to the principles of river basin regulation of the 1963 Water Resources Act, but with regions subject to control and coordination by a central NRA board. In July 1992, the government decided to establish a new Environment Agency which would include both the NRA and HMIP.

The Director-General of Water Services, Ian Byatt, saw the *raison d'être* of OFWAT, of which he was head, as being that water customers could not look to market mechanisms to protect them from unnecessarily high charges or a poor service, or

**A million gallons of water pass over the weir each day at the Grove, Carshalton in Surrey. The weir, which attracts many wildfowl, won a Civic Trust Award in 1971 for Southern Water.**

both. His object was to achieve *through regulation* the same balance as would otherwise be achieved by competitive markets. He would protect customers against their suppliers making excessive or undeserved profits, excessive price rises and 'ill-considered proposals for capital investment'. He would ensure that charges were 'fair' by comparison between different classes of customer, so that domestic users and industry each paid their 'proper' share. A company's costs were likely to cover much else besides the mechanics of water supply and sewage, such as their duty under the Act to conserve the environment. The Director-General of OFWAT said:

> I am concerned to dispel the misconception that environmental improvements are justified irrespective of their cost. Everyone welcomes moves to improve the quality of our drinking water, bathing waters and rivers. However, these improvements require massive capital expenditure programmes. These programmes will be paid for by the customer. Politicians and environmentalists must be sure that environmental proposals are soundly costed, and that the efficiency of different solutions is examined. Costs must be justified. The test is not just whether solutions achieve their objectives but whether they do so in a cost effective way.

To assist in protecting and considering customer interest, the Director-General appointed ten Regional Customer Service Committees. Drawing from a wide range of interests, these committees provided a local focus for consultation between the companies and customer representatives and an independent appeal mechanism for any customer dissatisfied with service or prices.

The DWI was formed to give, for the first time, a national body responsible for ensuring water companies met the new standards for drinking water quality. They would investigate any significant quality problems, audit compliance with investment programmes and carry out independent inspections of water supply plants and processes. Where the new standards were not being met they would lay down compliance programmes that companies would have to meet. If any company was shown to supply water unfit for human consumption it would risk prosecution.

In the organisation of the country's water supply and sewage service therefore, Government was still very much in evidence. It was a well-structured compromise. As Michael Carney said, 'private ownership combined with public regulation provides both the market dynamism so necessary in the efficient and economic production of goods and services, and the degree of public control so essential when a private monopoly is responsible for a basic product like water'. In a sense, OFWAT and the NRA could be said to be pulling in different directions – and thoroughly beneficially. OFWAT looks after performance and sees that customers get value for money; the NRA, the physical regulator, sees that the suppliers keep to the standards required to maintain and improve the water environment.

In the first ten years of operations under the reorganisation, the ten water supply and sewage companies together with 29 water-only companies planned to spend more than £28 thousand million on improving the quality of drinking water and treating wastewater. At 1989 prices that was more than double what the publicly owned water authorities were authorised to spend by successive governments during previous decades. In real terms the expenditure on wastewater was three times as much. A publicly owned and publicly funded water industry – albeit embracing the statutory companies which were not publicly owned – could never have embarked on a ten-year investment programme on that scale. Reassuringly, at the head of the new business-orientated water and sewage companies, were experienced businessmen of high calibre – who were already running the independent 'authorities' before privatisation.

## Most Controversial, Least Admired

This privatisation was the most controversial and, from all the research done, the least admired of the privatisations of Mrs Thatcher's last term as prime minister. Given the size of the investment – £28 billion for ten years – new or imminent EC directives, the backlog of mains and pipe renewal to make good, and the effect of all this on water prices, privatisation always seemed more appealing to those in the industry who knew what they were doing than to the industry's customers who had always pulled the chain and turned the tap without ever worrying where the water went to or came from.

It was no easy task for the government to convince the many genuine doubters that water privatisation was a good thing. The independence of OFWAT and the NRA helped. But public disquiet and debate wore on. Writing in *The Times* in March 1989, Lord Wyatt said the opinion polls suggested that more people were more hostile or indifferent to water privatisation than to any other. Irrational, atavistic feelings were at work, he said. It was vaguely felt that nature's bounty, if not free, should at least be publicly supplied without a distasteful connection with profit. It was feared that otherwise prices would soar, and concern over quality and pollution of rivers and beaches, and the health hazards of sewage would diminish.

> Reason is a better guide than inchoate emotions. All water is privatised in France and the French are rather particular about what they drink. Twenty-five per cent of our water to-day comes from statutory companies owned by private shareholders; the remainder is from public water authorities.
>
> What we should be afraid of about water is it not being privatised. Public water authorities, all allowed to regulate themselves, will never set such exacting standards as private companies goaded by outside bodies making life very nasty, through their pockets and otherwise, if they ignore instructions.
>
> Profits will be hit by non-observance of regulations and, as in all other areas, the profit motive will be an incentive to much higher efficiency. True, the cost of purification measures will at first mean higher prices of water. That is nothing to do with privatisation, but is a vital part of the 'Green' campaign.

Seeing privatisation as making the water industry more accountable, 'environmentalists' welcomed independent regulation. Most of the industry wanted it. As Michael Howard, Minister for Water, told the National Water Conference in October 1988, the government saw the change as freeing senior managers from government intervention and having to compete for resources with other public services:

> Employees at all levels will be able to identify with independent, enterprising concerns with an exciting future. And the greater transparency of the new structure will make it clearer to the customer exactly what they are getting for their money. These are the opportunities I see for the future of the water industry.

While the change has been made in England and Wales, plans are being made to privatise the water services of Northern Ireland and Scotland, but there is still much work to be done.

OVERLEAF: **Maundown Water Treatment Works, Brendon Hill, Somerset.**

# CHAPTER SEVEN

# Too *vital to leave to chance*

MONEY FOR WHAT? • ANGLIAN REGION • DRINKING WATER QUALITY • SOUTHERN REGION • CONSERVING THE ENVIRONMENT • THAMES REGION • RING MAIN LONGER THAN CHANNEL TUNNEL • WESSEX REGION • SOUTH WEST REGION – THE CLEAN SWEEP • WELSH WATER

The water industry today is a complex, highly skilled business with the customer at the forefront of everything it does. In England and Wales privatisation created water businesses with the job of putting right years of public sector neglect, meeting ever-higher quality standards, protecting the environment, meeting growing demand from customers, whilst at the same time trying to contain the increase in charges. The modern water industry is the most capital intensive industry in the country. Its assets, valued at over £13 billion, include over 500 impounding reservoirs, almost 5,000 service reservoirs, over 2,000 water treatment works, over 8,000 sewage treatment works and over 20,000 pumping stations. The network of public water mains stretches over 186,000 miles, with a similar length of sewers, and the industry employs some 55,000 people.

For administration and financial discipline, water and sewerage companies sensibly separate the raising of raw water and the distribution of treated water from the disposal and treatment of wastewater. But the two operations are indivisible for producing an end product of clean water that complies with all the rules – wholesome fresh water. The water and sewerage companies' £14 billion effluent clean-up programme for 1990/2000 is well on course. This is three times as much in real terms as in the previous years, and is in addition to another £14 billion being spent on drinking water improvement.

With discharges from wastewater operations and other outfalls into rivers requiring statutory consents, and the introduction of new treatment plant, the pollution load which made water anything but wholesome is being cut month by month. The under-investment of the public sector years to 1989 cannot be corrected overnight. It was stated at the start that it would take ten years to make the treated effluents discharged from 4,300 sewage treatment works meet the standards which water customers deserve and the National Rivers Authority and the European Community require. After two years, however, the plcs' standards for drinking water, already good, are even higher. It has cost money, and completion of the exercise will cost more. 'Water has been taken for granted as one of life's free gifts,' said William Courtney, Chairman of Southern Water and of the Water Services Association, in January 1992. 'That is changing as prices rise. People are beginning to realise that it can be costly to provide this essential product at acceptable standards.'

Every day we treat more than 4,180 million gallons of wastewater from a population of 54 million in England and Wales. More than 96 per cent of the population are connected to sewers, the highest percentage in Europe. Since 1974 good progress has been made in spite of public sector financing restraints. And the impact of privatisation in 1989 has been dramatic in that, for the first time, the industry has had access to funds to enable it to invest in much needed wastewater projects.

Why does raw water need treatment? Even at the start of the water cycle falling rain absorbs dirt, dust, grease and chemicals from the air. When flowing over the ground, it collects mud, clay, decayed plant matter, and nitrates as well as bacteria derived from the soil, vegetation and animal waste products. Man-made pollution comes from sewage effluent or contamination due to farming, animal rearing, mining, industrial discharges, litter and suchlike.

Mine water pumping can lead to harmful mineral contamination and much fine suspended matter. Industrial manufacturers may discharge substances into the water which can cause taste and odour problems. Dissolved organic matter from peaty land can affect water's natural colour. The treated water should end up with no 'turbidity' or suspended matter, no colour, no smell, no unpleasant taste, no disease germs, no other organisms and no harmful mineral content.

To ensure compliance with standards, all the water companies are subject to a detailed technical audit by their water quality regulator, the Drinking Water Inspectorate. The companies give the local authorities and regional health authorities in their region the results of their own monitoring. They hold regular meetings with environmental health officers to establish lines of communication and resolve matters of mutual interest.

**Thames Water's *Bubbler*, a special craft to pump oxygen-enriched water into rivers in the London Region to counter sudden sags in dissolved oxygen levels.**

Loch Ness, the abbey and
beside it Fort Augustus
public sewage works.

The high quality of Britain's water reflects the success with which the organisations responsible for water supply and sewage carry out the latter. If the benefit of sewage being carried away by water, through artificial sewers to natural open watercourses and out to the sea, is not to be negated by its polluting the river which may often be used as a source of fresh water supply, it must be deprived of its contaminating potential before it is discharged. A water-borne sewerage system is not necessarily superior to a land-based cesspit system; the effluent is merely collected and discharged to rivers and sea. The main benefits come when money and engineering and chemical expertise are applied to processes to treat the foul sewage/ordure released from water closets and urinals, the dirtied water sent down the plugholes and into the waste pipes under baths, washbasins and sinks, and the noxious chemical-impregnated effluent from manufacturing and mining processes. In addition to its original *asaquare* function of carrying away surplus rainwater to prevent flooding, a modern system collects and treats most of the wastes produced by society.

It was this treatment process to which for many years the Victorians were unable to apply themselves. Treat foul sewage? They carried out disposal without treatment at a cost that has been seen. Sewage treatment before 1974 was carried out by local bodies. As late as 1974 it was still being done by as many as 1,400 local authorities of varying size, many too small to have qualified staff. At that time there were only 300 qualified sewage treatment managers in the UK. It was the poor relation of municipal service, with local councillors finding it politically more attractive to spend money on houses and other services. Effective sewage treatment needs investment and it needs skilled technicians who have to have time and money devoted to their training. Lord Nugent of Guildford who in 1974 was chairman of the National Water Council was appalled by the low standards of sewage treatment inherited by the new water

Opened in July 1991, Thames Water's Advanced Water Treatment Centre at Kempton in West London uses ozone and granular activated carbon to remove pesticides from drinking water.

Improving bathing water quality – a new package wastewater treatment operated by South West Water on the South Devon coast at Wembury.

**The sleek lines of the Cambridge Water Company's Bluntisham reservoir and towers.**

authorities. In Huddersfield the sewage treatment works was 'absolutely unbelievable with settlement tanks full to the top'. In another in the North West nothing seemed to be working at all. Raw effluent left the works little different from the state in which it entered.

The sewage that arrives for treatment is over 99 per cent water – consisting of wastewater from homes, offices and factories and sometimes storm run-off from roads and roofs. Treatment is designed to separate the relatively small quantities of polluting matter from the large volume of water: no longer sewage farms, but truly wastewater treatment works.

No two wastewater treatment works today are exactly alike. They differ in design; in the strength, contents, quantity and quality of wastewater received; and in the standard required for the final effluent discharged to the river. Each wastewater treatment works has the same role, however – to clean wastewater to a standard where it is able to be returned without damage to the environment where it will join the rivers which for so many suppliers are the main source of water they deliver, fresh and clean, to their customers.

## Anglian Region has Lowest Average Rainfall

Water supplies still come predominantly from local sources. In some regions this is mainly surface water in rivers and reservoirs, in others groundwater from beneath the surface. In the Anglian region, stretching from Humberside to the Thames, half of the sources are reservoirs and rivers, and half underground aquifers. It has always had the lowest average rainfall – 21 inches compared with 24 inches in the rest of England and

Wales, of which about 70 per cent is lost by evaporation. Every 50 years it can expect a drought, but the one which began in the summer of 1988 was of a once-in-every-200-years severity, exacerbated by the greater evaporation in the long hot summers. The 41 months to the end of December 1991 were the longest dry period of the 20th century, with only 79 per cent of normal rain. One million of Anglian Water's 3.5 million customers, who are supplied from underground chalk aquifers, were banned from using sprinklers and hosepipes for 15 months. This restriction was lifted in November 1991 and was not reimposed in 1992, as the drought entered its fourth year, because of the special measures taken to open up new resources.

Inevitably the drought revived calls to tow icebergs from the Arctic, build desalination plants or construct a national grid. Unfortunately water, unlike electricity, is bulky and very expensive to move long distances. A better solution is the development of regional grids and inter-regional transfers – solutions already being pursued by the industry. Anglian Water, for instance, is steadily advancing long-laid plans to transfer water from the lower reaches of the Trent, linking the Trent-Witham-Ancholme with the Ely Ouse-Essex transfer scheme.

All the water companies are working to avoid the need for any restrictions on water use, except perhaps under the most extreme drought conditions. This means investment in developing new resources and extending transfer and distribution systems. Developing new resources now requires years of investigation and consultation to ensure there is no environmental damage from the development.

Alongside developing new resources, companies are working hard to reduce leakage and waste. Extensive monitoring and control systems enable pressures to be matched to demand and major problems quickly identified. Sophisticated control centres monitoring key information every few seconds round the clock mean rapid response, greater efficiency and far less dependency upon manual operations. One operator monitors the operation of the whole network, controls the operation of the pumps and takes immediate action to deal with any fault. Alarms go off if any of the readings fall outside pre-set limits.

In long periods of dry weather the Essex Water Company, the amalgamation of the South Essex Waterworks Company (formed in 1861), the Southend Waterworks Company (formed in 1865) and several local water undertakings in the region, makes use of the Ely-Ouse Transfer Scheme, opened in 1971. The company's head office building in Chelmsford was once (in 1899) the factory in which Guglielmo Marconi made components for his revolutionary 'wireless' telegraph transmitters and receivers. Between 1 January 1988 and 31 March 1992 the company invested £42 million in capital expenditure projects. Throughout the 1970s Tendring Hundred Waterworks successfully integrated the water undertakings of the four local authorities which had been supplying customers in Clacton, Brightlingsea and Wivenhoe. It developed four boreholes in Suffolk and embarked on the Ardleigh Reservoir Scheme, by which the winter flood water of the River Colne was impounded in a storage reservoir constructed in the Salary Brook.

## Drinking Water Quality

Providing sufficient, and sufficiently safe, *drinking* water is perhaps more of a problem. For Bernard Henderson, chairman of Anglian Water, consideration of Britain's drinking water requires 'a bit more science and a bit less emotion'.

Potentially, the greatest threat to health from drinking water arises from bacterial contamination. The virtual absence of outbreaks of water-borne disease via the public

**Rutland Water is the largest reservoir in the Anglian Water region, with walks and picnic sites at regular intervals along its 24-mile circumference.**

OPPOSITE: **Bewick swans and wildfowl on frozen flooded fields known as the Ouse Washes – a picture taken from one of the Wildfowl and Wetland Trust hides.**

water supply over the last 50 years is testimony to the success of water suppliers in protecting the nation's health. Half of the EC standards of 1985 related to aesthetic quality – the way water looks and tastes – and are concerned with naturally occurring substances which have no implications at all for health. All drinking water contains natural chemical substances, particularly mineral salts of calcium and magnesium. The amounts of these vary from area to area, but the vast majority are totally harmless and indeed without them water would taste flat and unappetising.

Groundwater pumped up from aquifers and water permeable rocks, which provides nearly a third of the water in England and Wales, is intrinsically purer than surface water, since many pollutants are naturally filtered out as it passes through the ground. Nonetheless groundwater can be contaminated if, for example, a poorly operated waste disposal site allows drainage water to percolate into the aquifer.

In 1987 the Department of the Environment found that 62 per cent of the 100 landfill sites they inspected took no measures to prevent groundwater ingress. Groundwater in agricultural areas is at increased risk of contamination as nitrate-based fertilisers and pesticides can leach into the supply. High nitrate levels in water supplies are predominantly to be found in eastern and central England in areas where rainfall is low and intensive arable cropping is practised. Nitrate levels in water supplies have been of concern since a relationship was established in the 1950s between nitrate and the so-called Blue Baby Syndrome. In the UK, however, the disease is virtually unknown – the last case was reported in 1972 and there have been only 14 cases in the last 35 years, all associated with private well water.

Nitrate, a compound of nitrogen and oxygen, is a normal part of human diet found in many foodstuffs. Farmers enrich their soil for high productivity by feeding it with fertiliser containing nitrate which can leach from the ground not only into underground water stores but into rivers and streams. At the levels currently found in public water supplies, however, nitrates do not pose any known significant risk to health.

Britain is fortunate in being an island. River and water pollution problems faced in the UK are dwarfed compared with those faced by countries bordering on international rivers such as the Rhine.

In providing such a vital public service, Britain's water suppliers have every reason to play safe. As most are commercial plcs it is something they *wish* to do; as law-abiding businesses they have no wish to break the law. For both reasons they set up elaborate continuous monitoring operations to tell them if and when the quality of their water in any part of their region is falling below the mark.

## Developing New Resources in Southern Region

Quantity is the concern of Southern Region's Mid Kent Water Company, the Folkestone and Dover Water Services Limited and the parts of Kent supplied by Southern Water. In view of the exceptional drought conditions, drought orders were obtained in 1992 to restrict various non-essential uses of water throughout most of Kent.

Southern Water's beautiful Bewl Water reservoir covering 770 acres was opened in 1975. The reservoir allows Southern Water to abstract water from the River Medway at Maidstone, treat it and supply it to much of North Kent. Mid Kent Water Plc has made a 25 per cent capital contribution to the cost of the scheme and is entitled to 25 per cent of the yield, part of which can be taken from Southern Water's Burnham Treatment Works and part direct from the Bewl Water reservoir, and treated at Mid Kent Water's Bewl Treatment Works. Mid Kent Water Plc was previously a statutory company

Southern Water's SS
*Frances Mary* takes
visitors on a trip round
beautiful Bewl Water,
near Lamberhurst in East
Sussex. She was brought
down from Loch Lomond
by road.

founded in 1888 and incorporated two years later. In 1970 the statutory Mid Kent Water
Company was joined by the Maidstone Waterworks Company, formed in 1860.

In the 1970s Mid Kent did a substantial amount of work in cooperation with Southern
Water, when it was an authority, to develop proposals for a reservoir at Broad Oak near
Canterbury, for which the government refused to give permission. The scheme was
never entirely abandoned, however, and Southern Water, Mid Kent and the Folkestone
and Dover Water Services Limited are currently progressing proposals for the reservoir
which would impound part of the Sarre Penn Valley with water from the River Stour.
Southern Water also plan a joint promotion with the Eastbourne Water Company to add
to their capacity by quadrupling the amount of water held in their Darwell Reservoir
near Hastings.

In the south of the region is the Mid-Sussex Water Company formed in 1881. Its first
source was a well at East Blatchington which unfortunately started drawing in salt water
through overpumping. The company looked for another source and had talks with
landowners who had springs. In 1914 a reservoir was built at Piddinghoe to serve
Newhaven. To supply the large number of troops stationed in the area during the First
World War, when consumption exceeded 550,000 gallons a day, an additional 12-inch
pumping main had to be laid. There were plenty of men around, but none available for
the chores of Civvy Street, so Mid-Sussex appointed a woman waste inspector at 30
shillings a week, work the directors considered 'quite suitable' for her. Once again
increased pumping led to salt intrusion, but the manager felt it would be 'too much to
ask the War Department to reduce the number of troops at this juncture'. He felt
justified in complaining, however, of the great waste of water by transient civilians
through their 'inordinate desire for hot baths at all hours'.

Along with every other water supplier in the country, Mid-Sussex never stopped
looking for new ways to reinforce its supplies. By the 1970s the only practical major

The inside of Southern
Water's cavernous
reservoir at Hastings
resembles a cathedral
crypt.

**This 'Kentish barn' is in fact a pumping station on the intake lagoon at Bough Beech in Kent.**

**OPPOSITE: Most of Southern Water's supply comes from boreholes – here they are using the latest mobile drilling equipment to sink one into the chalk of the South Downs.**

source remained the River Ouse. Southern Water constructed a river-regulating reservoir to keep up the flow in the Ouse at Ardingly on the Shell Brook, and to enable the company to continue to abstract water at Barcombe. It was, as was usual for such projects, a long drawn-out process. As the company's historian records:

> New reservoirs are an emotive subject: they bring forth a formidable army of objectors, conservationists, naturalists, landowners, ramblers and riders, agriculturalists and archaeologists. When the proposals for Ardingly came before a Public Inquiry not a single objector remained. The credit for this must go to the senior members of the staff both of the company and the [Southern Water] Authority who spent days and often nights explaining the scheme and listening to the views of those who might be affected. The landowners, including the National Trust, showed a breadth of view and public spirit which ruled out the question of compulsory purchase.

Mid-Southern Plc draws most of its water from more than 100 boreholes supplemented by additional water from a pumping station at Egham. The French SAUR Group have a controlling interest in Mid-Southern. In 1991 the SAUR Group formed 'South East Water

**Southern Water's treatment plant at Horsham, using the N-viro composting process.**

Limited' by bringing together three other water supply companies it owned: West Kent, Mid-Sussex and Eastbourne.

The French Compagnie Générale des Eaux is the majority shareholder of Folkestone and Dover Water Services Limited, the first towns in Kent to have a public water supply operating under the Waterworks Clauses Act of 1847. It is cooperating with Southern Water and Mid Kent over the Broad Oak reservoir scheme. At the other end of the region's coastline Portsmouth Water Plc, formed in 1857, draws 40 per cent of its water from Havant and Bedhampton springs, the largest source of its kind in the UK, and the rest from the River Itchen and boreholes.

## Conserving the Environment

The people of the United Kingdom benefit from the country's water supply industry not only as paying consumers of water but as members of the public at large who admire scenery and enjoy engaging in open air sport, studying nature and exploring the country. It is a by-product that for the most part is a freely available green bonus, although reasonable payment for some specially provided water recreation facilities helps to reduce water bills.

The 1989 Water Act imposed on the water and sewerage companies and the water supply companies in England and Wales certain general duties in respect to conservation, public access and recreation. These were to further the conservation and enhancement of natural beauty; 'to have regard to the desirability of protecting buildings and sites of archaeological, architectural, or historic interest, and giving the public access'; and to ensure that their land and stretches of water were made available for recreational purposes 'and in the best manner'. In doing so they must take account of the needs of the sick and disabled, and be guided by the code of practice prepared by the Secretary of State for the Environment and the Secretary of State for Wales in consultation with the Countryside Commission, the Nature Councils, English Heritage and the equivalent body for Wales (Cadw), the Sports Council and other similar organisations.

Conservation means keeping land, on which 'works' of any kind are being imposed, as much as possible as nature created it, not transforming it into an eyesore by spoiling the natural composition of shapes and colours with a man-made construction that makes a blot on the landscape. In the jargon of the day, in all their activities Britain's water suppliers are expected to be green-conscious and environmentally friendly. As Peter Soulsby, scientific manager of Southern Water's Hampshire division says, environmental responsibility is the added value that should be built into every drop of water supplied. And it is. Some 140 species of bird visit the company's Ashford Wastewater Treatment Works, including wrynecks, black-necked grebes and red-

**Heron on a willow tree in Syon Reach, on the Thames.**

OPPOSITE: **Kingfisher on a fishing post in a feeder of the River Test, Hampshire.**

**A family of mallard ducks on the River Derwent, Yorkshire.**

**Dragonfly breed on fast-flowing water in southern England.**

wings. A pair of kestrels have been spotted on the Isle of Sheppey's Queenborough works. With Tunbridge Wells Borough Council Southern Water has also helped to provide new homes for barn owls in Kent; preserved butterflies at Mill Hill in Sussex where the rare chalk-hill blue makes its home; placed nesting boxes for bats in the trees on the small island in the centre of Carisbrooke Pond on the Isle of Wight; and made a dragonfly pond on the bank of its Weir Wood Reservoir.

Conserving wildlife, the flora and the fauna, takes time and care; but saving water for human use takes even more. Doing so by reducing leakage on its 7,500-mile pipeline network has been a high priority for Southern Water.

## The River Thames and its Region Will Serve 7½ Million by 2001

Stretching between Anglian, Severn Trent, Wessex and Southern Water, Thames Water manages its water and sewage services on a big scale. Up to 1989 its region had only experienced seasonal fluctuations in the amount of water available of plus or minus six per cent of the average daily supply. Indeed, during the previous ten years they had been able to increase the daily supply by about 11 per cent – from 540 million gallons to 600. The resident population of the region, from Banbury in Oxfordshire southwards to Reading in Berkshire, where Thames Water has its headquarters, and from the Thames estuary to Swindon (with an even larger sewerage area), decreased slightly over the four years to 1983, but is expected to grow from 7 million to 7½ million by the year 2001.

The principal source of water for abstraction in the company's region is of course the Thames. The river's catchment area is a lowland river basin which contains extensive aquifers including Cotswold limestone and Chiltern chalk, which normally are replenished naturally during the winter months, but which in 1991/2 were affected by only half the average rainfall.

Thames Water draws about three-quarters of its water from the River Thames and River Lee and the rest from groundwater sources. It takes the water to 22 storage reservoirs capable of holding 45,000 million gallons located in the Thames Valley, the lower Lee Valley, Farmoor near Oxford and Grimsbury near Banbury. Ninety-four per cent of this stored water is in the Thames Valley and Lee Valley reservoirs, a nominal 100 days' supply.

In the Lee Valley, Thames region has a water supply company, the Lee Valley Water Company, now part of Three Valleys Water Services Plc, which was formed from a number of water supply undertakings which had been supplying a million people in north London, rural Essex, Hertfordshire and Bedfordshire for 100 years or more. Apart from its own sources, Lee Valley takes a bulk supply when it needs it from Thames Water and from Anglian Water's Grafham Water reservoir. It has no rivers or lakes in its area capable of providing a water supply, and relies on wells and boreholes. It was created in 1960 as an amalgamation of the Barnet District Water Company and the Herts and Essex Water Company. Ten years later, with the Colne Valley Water Company and the Rickmansworth and Uxbridge Valley Water Company, it promoted the Three Valleys Water Order which provided for the abstraction and treatment of water from the River Thames. The three companies pooled resources to build a waterworks at Iver.

The Colne Valley Water Company, dating from 1873 and now part of the Three Valleys Water Services Plc, supplies an area stretching from Harpenden to Harrow and Wembley. Its 600 million gallon Hillfield Park Reservoir, covering 120 acres, is the only large open reservoir in Britain to be built for storing water pumped from underground.

OPPOSITE: **When this water main burst, it took an East Surrey Water Company team eight days to repair it, working 24 hours round the clock.**

Clear, clean water in the Colne Valley Water Company's Harrow-on-the-Hill reservoir.

The third partner in the Three Valleys Scheme, the Rickmansworth Water Company, had also relied entirely on underground water from its foundation in 1884 until 1965. It contributed to the new reservoir at Iver and built additional service reservoirs, including one of 32 million gallons at Harefield, at the time the largest reinforced concrete covered reservoir in the country.

All the advanced control technology in the world could not prevent water levels in the five North London counties of the Three Valleys falling in 1992 to their lowest since 1903, or the months of January, February and March of that year being the driest since Bonnie Prince Charlie raised his standard in 1745. The three companies who operate as a group, Three Valleys Water Services Plc, which is French-owned, applied for a drought order to conserve what was left.

Also French-owned, the North Surrey Water Company supplies nearly half a million people living to the south of Heathrow Airport. In 1988, North Surrey was acquired by Compagnie Générale des Eaux (General Utilities in the UK).

Thames Water has all the equipment for supplying its vast 3,450,000 acre region with 18 Albert Halls (604 million gallons) of water every day, but with the clouds in the early 90s refusing to precipitate, it is pressing on with the implementation of its long term, ten year programme of extension and improvement on which it is spending £1 million *a day*. It is a sum which the successor of even the Metropolitan Water Board admits was inconceivable expenditure before privatisation in 1989. At the centre of the programme is its London Water Ring Main Project.

Up to now London's water has been fed from a network of large diameter surface trunk mains which radiate across the metropolis from the big treatment works in the Thames and Lee Valleys. It is energy intensive, requiring continuous pumping of water across long distances, with re-pumping once or even twice to reach the extremities of the system. In April 1985 the then Thames Water authority produced a paper called *The*

*London Water Supply in the 21st Century.* It postulated two ways of producing the greater volume of water its forecasts predicted it would need in the near future. They could either renew and enlarge hundreds of miles of conventional trunk mains and cause mammoth disruption of London's road traffic, or build a unique water ring main in a tunnel encircling London.

## Ring Main Longer Than Channel Tunnel

Work began on what resembled a giant bicycle tyre in 1987. The tunnel itself was to be 50 miles in circumference and sunk 130 feet underneath the streets of London. For the most part it was eight foot wide, large enough to drive a car through. This huge feat of engineering is longer than the Channel Tunnel. When it is finished, water will enter the ring main from the company's water treatment works which have the capacity to ensure that the circular main is always completely full. The water in it does not 'flow' – it can move in either direction. It is a circular underground storage reservoir of treated water

**Looking up one of the vertical shafts sunk by Thames Water for the London Ring Main Tunnel.**

which, moreover, does not have to be pumped into it; it reaches the tunnel from the works by gravity. Due to be finished in 1996, the London Tunnel Ring Main will be able to move 285 million gallons of water a day. It will supply about half of London's present-day demand. Water will be raised from the tunnel up through 12 shafts from Ashford Common in the west to Stoke Newington and Coppermills in the east, from Ealing in the north to Surbiton and Streatham in the south. The unmanned shafts will be controlled by computer from a central control centre. Thames Water envisage extending the tunnel to 87 miles in the 21st century – equivalent to nearly two Channel Tunnels in length.

It is the concentration of customers in so small and tightly built-over an area as London that calls for a piece of engineering as elaborate as the Ring Main, half of which has already been completed.

Not all Thames Water's water is underground. On ten major reservoirs Thames Water have floated rafts to give safe nesting at ground level near water to the common tern, which will not breed where it might be disturbed. It arrives from Africa in April and flies back again in October. In the grounds of its elegant Dancers End Pumping Station, near Tring in Aylesbury, are to be found 100 plant species including adderstongue, spiked sedge and chiltern gentian, a rare plant only found high in chalk hills. Among the butterflies that visitors can see at Dancers End are ringlet, meadow brown and marbled white. The site has one of Britain's largest badger sets, and provides a home for the uncommon Daubenton's bat. Thames Water has developed this wonderful natural playground with the Berks, Bucks and Oxon Naturalists' Trust.

### No Restriction on Water Use in Wessex Region

The task of a water supplier in the less congested region to the west of the Thames region, however, is no less sophisticated. The regional headquarters of Wessex Water, which the authority built in 1976, has a system capable of monitoring and controlling locations where, automatically without human intervention, water is raised, treated, pumped and distributed. As elsewhere, it has taken the place of the need for people to tour reservoirs and pumping stations round the clock across an area of 2,500,000 acres, a practice that now belongs to folklore. It is a system custom-built to serve a Wessex

From this computerised panel a single Wessex Water engineer can control and monitor all the company's operations throughout its wide region.

Wessex Water's wastewater treatment works at Avonmouth.

which, as Graham Harrison, one-time secretary of Wessex Water, points out, is 'more extensive than Thomas Hardy's, if less than Alfred the Great's'. It is a region of contrasts with large conurbations in the north and south. A company with a £1.3 billion ten-year investment programme, in May 1992 it moved into the top 200 of Britain's listed companies assessed by market valuation, with an equity value of £505 million compared with £302 million in 1990. The success of the Wessex integrated control system is demonstrated by the fact that despite periods of very low rainfall there have been no restrictions on water-use in Wessex Water since the 1976 drought.

The Bristol region's water supplier is Bristol Water, now a plc after 145 years as a statutory organisation. The company, among the largest water supply companies in the country, supplies over a million people in an area of nearly 1,000 square miles. Bristol Water has two major French shareholders, but it remains independent and locally managed.

At the southern end of the Wessex Water region, the Bournemouth and District Water Company is the supplier. With all the authority of a company which had been in business since 1863, it strongly attacked the idea, mooted in the Labour government Green Paper of 1975, that statutory companies should be integrated with the regional authorities.

On the eastern flank of Bournemouth is the West Hampshire Water Company which celebrates its centenary in 1993. Biwater Ltd acquired major shareholdings in both companies in 1989, and the two aim to operate as one before the end of 1994, supplying an area of 460 square miles. Together they are building a dual-flow strategic link to carry water between Alderney and Christchurch to optimise joint resources and to enhance security of supply.

Wastewater treatment must not only be effective but safe. All 39 of Wessex Water's

Analysing samples of customers' tap water at Wessex Water's Saltford Laboratories.

OVERLEAF: Submerged aquatic plants such as water crowfoot and starwort thrive in the clear waters of Hampshire's River Itchen which, like the nearby River Test, attracts fly-fishermen.

**Filter gallery where water is chemically treated at Maundown Treatment Works in Somerset.**

**After passing through micro-strainers, water flows out over a contact tank before treatment.**

bathing waters complied with EC directive bacteriological standards in 1990, but they have set aside £180 million to eradicate as much as possible of the pollution elements of the Severn estuary which are not natural phenomena. Already cod, salmon and even seals are reappearing after many years' absence. Until the late 1960s Bristol's raw sewage was pumped twice a day into the River Avon which also runs into the Severn Estuary. The river was chlorinated to keep the smell down. Construction of new sewers and treatment plans has been continuous since the mid 1960s. A series of trunk sewers carries the waste away to a treatment works at Avonmouth. Wessex Water has committed around £22 million to completing a new wastewater system for the Bristol conurbation, with Phase One of this scheme finished in 1990 and Phase Two, which will make the whole system operational, finished towards the end of 1994. All the city's wastewater will then be properly treated.

At Avonmouth works, Wessex Water are building the world's largest version of Swiss Combi's advanced automated drum drying plant to convert wet sludge into dry pellets for sale as a soil conditioner, fertiliser or as fuel. It is more environmentally sound than any alternative process. Wessex Water are investing a lot of money in wastewater treatment which it conducts as a separate activity to water supply. 'But,' says Nicholas Hood, the company's chairman, 'we shall continue to care as much for the amount of our customers' charges as for the quality of our customers' environment – there is a link between what our customers wish to pay and what our customers should pay for environmental improvements.'

Walkers in Wessex Water's Tucking Mill site can spy dark green fritillaries, and at Winsley reservoir take snaps of green-leafed orchids; admire untouched Mockbeggar Lake, the 10,000 trees the company have planted round Blashford Lake, the sand embankment at Upton Heath built for lizards to lay their eggs in, the rare pearl-bordered

fritillaries and the common twayblade orchid on Bridport Main, and the 18th-century ornamental lakes at Otterhead on the Blackdown Hills. Wessex Water is funding a study of kingfishers and dragonflies and the breeding habits of captured flamingoes. Bristol Water's Chew Valley Lake is the third most important reservoir in Britain for wintering wildfowl with as many as 250 species in and around it. From July to February it hosts 4,000 duck and by mid-winter it is home for around 40,000. There too is one of the largest colonies of the rare green-winged orchid. At the Herriotts nature reserve nesting islands have been created and reed beds managed so that bearded tit, ruddy duck and

**Rainbow trout reared in a series of fish ponds beneath Clatworthy reservoir are used to stock several reservoirs as part of the amenity facilities provided by Wessex Water.**

**Fishing at Bristol Water's Blagdon Lake. In 1904 it became the first reservoir in the country to be opened for public fishing.**

garganey have nested in recent years. Blagdon Lake, another haven for wildfowl, has fringing flower-rich meadows which include five orchid species, supports 18 species of dragonfly including the Ruddy Darter, and eight species of bat feed there in summer. All meadows, marsh vegetation and forestry – some 130,000 trees have been planted around Chew Lake since it opened – are managed for conservation.

### Renewing Sewerage Network in South West Region

Wherever people live, in crowded London or the rural West Country, they still use 25 gallons of water every time they use their washing machine and slightly more if they have a bath. So South West Water has to find 110 million gallons every day for its customers in Devon and Cornwall and part of Dorset – about 30 gallons a head. The 1½ million population it has to serve is 15 per cent higher than in 1971. With its large number of beaches and holiday sites, tourism is a major industry in the region and it has to plan for an influx of 2¼ million visitors every year. To keep abreast of demand, South West Water quadrupled water storage since 1974 to 156,000 million gallons, and have a £475 million water supply improvement programme scheduled for 1990–2000. It spent

OPPOSITE: **Building the control towers and dam for South West Water's mighty Roadford Lake near the Devon and Cornwall border, designed to hold 8,000 million gallons and opened in 1990.**

£120 million on more than 300 improvement schemes in 1990/1, more than double the investment of the previous two years. It has now increased its rate of investment by a further 75 per cent to more than £4 million a week. Recent projects include building three reservoirs at Wimbleball on Exmoor with Wessex Water, at Colliford on Bodmin Moor and (in 1990) at Roadford, a vital link in its water resource strategy. With the completion of the South Devon Spine main between Plymouth and Totnes it will reach South Hams and Torbay. In 1990/1 the company spent £6.5 million on cleaning and relining 130 miles of water mains at 18 locations.

South West Water is also busy relining old sewers by 'moiling' – by polyethylene slip-lining and ferro-cement lining. In 1990/1 it spent £15 million on replacement, renewal and extension of the sewerage network. Farmers are pleased to have treated sludge as manure, but South West Water also dispose of sludge to landfill with the remaining 20 per cent discharged from Exeter and Plymouth to deep sea disposal sites under licences granted by the Ministry of Agriculture and Fisheries. Sludge disposal at sea will end by 1998 so alternatives are being tested and developed. All sludge disposal operations are fully monitored and marine investigations are very carefully managed through the oceanographers and environmental scientists at the Marine Centre at Plympton.

With the highest ratio of coastline to land area of all the water and sewerage companies in England and Wales, South West Water has 132 'bathing waters' which have to be maintained to EC standards of cleanliness. It is investing £435 million on an investment programme called The Clean Sweep, a coastal wastewater treatment improvement programme involving 33 schemes which will benefit 81 bathing waters. Largest in the programme is the Penzance and St Ives Scheme. Of this Bill Fraser, the company's managing director, says:

> Forty-seven short sewage outfalls discharging raw sewage into the sea just a matter of yards from beautiful local beaches is a legacy of a century of neglect and under-investment. Now, as a privatised water company, we have the finance and we have been able to use it to achieve a comprehensive engineering and scientific solution to the problem. The massive improvement scheme ... will replace the dilapidated Victorian infrastructure that we conceived when hackney carriages, gas lamps and night soil carts were thought to be fashionable.

Located just south of the famous Jamaica Inn, South West Water's Colliford Lake is a tranquil setting for birdwatchers and walkers. Fans must obtain a birdwatching permit to enter the 338-acre Loveny nature reserve. At Burrator walkers can see one of the largest concentrations of hut circles on Dartmoor.

## Welsh Water Supplies Wales

Dŵr Cymru, Welsh Water's region, is a large one because it serves the whole of Wales except for that part of the River Severn catchment which lies within the Principality, but the region involves large parts of the River Dee and River Wye catchments which are in England. In the north-east corner of the region, water supply is handled by the Wrexham & East Denbighshire Water Company and by the Chester Waterworks Company which takes its water from the River Dee. They are heirs to the operation started by John Tyrer in 1600, taken over by John Hopkins and John Hadley in 1692 and then by the City of Chester.

Welsh Water's first sources were the catchment areas of the Rivers Taff and Usk, but

OPPOSITE: The operation being mounted by South West Water at Bude in north Cornwall for their sewerage and sewage treatment scheme – building the long sea outfall as part of the company's huge 'Clean Sweep' programme.

by the early 1970s they were becoming inadequate. Demand was rising and by the year 2001 it is expected to reach about 165 million gallons a day, whereas existing resources can only provide 125 million gallons a day. To bring the required water to the one-and-a-quarter million people who live in South East Wales, Welsh Water built a £28 million system of pumps, pipelines, treatment plants and storage facilities right across the County of Gwent from the River Wye, the largest river in Welsh Water's area which, as well as feeding the Wye Transfer Scheme, provides water to large areas of Herefordshire and Gloucestershire and to parts of Powys and Gwent. In addition, from the three early Elan Valley dams, plus the fourth at Claerwen added in 1952, 66 million gallons of water flow to the Midlands each day and on the way serve areas such as Llandrindod Wells. The nerve centre of the Transfer Scheme is the Court Farm Treatment Works, built in 1961 to take water from the Usk. Through it Wye water can now serve Llanwern steel works and supply drinking water to Newport, so freeing Usk water for use further west. It is what the company's chairman John Elfed Jones calls 'a Welsh Water cocktail to quench a giant thirst':

> The Wye Transfer, and limited expansion of some Brecon Beacons reservoirs, will ensure supplies for South East Wales for the foreseeable future, but water is too vital a service to leave to chance. Just as the first thoughts of the Wye Transfer came close on the heels of the Llandegfedd water scheme 20 years ago, so today Welsh Water is monitoring trends in water use and keeping contingency plans up to date for possible future sources.

**Welsh Water's programme for improving bathing waters includes Aberystwyth.**

To realise its vision of what Wales needs by way of water supply, Welsh Water is leaving as little as possible to chance by investing some £845 million over ten years.

There is fishing on many of Welsh Water's reservoirs – Alaw, Cefni, Brenig, Celyn. The fly fishing at Llyn Cefni has been leased to the local angling association (with access to the public by day ticket), but anyone can obtain a permit and licence from a coin-operated dispenser at Llyn Alaw for fly fishing, spinning or worming. At Llwyn-on reservoir there is a popular managed fishery. Every year Welsh Water welcomes hundreds of people who come to fish the Elan Valley and Claerwen reservoirs and nearby streams and natural lakes. In 1991 the World and Commonwealth Fly Fishing Championships and Home Fly Fishing International were held at Llyn Brenig.

Welsh Water's reservoirs provide every kind of opportunity for bird watchers. At Llyn Alaw visitors can see wintering wildfowl and passage waders from the bank, and there is a bird hide, as there is at Llyn Cefni. Holidaymakers can walk or pony-trek on Llyn Brenig in the wild Denbigh moors with, as the company say, 'a freedom unusual in this day and age'. They can see all kinds of birds of prey on the Elan Valley Estate including the red kite and buzzard. They can admire too the masonry dams built at the beginning of the century and the old stone cottages and school of Elan Village created for the families of those who built the famous reservoir and aqueduct. At the peaceful Llyn Brianne reservoir in the hill country of mid-Wales the whole area is rich in birdlife and surrounded by the most beautiful countryside. Herons and kingfishers abound in the equally tranquil Lliedi reservoirs, the so-called Swiss Valley, in Dyfed. At the Herefordshire Waterworks Museum at Broomy Hill in Hereford are some of the finest pumping engines in the country.

**Llyn Brianne reservoir, part of Welsh Water's Tawe Transfer Scheme, is the major supplier of water to a large part of South West Wales including Swansea.**

OVERLEAF: **An industrial rubbish dump, one cause of contamination that the water companies have to contend with.**

# CHAPTER EIGHT

# Friends of the water environment

NORTHERN IRELAND'S SILENT VALLEY · NORTH WEST REGION · PLENTY OF RAIN IN
SCOTLAND · NORTHUMBRIAN REGION · YORKSHIRE REGION · SEVERN TRENT SERVES THE
HEART OF ENGLAND · HELP FOR DISABLED PEOPLE

**Drought in the not-so-Emerald Isle. Seedlings have appeared in the polygonal cracks formed as the mud dries out at the side of Coole Lake in Northern Ireland.**

The Emerald Isle is so called because of its verdure, the bright green colour of the landscape caused by so much rain. Between 34 and 37 inches of rain fall on Belfast every year and up to 60 inches in many of the catchment areas. Between Christmas and Easter 1992 it rained somewhere in Northern Ireland every day. There is no need usually to interfere with the use of hosepipes or sprinklers but the region still has to contend with all the other problems associated with water supply in other parts of the United Kingdom – particularly how to forecast rising demand and how to meet it.

The people of Northern Ireland were restricted in their use of water in 1976 but not to the same extreme extent as on the UK mainland. An intensive leak reduction programme in Belfast helped to keep consumption down, and from 1979 to 1981 demand dropped owing to the economic recession, exaggerated by the fact that many of the major industries were fibre manufacturers and tyre manufacturers who are particularly heavy water users. After 1981 water consumption, excluding leakage, began to grow again at a rate of about 3 per cent a year.

Use of general sources by interconnection reduced the operating cost of pumped sources. It allowed sources in surplus to augment those close to their limit. The large gravity source of the Silent Valley which required minimal treatment was by far the cheapest. The large Lough Neagh pumped sources at Dunore Point and Caster Bay were slightly cheaper than the medium-sized gravity sources of Lough Fea, Bally-sallagh and Lough Macrory. Care was taken not to abandon small sources purely on the basis of size, since occasionally a very small source of high quality raw water, needing little or no attention, could be economical.

In the eastern part of the province the development of larger sources feeding towards Belfast built the core of a conjunctive use system. Over the years it was extended until the whole of the Water Service's Eastern Division, and part of the Northern and Southern Divisions, could be considered a single large integrated system. The major sources supplying Belfast are more than capable of meeting future demands en route.

In 1992, 97 per cent of Northern Ireland's population of one and a half million are connected to public water mains and sewers. On average about 150 million gallons of water are supplied daily to 470,000 homes and 70,000 businesses and farms – an average household taking some 90 gallons a day. For this the Water Service maintains 13,000 miles of water mains, 90 water treatment works and 470 reservoirs. Out of a budget of £144 million in 1992–3, they will spend £95 million on the treatment, supply and distribution of water and the treatment and disposal of sewage, and £49 million on their capital works programme. Development of the new water source for the eastern part of Northern Ireland was part of its ten-year capital investment programme with the general aim of maintaining water quality and improving sewage services and, along with other UK water suppliers, complying with EC directives. The Water Service's normal annual budget, excluding wages, amounts to about £30 million for capital works and £66 million for operation and maintenance. It is closely involved all the time with district councils in the consultation process, particularly in establishing the priority of schemes within a council's district. On all major policy issues, the Northern Ireland Water Council is the statutory body charged with advising the Water Service in the exercise of its functions under the Water and Sewerage Services (Northern Ireland) Order 1973. This helps the Water Service to achieve a balance between conflicting interests in water and sewage matters. Membership of the council represents agriculture, angling, industry and commerce, tourism, trade unions and local government.

In November 1990 the Secretary of State for Northern Ireland announced that he proposed to transfer the water and sewage services, currently carried out by the Department of the Environment's Water Service, to a government-owned company. The creation of the company will separate the department's regulatory functions from the delivery of water and sewage services. The target date for the transfer is summer 1993.

'Before-and-after' views of Hog Park Point on the shores of Lough Neagh in Northern Ireland, the largest freshwater lake in the British Isles – currently being considered as a major new water source to supply the Greater Belfast area in the next century.

## Conjunctive System in North West Region

Across the Irish Sea to the only slightly less verdant acres of Lancashire and Cumbria, North West Water is also confident that it has enough water from its boreholes, rivers and lakes to meet demand until well into the next century. It had no need for hosepipe bans or drought orders in 1991, in spite of the long hot summers of 1989 and 1990. In the Lake District, where it obtains up to 30 per cent of its piped supply, the annual average rainfall is 93 inches. There the Thirlmere reservoir, built in 1894 and now enlarged, supplies 45 million gallons a day to Manchester and parts of Lancashire. Behind its 56 foot high dam it can hold 9,000 million gallons of water, which is then conveyed to Dunmail Raise treatment works and thence by gravity along its 96-mile aqueduct to storage reservoirs at Manchester. The other Lake District supplies come from Haweswater, Ullswater and Lake Windermere, England's largest lake. Water from Windermere and Haweswater is transferred to Watchgate treatment works near Kendal and delivered some 90 miles to Manchester with connections along the route to other centres in South Cumbria and Lancashire.

North West Water is engaged in replacing and refurbishing old pipes, bridges and the structure of the great aqueduct which will be 100 years old in 1994. It will take years to finish and when the work is done it will have cost around £8 million, all part of the £4.3 billion ten-year investment programme. Apart from the Lake District aqueducts, North West Water has to maintain 23,000 miles of water mains. As in Northern Ireland, it has a 'conjunctive' system by which it can tap in to the large aqueducts so that, when smaller local reservoirs are hard put to meet demand, supplies from these sources can come to their rescue. It raises more than half its water from the Lake District, the Pennines and the Peak District. Of the remainder about a quarter comes from rivers, mainly the Dee, with boreholes and a few streams providing the rest.

North West Water has replaced the 26 outfalls which once discharged untreated wastewater into the Mersey estuary with the first wastewater treatment works (at the abandoned Sandon Dock) to service the Liverpool and Bootle areas and their total population equivalent of a million including industry. A 16-mile interceptor sewer is being built to Crosby in the north and Speke in the south, costing more than £150 million. At Sandon Dock it will treat flows up to five times the normal dry weather flow. North West are midway into a 1989–94 scheme to improve over 40 wastewater treatment works on the Mersey basin or divert their load to more modern works. By the year 2000 it will have spent more than £2 billion on improvements to sewerage and to treatment works in the North West region as a whole. It has launched Europe's largest sewer study in Greater Manchester involving the inspection of some 2,200 miles of pipes.

The North West region includes more designated land than that of any of the other privatised water companies: 16,200 'environmentally sensitive' acres, 36,000 acres of sites of specific scientific interest, 27,000 acres of outstanding natural beauty, and three National Parks covering 62,000 acres. They cover the catchment areas of Haweswater, Bowland, Longdendale, Thirlmere, Rivington, Goyt Valley and the South West Pennines. To help with the work of conservation, North West Water enlist members of the British Trust for Conservation Volunteers who put in around 6,000 work days every year, making and repairing footpaths, hedge laying, trimming ponds and clearing small woodland. North West Water's reserve, known as Swallows Wood, at Hollingworth Reservoir near Glossop is a varied wetland and woodland habitat which was created on a drained reservoir.

OPPOSITE: **Inside North West Water's 15-mile interceptor sewer at Liverpool which runs between Crosby and Speke.**

The 'Keep Out' notices have been removed from all but operationally sensitive areas, and the public are encouraged to enter and enjoy the landscape which the water companies are at pains to make attractive for them. Most people come for the most leisurely activity, walking.

OVERLEAF: **Strong winter winds whipping up surface water on Wastwater in the Lake District.**

## Plenty of Rain in Scotland

Further north the three groups who organise Scotland's water supply, the nine Regional Councils, the three Islands Councils and the Central Scotland Development Board, likewise have none of the worries of their Southern England counterparts about shortage of the raw material. There is always plenty of rain in Scotland. If there should by chance be a severe drought, the Central Scotland Water Development Board, as an independent bulk supply authority, has a large strategic reserve capacity for users in its area who constitute about 80 per cent of Scotland's whole population. To be on the safe side and leave nothing to chance, it has commissioned a survey to identify demands and alternative ways of meeting them well into the next century.

Customers served by the water undertakings of the Regional Councils vary from 2½ million in Strathclyde to 90,000 in the Borders Region. The areas of supply in Scotland also vary immensely; they range from Fife's modest 600 square miles to Highland's vast extent of 9,800 square miles. Strathclyde supplies 240 million gallons of water a day; Borders 8 million.

In 1990, Strathclyde embarked on a programme of remedial action to improve most supplies to meet the required standards. Modernisation or replacement of water treatment facilities throughout the region was to be undertaken in a programme of 145 projects costing more than £265 million. Some 5,000 miles of existing main known to be in unsatisfactory condition were to be renovated or replaced at a further estimated cost of £350 million.

Out of a population of just over 500,000, some 460,000 of the people in Grampian Region receive a public water supply from sources such as impounding reservoirs, rivers, springs, wells and boreholes. Of these, river abstraction makes up about three-quarters of the 36 million gallons which the authority supplies on average every day. It uses more than 100 sources, of which 11, including a bulk supply from Loch Lee in Tayside Region, contribute about 85 per cent of current average output. The most important source is the River Dee from which Aberdeen has been getting its water since 1830. They also draw it from the River Deveron at Turriff, from where water is supplied to much of the region from Aberdeen northwards. The River Spey abstraction scheme, which will supply water to most of the northern coastal areas, should be operational by 1994.

The Grampian Regional Council accepted in 1975 the recommendations of a commissioned water resources study for the development of water supplies in the north east. These suggest an additional abstraction scheme from the River Dee in the Cults Area, with river regulation provided by an impounding reservoir on the Water of Dye, and direct abstraction from the River Spey near Fochabers. The consulting engineers' New River Dee Abstraction Scheme involved building a reservoir on the Water of Dye at Tillyfumerie, but after discussions with fishery interests this was considered undesirable. The 1980 Water Order allowed for a total abstraction of 16 million gallons a day from the Dee half a mile downstream from Morrison's Bridge – 'the Shakin' Briggie'. To allow fish to run in low flows, abstraction had to stop for six hours a day when the flow at Park near Drumoak was shown to be less than 140 million gallons. In the event, the scheme took the form of an intake below the bed of the river – six adjacent concrete boxes with stainless steel distributor plates supporting layers of washed river gravel and crushed granite. It was not intended to serve as a filter, but rather to reduce the velocity of the flow of water so that it presented no problem to returning salmon.

**Haggloader at work at the face of the tunnel being built for Grampian Regional Council's Aberdeen Long Sea Outfall.**

OPPOSITE: **Grampian Regional Council took special measures not to disturb the salmon in the River Dee, from which Aberdeen receives most of its water.**

## Northumbrian Region Had First Water Grid

Abstraction from the River Wear and the River Tyne is to a large extent affected by Northumbrian Water's Kielder Water reservoir. This was built because of the uneven distribution of rainfall in the region. The first idea was to exploit the higher rainfall in the west, but a north–south strategy was selected when it was shown that the first plan would involve the construction of six reservoirs. Opened by HM The Queen in May 1982, Kielder was the first example of a regional water grid system in the UK. It involved a large regulating reservoir at Kielder in the valley of the North Tyne River, and the piping of the water south from the Tyne to the Wear and Tees. Kielder reservoir boosted the potential of the Tyne, Wear and Tees and ensured adequate wholesome water to domestic users, and 'fit to use' water to industrial customers, for many years to come. It is three-quarters of a mile long and its dam is 167 feet high. It holds 44,000 million gallons of water and took four and a half years to build. Flooding started in the winter of 1980 and it took two winters to fill. It is one of the largest man-made lakes in Northern Europe. With a surface area of 2,680 acres, it is larger than Ullswater and three-quarters the size of Lake Windermere. The whole Kielder project cost £167 million, some of which was borne by grants from the European Community's Regional Development Fund and loans from the European Investment Bank. The water made available through the project is not just for consumers in the immediate area but throughout the north east. The reservoir is linked to existing water supplies by a sophisticated telemetry system.

Water released from Kielder Water flows down the Rivers North Tyne, Wear and Tees. At Riding Mill it is abstracted at Britain's largest pumping station. Further down the Tyne at Ovingham, the Newcastle & Gateshead Water Company have an abstraction point to supply the Tyneside area. From Riding Mill the water travels in a buried pipeline to the highest point of the aqueduct at Letch House four miles away, and then through a three-mile tunnel to the 44 million gallon header tank for the system, Airy Holm reservoir. For the next 20 miles the water goes along a concrete-lined tunnel under the Durham fells. At Frosterley the water can be released into the River Wear and at Eggleston into the River Tees. This transfer system brings water from Kielder to 85 per cent of the North East region and its densely populated area. Northumbrian Water provides water to about 40 per cent of the people living in its region and wastewater services to nearly everyone in the region.

Water for over 60 per cent of the people living in the Northumbrian region, which covers 3,600 square miles south of the Scottish border down to North Yorkshire east of the Pennines, is supplied by the Newcastle & Gateshead and Sunderland & South Shields Water Companies which, in March 1992, merged as 'North East Water Plc'.

Water has been raised from the River Tyne and piped to Tyneside since that wheel driven pump was put to work on the river bank in 1680. Three hundred years later, North East Water supplies a vast area. The Tyne Abstraction Scheme of 1976 gave its submersible pumps the capacity to draw up to 100 million gallons a day. It brings water to the people of remote Lindisfarne Island off the North Northumberland coast from a borehole and iron removal plant.

By 1902 the Sunderland & South Shields Water Company (founded 1852) was already operating nine groundwater sources – magnesian limestone aquifers. Together with Durham County Water Board the company built Burnhope reservoir to the head of Weardale (now owned by Northumbrian Water Group Plc as the successor of the Durham Water Board). To meet the rising demand the Derwent reservoir was built at Consett, County Durham, and opened in 1966. These two old-established

suppliers, merged as North East Water Plc, now serve 1.3 million customers. The people of Hartlepool are supplied by the region's third water supply company, Hartlepools Water Company.

In 1958 the Tyneside local authorities decided that the community could no longer be expected to tolerate the filth and smell suffered by those living and working alongside the River Tyne and the adjoining beaches. So in 1966 they set up the Tyneside Joint Sewerage Board to promote the construction of a sewage collection and disposal scheme. They prepared what at the time was the largest single clean-up scheme of its kind ever undertaken in Britain. The Northumbrian Water Authority (Northumbrian Water Group Plc since 1989) inherited this Tyneside Sewage Treatment Scheme in 1974. It has interceptor sewers running parallel with each bank of the Tyne and with the coast on the north and south sides of the river. These divert most of the wastewater from the old outfalls and carry it to the major treatment works at Howdon. Like many other parts of Britain, Tyneside has a combined sewer system, which means that rainfall and domestic and industrial sewage find their way into the same pipe. The old outfall sewers discharged both storm water and the domestic and

**Northumbrian Water's Kielder Water, one of the largest constructed lakes in Northern Europe, covering 2,700 acres, was opened by HM The Queen in 1982, the first regional water grid system in the UK.**

industrial sewage straight into the Tyne. In the new scheme storm overflows have been built where the old outfall sewers join the new interceptors.

Construction of the new system began in 1973. More than half the Tyneside Sewage Treatment Scheme was in service by the end of 1983 and the flow of raw sewage to the river was reduced by 60 per cent. By 1990 it had cleaned up 20 miles of the Tyne estuary and 8½ miles of beaches. Completion is expected in the next few years.

Northumbrian Water's clean-up at Seaton Carew has given archaeologists the opportunity to examine evidence of a Romano-British settlement and the remains of a 12th-century village – and has won a grant from the European Development Fund.

Trout fishing is offered on all its 13 main reservoirs under direct control. It has leased all but four to local angling clubs, though a limited number of non-members can fish there on a day ticket. It has no need to stock Selset and Balderhead with fish since they have long been the home of wild brown trout. Many spend a fishing holiday at Kielder Water, staying in one of the log cabins in Leaplish Waterside Park. The *Kielder Ferry* leaves the jetty at Tower Knowe visitor centre on regular trips round Kielder Lake and, if asked, the captain will put in at Leaplish where boats, canoes, wetsuits and sailboards are for hire and passengers can abandon ship for a sail, a windsurf or a swim. Kielder Water has staged not only water-ski and power boat championships but marathon swims.

Northumbrian Water has provided plenty of picnic places, barbecue areas and walks at Kielder and the Valley of the River Tyne – 'no crowds, no parking problems, good roads'. Inside Kielder Castle, an old hunting lodge, is an exhibition on the development of the surrounding forest. Cyclists can pedal a machine hired from Hawkehope car park round the cycle route, back-packers can take an orienteering course, children can go pony-trekking and mums and dads can munch sandwiches in the picnic area.

The modern architecture of Yorkshire Water's Harlow Hill water treatment works in Harrogate.

## Yorkshire Region's Water Transfer Scheme

South of the region, customers benefit from another water transfer scheme, the £200 million Yorkshire Grid which the regional supplier, Yorkshire Water, is augmenting by a long-term development of sources in the Vale of York. Most of the water in the region is collected in impounding reservoirs such as that at Thruscross in the hilly area to the west of the region, where there is high rainfall and a suitable catchment area, and the water can flow to the treatment works by gravity. In the east of the region, Yorkshire Water has sunk boreholes into the water table. In 1992 it invested £300 million in Yorkshire and plans to spend a similar sum every year until the end of the century – around £1 million every working day.

Yorkshire Water has pressed ahead with refurbishing its Ingbirchworth water treatment works and opened new water treatment plants at Fixby, Longwood, Kirkhamgate and Harlow Hill. It is applying its well-proven flotation technology at the £20 million project at Graincliffe; and using technology which enables it to treat both reservoir and river water at the treatment plant being built at Headingley to open in 1994. The major thrust of Yorkshire Water is directed towards the improvement of the aesthetic quality of its water.

Inside Yorkshire Water's region is an area of 131 square miles served by the region's only water supply company, The York Waterworks Plc, whose origins go back to 1677 when Henry Whistler obtained a 500-year lease from the City Council of Lendal Tower at a peppercorn rent which still has nearly 200 years to run. Now a protected ancient

Lendal Tower, which the
York Waterworks
Company adapted as
their board room in
1932. Henry Whistler
obtained a lease of the
tower for the company
from York City Council
in 1677.

monument, the company adapted the tower in 1932 as its board room. In an eight-year modernisation programme after World War Two, the company created additional water storage capacity at Acomb Landing, having earlier constructed Siwards How Water Tower which, with a capacity of 100 million gallons, was the largest water tower in Great Britain.

The River Aire running through the Yorkshire Dales to the Humber Estuary in Yorkshire Water's region carried water-borne waste from almost two million people and, below the point where it meets the River Calder, from almost 80 per cent of the region's industries. To make the Aire capable of sustaining fish life from its source at Malham to its confluence at Goole, Yorkshire Water have embarked on a £130 million programme to improve its wastewater treatment works, and to upgrade, rebuild and phase out obsolete works. It is now halfway through a decade of investment. It has already begun eight schemes and is spending £53 million on upgrading sewerage in

**The Don Valley
Interceptor Sewer
beneath Sheffield in
Yorkshire Water region.**

**Plastic bacteria bed
medium used by
Yorkshire Water in their
wastewater treatment
works.**

Bradford alone. Coarse fishing has already returned and herons have been sighted just upstream of Leeds below the discharge from the main Bradford wastewater works. It has just opened its rebuilt Blackburn Meadows wastewater treatment works ahead of schedule.

Almost all the water companies possess reservoirs, man-made and natural, to which they invite the public at large to come and fish for rainbow trout and brown trout, and mainly both, as well as a variety of the usual coarse fish. Yorkshire Water will lease a reservoir to a fishing club. In 1990 it stocked its Thornton Steward and Washburn Valley waters with rainbow trout every fortnight. At the end of the season it had dowsed the deep with 30 tons of them.

All the sailing on Yorkshire Water's reservoirs is club-based – 14 clubs, several with windsurfing sections. Demand for sailing in this part of Britain from Yorkshire Water is considerable since there is a lack of such inland water facilities within Yorkshire and Humberside. More than 100 boats take part in the Pennine Sailing Championships sponsored by Yorkshire Water on its Morehall reservoir. Rowing clubs are active on Damflask Reservoir near Sheffield, and schools and scout groups indulge in canoeing on Scout Dike and Scammonden reservoirs; in 1992 the company opened up Cod Beck Reservoir in the North York Moors National Park for canoeing.

In accordance with their 1989 Water Act duty, all the water companies take the greatest care not to destroy, and if possible preserve, any archaeological finds which come to light in the course of laying pipelines or building waterworks, and they display any of them which they think will interest visitors. Yorkshire Water knew of the Roman settlement which had occupied the site of the depot it was going to build at Catterick Bridge and asked archaeologists to record and advise on any items of interest it unearthed. They duly found two Roman skeletons which had lain buried for 1,700 years with several pieces of pottery. At the Springhead Museum less ancient relics are on display – 400-year-old wooden water pipes and a 40-ton Cornish beam engine.

## Severn Trent Serves the Heart of England

Below Yorkshire Water's region, the heart of England is served by Severn Trent Water. The latest piece in its complex water supply network, Carsington reservoir, was opened by HM The Queen in May 1992. Into this reservoir comes water which has been pumped out of the River Derwent six and a half miles away at Ambergate. When the river is low the compensation water is pumped back from Carsington into the Derwent. The project has cost £107 million, most of it going on the 4,000 foot-long dam and aqueduct. The drinking water supply of three million people in the East Midlands is now secured. They are only a part of Severn Trent's vast region, stretching from the Bristol Channel to the Humber and from mid-Wales to the East Midlands, consisting of 8,000 square miles taking in the basins of two of the country's greatest rivers: the Severn and the Trent. Sixty per cent of its water is for domestic use and 40 per cent for industry. In addition, industry itself takes three times this amount directly from rivers, returning the treated water after use. More than half Severn Trent's water comes from rivers and reservoirs and the remainder from underground. Its largest reservoir is at Lake Vyrnwy in the Welsh mountains holding 13,000 million gallons – enough to fill 702 million baths they say. It covers 1,120 acres.

Birmingham, England's second largest city in the centre of Severn Trent's region, has been supplied since the turn of the century with water from the Elan Valley reservoirs built by Birmingham Corporation. After the water industry reorganisation in 1973, ownership of the reservoirs and treatment works of the Elan Valley passed to Welsh Water, though the water still flowed to Birmingham along that 72-mile aqueduct which lies in the Welsh Water region. Some water from the Elan Valley also supplies people in the Welsh Water region, living in a few private houses and farms along the route of the aqueduct.

South Staffordshire Water Plc, established in 1853, is the largest of the water-only supply companies. It serves one and a quarter million people in an area of 580 square miles. Its supply area includes a great diversity of industrial customers – the historic engineering industries of the Black Country and vast electricity generating stations and breweries. It has recently negotiated a ten-year contract for the supply of water to the huge new Toyota motor car factory at Burnaston in Derbyshire – in the course of negotiations the company surprised and delighted its would-be customers by producing the draft contract in Japanese. Instead of laying new pipes it has pioneered the 'high tech-low dig' technology of scraping and relining them and was the first to use the 'airknife'.

The approach of the East Worcestershire Waterworks Company, the second water supply company in the Severn Trent region, to the problem of leakage control has been to create closed leakage zones of between 500 and 2,500 properties fed by a single zone meter. In September 1985 the company adopted a policy of metering all new supplies and charging developers the cost of meter installation. It was one of several taking part in the National Water Metering Trials, employing a high-tech metering system and a seasonal tariff which will identify and charge additionally for high demands over the summer months.

Formed in 1877, East Worcestershire, in which the Biwater Group has a controlling interest, set up a central control room at its Sugarbrook pumping station in the 1960s, and in 1982 turned this into an eight-channel microwave radio station to pick up the spine points within its area and the main ultra-high frequency scanning stations – high technology stuff.

Severn Trent Water's large investment programme to keep its wastewater treatment

**A steel water main pipe being lowered onto the bed of the River Dove, as part of the work undertaken by the South Staffordshire Water Company to supply water to the Toyota site at Burnaston in Derbyshire.**

plants up to date, so it continues to meet National Rivers Authority standards, include major schemes at Minworth and Coleshill works where it is spending £65 million to increase and improve capacity and to provide a new sludge incineration and disposal plant.

In March 1990 the Secretary of State for the Environment announced the Government's decision that from 1998 they would not permit any treated sludge to be dumped at sea. As a consequence all regional water supply and sewage companies are taking more interest in methods of disposing of sludge by incineration or dewatering. Several of them are making such developments a fundamental part of their sludge utilisation strategies. HM Inspectorate of Pollution have set standards for the process as 'Best Available Technology', and for any discharges to air, water and land. During the 1987–8 session of Parliament the Environment Committee noted:

> With constraints on traditional disposal routes to sea and land, we consider that incineration of sewage sludge may increasingly become the preferred option. For the future, other disposal routes which convert sludge into useful products will seem more desirable, and their viability should be researched and reviewed thoroughly.

There are other options, however – more recycling to farmers as a soil nutrient; as landfill with other waste materials which together might generate methane gas; composting to produce alternatives to peat; or pasteurising and drying to give soil conditioner that can be bagged for sale even in supermarkets. Each company will have to decide the alternative method of sludge disposal most suited to its circumstances before the sea ban comes into operation in 1998.

Providers of sewage treatment services are committed to meet four main requirements: to remove risks to public health by preventing the spread of disease; to avoid unpleasant and offensive sights and smells on and off the treatment works; to enable the watercourse into which the treated wastewater is discharged to meet its varying uses; and, of course, to serve legal conditions of discharge.

Since, unlike most major UK water and sewage companies, Severn Trent Water has no coastline, it has never disposed of sludge into the sea. Where, as at Coleshill, it does not incinerate, it arranges for the sludge from rural wastewater works to be applied to farmland as fertiliser. It has 1,063 wastewater works, including one of the largest in the UK, and 2,251 pumping stations. The £2.2 million wastewater scheme in Leamington Spa will go a long way to further improve the water quality of the river. There are plans for a £6 million improvement programme at Mansfield wastewater treatment works. And Severn Trent is halfway through a planned ten-year programme to survey all strategic sewers by closed circuit television.

The investment in better sewage treatment improves the quality of rivers and increases fish and other water life. Severn Trent also takes direct action to improve fishing. Severn Trent Water incorporated new fishing platforms into the design of the dam it reinstated at Holmer Lake near Telford and, while the work was going on, with the help of the Telford Anglers Association it safely removed the fish stocks for replacement when coarse fishing resumed. Severn Trent Water has three directly managed fisheries, Ladybower, Foremark and Draycote.

Ramblers as well as fishermen benefit from the concern for the environment. Severn Trent Water recommends stout footwear for the 2½-mile Llyn Clywedog Scenic Trail in Wales with 14 stops on the way at a dingle (hill), to see a redpoll (finch), to watch the sailing, sheep grazing, a fox warming itself on the hillside, voles and polecats, the yellow

Hatchery-reared trout alevins, shortly after hatching, with the enlarged yolk sacs which sustain the fish for the first few weeks of life before they begin feeding.

OPPOSITE: Severn Trent's Carsington reservoir opened by Her Majesty The Queen in 1992.

tormentil among the grass and the small copper butterflies that flutter overhead. The company has built railed steps to help the elderly up the Clywedog Gorge Trail to see the old Bryn y Tail lead mine which closed in 1884.

## Help for Disabled People

The 23 water companies in England and Wales make equal efforts to provide recreational facilities like fishing on their reservoirs. Bristol Water's amenities have already been described. South Staffordshire Water Plc offers some of the finest fishing in the country at Blithfield Reservoir near Abbots Bromley. Altogether some 30,000 trout from its own fish farm go into Blithfield every year. Further south, West Hampshire Water Company has been managing the Royalty Fishery on the River Avon, the River Stour and in Christchurch Harbour for 60 years. In Northern Ireland fishing is permitted at a number of reservoirs where the fishing rights have been leased either to the Department of Agriculture for Northern Ireland or to individual angling clubs. It is a long list.

For the fit and healthy, casting a line from the bank means standing up but all the water companies with fishing facilities make the sport available to disabled people, in the same way that they make it easier for them to walk their trails and admire their scenery. And not only for fishing from the bank: at Welsh Water's Llyn Brenig reservoir for instance, as at many throughout Britain, the fishing boats can take a wheelchair safely by carefully rebuilding the boat. Disabled visitors wear a life jacket which is lent to them for the day and there must be at least two or three people in each boat. The company's rangers will help clamp any special seat brought by the disabled owner to

This sensory garden with moving water, textured surfaces and aromatic plants, created for pupils at the Royal School for the Blind in Liverpool, was financed by North West Water.

the ordinary boat seat. Welsh Water has built two fishing platforms giving improved casting height and reach for wheelchair fishers and the path to the platform can be negotiated by a self-propelled chair. Wessex Water has adapted Tucking Mill for wheelchair bound disabled fishers. South West Water has specially developed 'Wheely boats' at Wimbleball Lake, Kenrick and Farnworthy Reservoirs and at Argal near Falmouth. The companies also make it easier for disabled people not just to watch but take part in more strenuous sporting action than fishing, by helping participation in the faster-moving watersports on and under the water. North West Water has converted a disused keeper's house at their Cowm Reservoir near Rochdale, which had been empty for a decade, into a clubhouse for the British Disabled Water-Ski Association; and water-skiers use the reservoir every day.

**Wessex Water's Tucking Mill near Bath has been adapted for wheelchair-bound anglers, who have exclusive use of the reservoir.**

OVERLEAF: **Icicles beneath Culham Bridge, beside the River Thames.**

# CHAPTER NINE

# The future – bright and clean

In the last decade of the 20th century there is nothing hit-or-miss about the way water comes through the nation's taps. It is a highly sophisticated, high-tech operation devoted not, like a manufacturing process, to converting a mix of raw materials into something else, but where a single raw material is also the end product, and the process, apart from organising how it comes to the tap, is devoted to making sure it comes clean.

There will be no stopping the momentum of improvement, the change for good – rather, it will continue to accelerate. Future generations will look to the 1980s as the enlightened era in which three forces combined to produce almost revolutionary change within the water services of the United Kingdom.

## Forces for Change

Since 1945 British people, like most people world-wide, began to expect and demand a better quality of life. In the case of water this was reflected in dissatisfaction with the quality of drinking water and growing concern about its safety, as well as its taste, colour and smell.

The environmental movement, which for many years had been the concern only of a small group of zealots, took advantage of these rising expectations and began to gain popular support, especially among young people. The state of Britain's rivers and bathing waters became a focus of attention, and traditional practices such as disposal of raw sewage to sea became unacceptable.

At the same time the European movement and interference was growing apace, and the European Commission began to oblige national governments to reassess their priorities and to review their own standards in the light of the best achieved elsewhere in Europe. While water standards in the UK were still among the best in Europe, the country's position had been slipping as countries like Germany, the Netherlands and Denmark invested substantially to improve their water systems. Even the quality of the water in France could no longer be treated as a music-hall joke. Indeed, French water companies with high professional standards have been taking over some of the smaller water-only companies in England.

The privatisation of water authorities in England and Wales was to some extent a response to these changes, and itself contributed to increasing the pace of change.

A major challenge for Britain's fresh water suppliers in the coming years will be to ensure adequate water supplies without damaging the environment. The proportion of UK rainfall used for public water supply is low – only about 8 per cent. Even so, developing new resources to meet growing demand will become more and more difficult. Increasingly water will have to be abstracted from the lower reaches of rivers to minimise the abstraction impact on river flows. So the water in the rivers has to be of

OPPOSITE: **Water is vital to life on earth. Natural water can provide a magical element to a landscape. Here it plunges down Pistyll Rhaeder, the highest waterfall in Wales.**

**Thames Water's Chinese-style pumping station on the Isle of Dogs – an award-winning design by John Outram.**

the highest quality, which means sewage treatment methods in their turn must be highly effective, since inland sewage treatment works all discharge into rivers.

It will be of the greatest importance that the suppliers make the fullest use of what resources are available. Up to 25 per cent of the water the suppliers put into the distribution system today is unaccounted for. Some of that is water used for firefighting and for flushing mains and about a third of the loss is from their customers' own pipes and plumbing. Locating and repairing leaking pipes is expensive. In the past, suppliers have always found it cheaper to develop new resources than to seek out and stop all but major leaks. But today their attitude is changing as the cost of supplying water increases, environmental concerns grow and new resources become increasingly expensive to develop. All the suppliers are putting greater effort than ever into leakage control, and have set themselves ambitious targets for reducing leakage levels over the coming years.

One way of reducing the amount of water wasted, which is likely to feature more prominently in the future, is metering. In May 1992 OFWAT told companies to extend the metering option. Trials have indicated that there is a reduction of about 10 per cent in water demand when meters are installed, and yet an opinion poll commissioned by OFWAT in 1992 showed that only four in ten customers were aware that they could opt for a meter.

At present most domestic customers pay charges based on the rateable value of their premises. The government has given the water industry until the year 2000 to introduce a new charging system not linked to rateable value. More widespread metering could reduce consumption; it would certainly make leak detection easier. But the cost on average of around £200 for supplying and fitting the meter has to be weighed against the likely benefits. In some areas, particularly where developing new resources would be very expensive, metering would be the answer; in other areas, probably not.

Whatever happens to methods of charging there is no doubt the technology employed in the water and wastewater industry will change at a faster pace. For many years there was little change in basic processes and systems. More recently the need to meet higher standards with increased reliability and greater efficiency has required new technology. All the companies are seeking ways to accelerate change to keep pace with and, if possible, anticipate new requirements. The introduction of chemical rather than civil engineering techniques, the use of standard designs and pre-fabrication, new materials, more sophisticated controls – all are playing a growing part in reducing capital costs and improving efficiency and consistency of operation. The moves towards absolute standards will require new techniques – for instance, physical methods of separation such as membrane systems may become necessary.

So old, inherited problems have been tackled and solved over many years with the greatest vigour and effect. The will, lacking for so long before, to free the public water supply from contamination by sewage is now established, and a wholly effective means of doing so has been invented and is being applied. The need for change was triggered by the first revolution of the mid-18th century, when people migrated from the well-watered countryside into the towns and proper disposal of sewage, which had been no problem in the fields and valleys, soon become impossible. It took many years to perfect a treatment that works, but in 1992 the basic problem of contamination by sewage and wastewater has been solved.

The focus of today and for tomorrow is on how to free fresh water from contamination by the waste products of high-tech contemporary manufacturing and mining processes, and of intensive agriculture. This is the second revolution, the consequences of which

ABOVE: **All Britain's water companies are making a drive to ensure that all the water they draw from their various sources reaches the customers' taps – and are accelerating efforts to stop leaks, as Wessex Water engineers are seen doing here.**

LEFT: **Southern Water's Leakage Patrol at work.**

OVERLEAF: **Drought dries up the water supply; sub-zero temperature freezes it solid – as at Nant Gwyllt reservoir in the Elan Valley.**

Engineers inspecting their water mains and sewers by closed-circuit television, which gives them (*below*) this view of the inside of a sewer.

are exercising the water industry and the environmental movement. The use of chemicals by industry, by people in their everyday home life, and by farmers using intensive methods to raise the yields of their crops, can contaminate drinking water just as severely as foul sewage, if not more so.

'Source protection zones', some covering tens of thousands of acres, are being drawn around boreholes and wells and springs in areas where pollution can seep through porous rock into drinking water supplies. Building new highways, railways, shafts and tunnels; mining operations, landfills, dumping of metal wastes, the use of pesticides and fertiliser sprays; the redevelopment of abandoned contaminated factory sites; use of septic tanks in sensitive rural landscapes – all are being restricted if there is risk of damage to water.

In 1989 the European Community began the process of prosecuting the British government in the European Court of Justice for the levels of nitrate in 28 supplies in East Anglia and Staffordshire, and for lead pollution of 17 supplies in Scotland. Chris Patten, the Environment Secretary of State, told Carlo Ripa di Meana, the EC Commissioner for the Environment, that the levels of nitrate at issue were close to the maximum levels permitted by the EC, and well within the level set by the World Health Organisation. The Commissioner thought Britain's six-year timetable for bringing about the desired improvement was too long, but took no further action. *All* the European Community requirements were incorporated into British law under the 1989 Water Act.

But is there an *absolute* standard? How safe is safe? The environmental pressure group Friends of the Earth maintain the public have 'a right' to fresh water which is always up to the legal standard.

'Wrong damn question,' say the Water Services Association. The question should be 'What are the priorities?' It would be outrageous, they say, to ask Britain's taxpayers to spend large amounts of money to reach absolute standards that are unnecessary. It is this point which Douglas Hurd, Secretary of State at the Foreign and Commonwealth Office, made in a letter in *The Economist* of 6 June 1992, in which he said that pressure groups had increased in power:

> They can certainly draw attention to an evil or to a gap in policy. But by definition they wear blinkers. Groups that never mention the cost to the consumer of environmental improvements are a topical case. They are not necessarily wrong, just single-minded. Members of Parliament have to weigh, balance and establish priorities.

The tropical elephant fish, *Gnathenemus petersi*, is used by Thames Water to monitor the quality of their river water intakes. This fish continually produces electric pulses at a rate of 300–500 per minute, which changes quite dramatically if chemical pollutants are present in the water. Electrodes in the tank constantly monitor the pulses and sound an alarm if there is a noticeable change.

And so do the monopoly providers of Britain's fresh water and sewage services. It is a difficult role, made more difficult by having to reach decisions no longer affected merely by public opinion in Britain.

The first to shake the Establishment out of its complacency were Edwin Chadwick, Charles Dickens, Michael Faraday and Charles Kingsley, who from London voiced the social impatience of the nation in an age of reform. But now attention must also be paid to what is being said in Brussels and to the views of the EC, now well supported, however, by Britain's Secretary of State for the Environment. There is no question of ignoring European attitudes, but the question is how much should customers be asked to pay to enable the suppliers to deliver water of higher and higher quality, *and* to achieve higher and higher environmental standards?

A glass of tap water anywhere in the UK and the discharge of treated wastewater into any of the country's rivers, are now far cleaner and 'safer' than even most people's parents enjoyed, let alone their Victorian ancestors.

At a time when it might seem that the matter was getting out of proportion, Jack Jeffery, chairman of North Surrey Water Company, gave a salutary corrective to an audience of doctors:

> I think we should also remember that the UK tap water is probably safer, by at least an order of magnitude, than anything else we ingest. We should do more to assess risk and the cost/benefit ratio to society; and bear in mind that some of our concerns about concentrations of parts per billion (remembering the resources required to remove these parts per billion) might just seem like self-indulgence to many in the Third World.

Which brings us back to WaterAid . . .

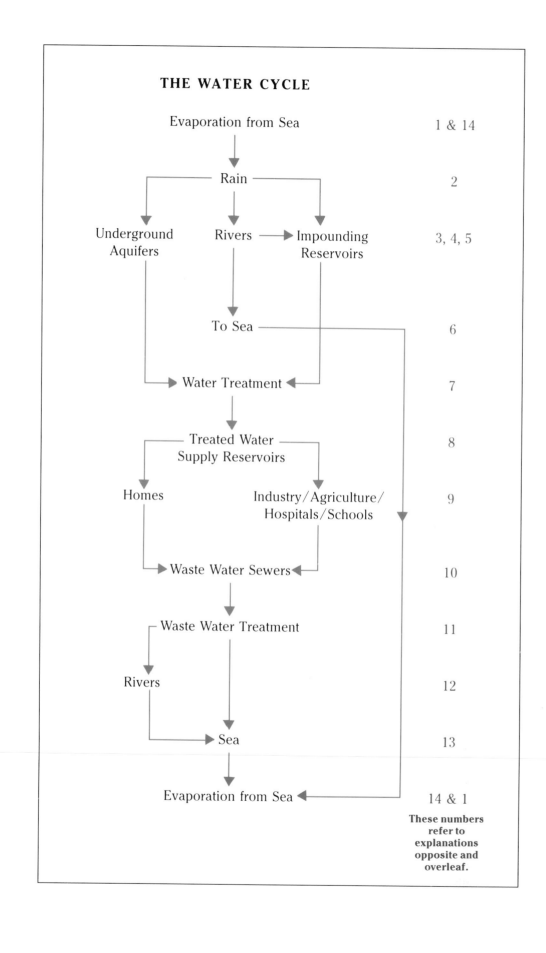

# THE WATER CYCLE

Evaporation from Sea      1 & 14

Rain      2

Underground Aquifers    Rivers    Impounding Reservoirs      3, 4, 5

To Sea      6

Water Treatment      7

Treated Water Supply Reservoirs      8

Homes    Industry/Agriculture/Hospitals/Schools      9

Waste Water Sewers      10

Waste Water Treatment      11

Rivers      12

Sea      13

Evaporation from Sea      14 & 1

**These numbers refer to explanations opposite and overleaf.**

# The Water Cycle

*'It is the continuous recycling of water which provides the earth with its constant fresh supplies.'*

(Paragraph numbers refer to the flow chart opposite.)

1. & 14. Moisture, most from the oceans and seas, is drawn up into the atmosphere by evaporation. As this water reaches the colder temperatures of the higher altitudes it condenses and forms clouds which are carried along by prevailing winds.

2. As the condensation increases, the weight of water can no longer be supported in the atmosphere and it returns in the form of rain.
   The west of the UK has a higher rainfall than the east because prevailing winds are generally from the west. As the moisture-laden clouds from the Atlantic cross the west coast and the land mass rises from sea level, so the air is forced upwards into higher altitudes where the colder temperatures start rainfall.

3. Rain which falls onto land where the underground rock is porous, usually chalk or limestone areas, soaks through the soil and is absorbed by the porous rock. These underground water-bearing rock stratas are called aquifers.

4. Rain which falls in areas where the rocks beneath the soil are non-porous, runs off into streams and rivers and back into the sea to begin the cycle over again.

5. A small proportion of this surface water is used by people. Either it is pumped from a river or surface run-off is retained by a dam to form an impounding reservoir.

6. As the river flows back into the sea so the cycle is repeated.

7. People and industry only use a small fraction of the water which falls as rain. The amount drawn from either underground aquifers or impounding reservoirs is strictly controlled by independent regulators. Licences, which limit the rate of abstraction, are granted for each source.
   Water from underground aquifers is obtained by sinking a borehole into the water-bearing rock. Water from these sources often contains dissolved minerals, principally carbonates of calcium and magnesium, which make it 'hard'.
   Water from impounding reservoirs is often softer because it has not come from underground so contains no dissolved minerals. People notice that soft water lathers easier than harder water.
   The level of treatment which drinking water requires, before it is introduced into the distribution system, depends on the source. Many borehole supplies only require disinfection. Surface water supplies from reservoirs normally require more complex treatment.
   Screening removes any larger debris and then microstrainers, very fine mesh rotating screens, remove algae and other small matter. Flocculating agents are

added which bind together any other impurities so the water can be further cleaned before passing through sand filters. Sometimes lime is added to neutralise any acidity in the water. All water is disinfected before it is put into the public supply system to kill any bacteria. Chlorine gas is the normal method but ozone is sometimes used. A residual chlorine level of no less than two parts per ten million is retained in the water to keep it germ-free right up to the customer's tap.

All public water supplies in the UK are closely monitored by the water suppliers. National regulatory bodies check that water suppliers are carrying out their obligation to meet the standards required by EC directives for the quality of drinking water.

8. After disinfection clean water is put into the trunk water mains distribution system, an interconnected network of underground pipes and treated water supply reservoirs. By using a trunk main network water can be moved around a region to put right any water shortages such as losses through any burst pipes. The clean water supply reservoirs act as a buffer to store and balance flows. Where needed, a disinfection 'top up' is carried out here to ensure the water supplied is completely safe.

9. From the treated water supply reservoirs the water is pumped or gravitates through water mains to the customers' premises. These may be private homes, hospitals and schools, industrial buildings or farms.

10. After use, wastewater must be treated to make it safe to be returned to the environment. Most is discharged into the sewerage system to be conveyed to a wastewater treatment plant. Unlike wastewater from our homes, wastewater from industry is monitored and controlled to ensure it does not contain any substances which can be harmful to the environment.

11. The level of treatment which the wastewater needs depends somewhat on the size of the receiving river and its use. The objective is to remove solids and soluble polluting matter which would deplete the river of oxygen so reducing oxygen necessary for wildlife, fish and plants.

    At the treatment plant the wastewater is first screened to remove solid material, like plastic and rags, before passing through a grit removal plant. The remaining decomposable solids are removed by passing the flow through settlement tanks where the solids sink to the bottom and form a sludge. This sludge is drawn off, treated and generally used on farmland in strictly controlled ways.

    The partially treated topwater, from the settlement tanks, then passes through a biological treatment stage. Bacteria, in the presence of oxygen, decompose the dissolved pollutants to reduce further the amount of oxygen the treated effluent might take from the river to make the river less healthy.

12. After passing through a final settlement stage the treated effluent is discharged into the river. Sometimes further 'polishing' or filtering of the treated effluent is required; this depends on the quality and size of the receiving river.

13. Where wastewater effluent discharges into the sea, it may be disinfected if the outfall pipe is anywhere near a bathing beach. All wastewater effluents must meet a quality standard set down in precise consents granted by national regulatory bodies.

14 & 1. As the river flows into the sea, the cycle continues.

# Conversion Table

Measurements in this book have been given in Imperial form through-out, with the exception of metric measurements in reported speech. Metric equivalents are given below:

| | | | | |
|---|---|---|---|---|
| 1 millimetre | = | 1000 micrometres | = | 0.0394 inch |
| 1 centimetre | = | 10 millimetres | = | 0.3937 inch |
| 1 metre | = | 100 centimetres | = | 1.0936 yards |
| 1 kilometre | = | 1000 metres | = | 0.6214 mile |
| 1 inch | | | = | 2.54 centimetres |
| 1 foot | = | 12 inches | = | 30.48 centimetres |
| 1 yard | = | 3 feet | = | 0.9144 metre |
| 1 mile | = | 1760 yards | = | 1.6093 kilometres |

| | | | | |
|---|---|---|---|---|
| 1 square metre | = | 10,000 sq centimetres | = | 1.196 sq yards |
| 1 hectare | = | 10,000 sq metres | = | 2.4711 acres |
| 1 sq kilometre | = | 100 hectares | = | 0.3861 sq mile |
| 1 sq foot | = | 144 sq inches | = | 0.0929 sq metre |
| 1 sq yard | = | 9 sq feet | = | 0.8361 sq metre |
| 1 acre | = | 4840 sq yards | = | 4046.9 sq metres |

| | | | | |
|---|---|---|---|---|
| 1 cu decimetre | = | 1000 cu centimetres | = | 0.0353 cu foot |
| 1 cu metre | = | 1000 cu decimetres | = | 1.3080 cu yards |
| 1 litre | = | 1 cu decimetre | = | 0.22 gallon |
| 1 megalitre | = | 1000 cu metres | = | 220,000 gallons |
| 1 cu yard | = | 27 cu feet | = | 0.7646 cu metre |
| 1 pint | = | 4 gills | = | 0.5683 litre |
| 1 gallon | = | 8 pints | = | 4.5461 litres |

# Bibliography

Anon, *Voyage Philosophique d'Angleterre*, 1786

Atkinson, D W and Cranwick, P D, *A Short History of the Water Supply to Kingston-on-Hull*, Yorkshire Water, 1974

Baker, M N, *The Quest for Pure Water*, New York, 1949

Bateman, John Frederic, *History and Description of the Manchester Waterworks*, 1884

Bedford, John, *London's Burning*, Abeldar-Schuman, 1966

Berry, G C, *Sir Hugh Myddelton and the New River*, Cymmrodorian Society, 1956

Binnie, G M, *Early Victorian Water Engineers*, 1981

Burnet, Gilbert, *History of His Own Time* (1703), Oxford University Press, 1823

Burnet, John, *History of the Water Supply to Glasgow*, 1869

Burton, W K, *The Water Supply of Towns*, 1894

Caroe, W Douglas, FSA MA, 'The Water Tower' [Canterbury], *Friends of Canterbury Cathedral Second Annual Report*, 1929

Central Advisory Water Committee, *Future Management of Water in England and Wales*, 1971

Cole, Catherine, 'Carfax Conduit', *Oxoniensia*, vols. xxix/xxx, pp. 142–66, 1964

Crawley, H, *History of Oxford's Water Supply*, 1615–1946 [MS Oxford Record Office]

D'Acres, R, *The Art of Water-drawing* (1659), Newcomen Society, 1930

de Rance, C E, *The Water Supply of England and Wales*, 1882

Defoe, Daniel, *A Tour Thro' The Whole Island of Great Britain*, 1724

Dickinson, H W, *Water Supply of Greater London*, 1954

Dracup, S B, 'Water Supply in Great Britain 1690–1950, A Brief History', *British Water Supply*, 1973

Fielding, F J (ed.), *The Speeches of Charles Dickens*, 1988

Fitzsimmons, M, Smith, J E and Stell, E, *A Brief History of the Water Supply of Chester*

Ford, Alfred Stanley, *Springs, Streams and Spas of London*, 1910

Gale, James, *Photographic Views of Loch Katrine*, Glasgow Corporation Waterworks, 1889

Gibb, Sir Alexander, *The Story of Telford*, 1935

Goubert, Jean-Pierre, *The Conquest of Water*, 1989

Hawkings, David J, *Water From the Moor*, An Illustrated History of the Plymouth, Stonehouse and Devonport Leats, South West Water/Devon Books, 1987

Hibbert, Christopher (ed.), *The Encyclopaedia of Oxford*, 1988

Hughes, Samuel, *A Treatise on Waterworks*, 1856

Jackson, Peter, *George Scharf's London*, John Murray, 1987

Jackson, Peter, *London Bridge*, Cassell, 1971

James, M R, (Introduction) 'The Canterbury Psalter', *The Western Manuscripts in the Library of Trinity College Cambridge*, vol. 2, Cambridge University Press, 1901

Jeffery, J, *Politics and Practice in the Supply of Water*, Medico-Legal Journal, 1991

Jenkins, Rhys, *The Collected Papers of Rhys Jenkins*, Newcomen Society, 1936

Jones, Philip E, 'Whittington's Longhouse', *London Topographical Record*, vol. xxiii, 1972

Keith, Alexander, *A Thousand Years of Aberdeen* [1972]

Latimer, John, *Annals of Bristol in the 19th Century*, 2pt., 1887, 1902

Leach, Joseph, *The Pipes, Pumps and Conduits of Bristol*, 1853

'London Water in Four Chapters', *All The Year Round*, Charles Dickens (ed.), 1861

Marwick, James D, *Glasgow: The Water Supply of the City*, 1901

McNicholas, J, *Looking Back*, Institution of Water Pollution Control, 1986

More, Thomas, *Utopia* (1516), J R Lumby (ed.), 1716

Muirhead, James Patrick, *The Life of James Watt*, John Murray, 1859

*The Notched Ingot: An Engineering Review and Miscellany*, 1959

Pumphrey, George H, *The Story of Liverpool's Public Services*, 1964

Rennison, R W, *Water To Tyneside*, A History of the Newcastle & Gateshead Water Company, 1979

Reyburn, Wallace, *Flushed With Pride*, *The Story of Thomas Crapper*, Macdonald 1969

Robins, F W, *The Story of Water Supply*, Oxford University Press, 1946

Rodwell, C Herbert, *Old London Bridge*, 1848

Serpell, C A, *The Institution of Water Engineers & Scientists' History, 1896–1987*

Shadwell, Arthur, *The London Water Supply*, 1899

Shepherd, C W, *A Thousand Years of London Bridge*, John Barker, 1971

Stanbridge, H H, *History of Sewage Treatment in Britain*, Institution of Water Pollution Control, Maidstone, 1976

Stone, John M, *Greenwich: Its Underground Passages, Caverns etc*, Greenwich & Lewisham Antiquarian Society, 1914

Taylor, J E, Jerrome, P A and Allnutt, A G, *Petworth Water Supply*, Sussex Industrial Archaeological Society, 1979

*Victoria County History of Gloucestershire*, vol. 14, Oxford University Press, 1988

Walker, David, *The Regional Water Authorities: Ten Years On*, Institution of Water Pollution Control, 1984

Walters, R C S, *The Nation's Water Supply*, Ivor Nicholson & Watson, 1936

*The Water Supply of London*, Metropolitan Water Board, 1961

Williamson, F, *George Sorocold of Derby, A Pioneer of Water Supply*, Derbyshire Archaeological & Natural History Society, 1936

Willis, Revd Robert, MA FRS, *The Architectural History of the Conventual Buildings of the Monastery of Christ Church in Canterbury*, 1869

Wilson, Charles A, *Aberdeen of Auld Lang Syne*, 1948

# Illustrations

The Publishers and the Water Services Association would like to thank Dr Heather Angel for her splendid work photographing water from all angles throughout the country. Her photographs appear on the following pages: 1, 16, 19, 20, 23, 34 (top), 40, 42–3, 52, 77, 78 (top), 79, 80–1, 110–11, 116, 132, 145, 146, 149, 150, 158, 163, 164–5, 169, 173, 174, 177, 186 (top), 188, 195, 196, 197, 204–5, 206, 207, 216, 220–1, 223, 230, 232, 234–5, 237, 238, 242 (bottom).

Thanks for use of their illustrations or photographs are also due to:

Nadav Kander (photographer): 2

Guildhall Library, London: 4, 50 (bottom), 51, 60, 63, 64, 65, 92, 94, 100, 130, 131, 133, 134, 137

Photographers International (photograph by Jayne Fincher): 6

WaterAid/Brian G. F. Mathews: 8

WaterAid/Jeremy Hartley: 9, 10

WaterAid/Framework: 11

Wessex Water Plc: 12, 13, 33 (bottom), 180–1, 202, 203, 233, 239 (top), 242 (top and middle)

Cambridge Water Company: 22, 120 (bottom), 121, 187

Trinity College Library, Cambridge: 25

Trustees of the Science Museum: 26, 28

City of Plymouth Museum and Art Gallery: 30

Greenwich Local History Library: 31

*The Engineer*: 32 (top)

The Pipeline Industries Guild (*Journal* 80, Summer 1982): 32 (bottom)

Thames Water archives, Greater London Record Office: 34 (bottom), 44, 50 (top), 95, 152, 154, 156 (top), 157

Edinburgh University Library (MS La.III.283): 35 (bottom)

Illustrated London News Picture Library: 37, 78 (bottom)

Institute of Agricultural History and Museum of English Rural Life, University of Reading: 39 (bottom)

Islington Archaeology and History Society, from Mary Cosh *The New River* (1988): 48, 49

Oxfordshire Studies, Oxford Central Library: 53 (drawing by William Foreman), 54

By courtesy of the Trustees of the British Museum: 57, 108, 109, 126, 127

Thames Water Plc: 58–9, 97, 112, 113, 123, 125, 183, 201

The Corporation of London Record Office: 61

By courtesy of the National Portrait Gallery, London: 62, 87

Kew Bridge Steam Museum: 73

Sussex Industrial Archaeology Society (drawing by R G Martin): 76

Yorkshire Water Museum: 89, 96, 117

Esler Crawford Photography, Belfast: 90

Mary Evans Picture Library: 99 (bottom), 107

Caradon Bathrooms Ltd., Stoke-on-Trent: 105

British Engineerium, Hove: 114

Ryhope Engines Trust: 115

Grampian Regional Council, Department of Water Services: 119, 153, 222 (photograph by courtesy of D Wilson Laing & Co., Blairgowrie)

The Institution of Civil Engineers: 120 (top), 129

South Staffordshire Water Plc: 122, 229

Neville Chadwick Photography, Wigston, Leicestershire: 128

Pictor International: 142–3

Dŵr Cymru Welsh Water Plc: 144, 212, 213

South West Water Plc: 148 (top), 186 (bottom), 209, 210

Severn Trent Plc: 148 (bottom), 231, 240–1

Bristol Water Holdings Plc: 149, 150, 208

Sutton District Water Company: 156 (bottom)

Northumbrian Water: 161

Donald M Fisher, FBIPP, Fisher Spence Associates, Inverness: 184–5

Anglian Water Plc: 189

Southern Water Plc: 191, 193, 194, 239 (bottom)

East Surrey Water Company Plc: 192, 199

Colne Valley Water Company Plc (photographer Nigel Wickens): 200

Telegraph Colour Library: 214–15

Department of the Environment, Northern Ireland, Water Service: 217

North West Water Group Plc: 219

Airfotos Ltd: 225

Yorkshire Water Plc: 226, 228

The York Waterworks Plc: 227

Christopher Wormell: 243

# Index

Emboldened entries refer to illustrations. In some cases there are textual references on these pages too. References to early water companies have been grouped regionally.